JAN DE PLOEY (ED.)

RAINFALL SIMULATION RUNOFF AND SOIL EROSION

CATENA VERLAG, MARGOT ROHDENBURG M.A., Brockenblick 8, 3302 CREMLINGEN 4 W.GERMANY

Submission of an article for publication implies the transfer of the copyright from the author(s) to the publisher.

Printed in West Germany:
Graphische Kunstanstalt W. Herr, 6300 Gießen

ISSN 0722–0723 / ISBN 3–923381–03–4

JAN DE PLOEY (ED.)

RAINFALL SIMULATION RUNOFF AND SOIL EROSION

CATENA SUPPLEMENT 4

CATENA VERLAG, MARGOT ROHDENBURG M.A., Brockenblick 8, 3302 CREMLINGEN 4 W.GERMANY

Printed in West Germany:
Graphische Kunstanstalt W. Herr, 6300 Gießen

ISSN 0722–0723 / ISBN 3–923381–03–4

PREFACE

This CATENA–Supplement may be an illustration of present-day efforts made by geomorphologists to promote soil erosion studies by refined methods and new conceptual approaches. On one side it is clear that we still need much more information about erosion systems which are characteristic for specific geographical areas and ecological units. With respect to this objective the reader will find in this volume an important contribution to the knowledge of active soil erosion, especially in typical sites in the Mediterranean belt, where soil degradation is very acute. On the other hand a set of papers is presented which enlighten the important role of laboratory research in the fundamental parametric investigation of processes, i.e. erosion by rain. This is in line with the progressing integration of field and laboratory studies, which is stimulated by more frequent feed-back operations. Finally we want to draw attention to the work of a restricted number of authors who are engaged in the difficult elaboration of pure theoretical models which may pollinate empirical research, by providing new concepts to be tested. Therefore, the fairly extensive publication of two papers by CULLING on soil creep mechanisms, whereby the basic force-resistance problem of erosion is discussed at the level of the individual particles.

All the other contributions are focused mainly on the processes of erosion by rain. The use of rainfall simulators is very common nowadays. But investigators are not always able to produce full fall velocity of waterdrops. EPEMA & RIEZEBOS give complementary information on the erosivity of simulators with restricted fall heights. MOEYERSONS discusses splash erosion under oblique rain, produced with his newly-built S.T.O.R.M–1 simulator. This important contribution may stimulate further investigations on the nearly unknown effects of oblique rain. BRYAN & DE PLOEY examined the comparability of erodibility measurements in two laboratories with different experimental set-ups. They obtained a similar gross ranking of Canadian and Belgian topsoils.

Both saturation overland flow and subsurface flow are important runoff sources under the rainforests of northeastern Queensland. Interesting, there, is the correlation between soil colour and hydraulic conductivity observed by BONELL, GILMOUR & CASSELLS. Runoff generation was also a main topic of IMESON's research in northern Morocco, stressing the mechanisms of surface crusting on clayish topsoils.

For southeastern Spain THORNES & GILMAN discuss the applicability of erosion models based on fairly simple equations of the "Musgrave-type". After Richter (Germany) and Vogt (France) it is TROPEANO who completes the image of erosion hazards in European vineyards. He shows that denudation is at the minimum in old vineyards, cultivated with manual tools only. Also in Italy VAN ASCH collected important data about splash erosion and rainwash on Calabrian soils. He points out a fundamental distinction between transport-limited and detachment-limited erosion rates on cultivated fields and fallow land. For a representative first order catchment in Central–Java VAN DER LINDEN comments contrasting denudation rates derived from erosion plot data and river load measurements. Here too, on some slopes, detachment-limited erosion seems to occur.

The effects of oblique rain, time-dependent phenomena such as crusting and runoff generation, detachment-limited and transport-limited erosion including colluvial deposition, are all aspects of single rainstorms and short rainy periods for which particular, predictive models have to be built. Moreover, it is argued that flume experiments may be an economic way to establish gross erodibility classifications. The present volume may give an impetus to further investigations and to the evaluation of the proposed conclusions and suggestions.

Jan de Ploey

CONTENTS

Jan de Ploey (Ed.):
Rainfall Simulation, Runoff and Soil Erosion
CATENA SUPPLEMENT 4, Braunschweig 1983

FALL VELOCITY OF WATERDROPS
AT DIFFERENT HEIGHTS AS A FACTOR
INFLUENCING EROSIVITY OF SIMULATED RAIN

G.F. **Epema** & H.Th. **Riezebos**, Utrecht

SUMMARY

Research on factors determining erosivity led to the necessity to study the relation between fall height and fall velocity for different drop sizes, generated in a rainfall simulator set-up.

For two different flow regimes occurring during the fall of drops (laminar and turbulent conditions) theoretical equations are derived, describing the relation between fall height and fall velocity. Experimental data on fall velocities for different heights of fall and drop diameters were gathered using infra-red beam interruption and a timer-counter.

The theoretical relation for laminar flow could not be corroborated. This is ascribed to oscillations in drop shape, resulting in variation of friction. The oscillations in drop shape and hence impact area, occurring mainly in the first part of fall may affect the results of erodibility studies with rainfall simulators using relatively small fall heights.

The theoretical equation for turbulent flow conditions was confined by the experimental data. During the fall under turbulent conditions the oscillation in drop shape is probably only minor and a constant friction is attained.

1. INTRODUCTION

The rainfall erosivity is the potential ability of rain to cause erosion. It is a function of the physical characteristics of rainfall (HUDSON 1971). Most expressions describing erosivity are related to kinetic energy or momentum, both per unit rainfall or per unit drop impact area. Even for recently developed indices (GHADIRI & PAYNE 1977, 1979, IMESON et al. 1981) the expressions can be described as (MEYER 1965, BUBENZER 1979):

$$E \propto d_{eq}^{p} \cdot v^{q} \qquad (1)$$

where   E is the erosivity

d_{eq} is the equivalent drop diameter (m)

v is the fall velocity (m/sec)

and   p, q are coefficients.

Alternatively (1) can be written as:

$$E \propto M^{y} v^{z} \qquad (2)$$

where   M is the mass of the drop (kg)

and   y, z are coefficients.

From the above it can be concluded that the velocity on impact is one of the important factors determining rain erosivity. The present article deals with the velocity as a function of fall height for different drop diameters.

The results of measurement on drop characteristics (fall velocity, drop shape and mass) at reduced heights of fall may be of special interest for raindrop erosion studies where vegetation is present and the portion of rainfall dripping from leaves and branches play an important role. Moreover, the determination of fall velocity and drop shape is most relevant for comparing erosion studies where simulators are used.

In order to measure the fall velocity after different heights of fall an experimental set-up was devised. Theoretically derived formulae describing the relation between fall velocity and height for a range of drop diameters are compared with the experimental data.

Exact knowledge of relevant drop characteristics is one of the important factors needed for the validation of the physically based erosivity indices. Such an index can be essential if the basic principles of the mechanics of erosion are investigated. From these principles a model of the erosion system with a sound physical base might be built, as advocated by MORGAN (1980).

2. THEORY OF THE RELATION BETWEEN HEIGHT OF FALL AND DROP VELOCITY

A downward (positive) force of gravity (Mg) and an upward (negative) directed friction force (w) act on a vertically falling drop

$$Mg - w = M\frac{dv}{dt} \tag{3}$$

where

g is the acceleration of gravity, (m/sec^2)
w is the force of friction (kgm/sec^2)

and

t is time (sec).

Under laminar flow conditions friction is proportional to velocity and (3) becomes

$$Mg - \alpha v = M\frac{dv}{dt} \tag{4}$$

where

α is a friction constant (kg/sec)

For turbulent flow conditions friction is proportional to v^2, so,

$$Mg - \beta v^2 = M\frac{dv}{dt} \tag{5}$$

where

β is a friction constant (kg/m).

For both cases (4) and (5) the relation between fall velocity and height of fall will be derived.

2.1. CASE 1; LAMINAR FLOW

Equation (4) can be written as

$$v' + \frac{\alpha}{M} v - g = 0 \qquad (6)$$

where $\qquad v' = \frac{dv}{dt}$

For $g = o$ a homogeneous solution for (6) would be

$$v = A e^{-\frac{\alpha}{M} t} \qquad (7)$$

where $\qquad$ A is a constant.

The particular solution for (6) can be found by assuming $v = \alpha$, then $v' = o$, and from (6) follows

$$\frac{\alpha}{M} \cdot \alpha = g$$

and

$$\alpha = g \cdot \frac{M}{\alpha} \qquad (8)$$

From (7) and (8) it can be concluded that

$$v(t) = A e^{-\frac{\alpha}{M} t} + g \cdot \frac{M}{\alpha} \qquad (9)$$

Equation (9) has to satisfy the condition $v(o) = o$ and therefore A can be calculated as

$$A = -g \cdot \frac{M}{\alpha} \qquad (10)$$

Equations (9) and (10) give

$$v(t) = -g \cdot \frac{M}{\alpha} \cdot e^{-\frac{\alpha}{M} t} + g \cdot \frac{M}{\alpha} \qquad (11)$$

or

$$v(t) = g \cdot \frac{M}{\alpha} (1 - e^{-\frac{\alpha}{M} t}) \qquad (12)$$

In (12) the fall velocity is expressed as a function of time. The terminal velocity v_f, for $t \rightarrow \infty$, then becomes

$$v_f = g \cdot \frac{M}{\alpha} \qquad (13)$$

Since the fall distance x(t) can be expressed as x(t) = v(t)dt, it is possible to find the relation between the distance of fall and time:

$$x(t) = g \cdot \frac{M}{\alpha} \int (1 - e^{-\frac{\alpha}{M}t}) \, dt =$$

$$= g \cdot \frac{M}{\alpha}(t + \frac{M}{\alpha} \cdot e^{-\frac{\alpha}{M}t} + B) \qquad (14)$$

Equation (14) must satisfy the conditions x(o) = o and t = o and therefore

$$B = -\frac{M}{\alpha} \qquad (15)$$

From (14) and (15) it follows that

$$x(t) = g \cdot \frac{M}{\alpha}(t + \frac{M}{\alpha} e^{-\frac{\alpha}{M}t} - \frac{M}{\alpha}) \qquad (16)$$

In (16) the distance of fall is expressed as a function of time.

From (12) and (16) it is possible to find the relation between fall distance and fall velocity by eliminating the time t.

From (12) follows

$$e^{-\frac{\alpha}{M}t} = -\frac{v}{g} \cdot \frac{\alpha}{M} + 1 \qquad (17)$$

Substitution of (17) in (16) gives

$$x = g \cdot \frac{M}{\alpha}(t - \frac{v}{g}) \qquad (18)$$

From (17): $-\frac{\alpha}{M} \cdot t = \ln(1 - \frac{\alpha}{M} \cdot \frac{v}{g})$

so: $t = \frac{M}{\alpha} \ln(1 - \frac{\alpha}{M} \cdot \frac{v}{g})$ \qquad (19)

Substitution in (18) gives

$$x = g \cdot \frac{M}{\alpha} \left| -\frac{M}{\alpha} \ln \left(1 - \frac{\alpha}{M} \cdot \frac{v}{g}\right) - \frac{v}{g} \right| \qquad (20)$$

2.2.   CASE 2; TURBULENT FLOW

Equation (5) can be written as

$$Mg - \beta v^2 = M\frac{dv}{dx} v \qquad (21)$$

or:

$$\frac{M \cdot v \cdot dv}{Mg - \beta v^2} = dx \qquad (22)$$

$$x = M \int \frac{v \cdot dv}{Mg - \beta v^2} \qquad (23)$$

Integrating gives:

$$x = -\frac{M}{2\beta} \ln (Mg - \beta v^2) \qquad (24)$$

so:

$$(Mg - \beta v^2) = e^{-2x \cdot \frac{\beta}{M}} \cdot K \qquad (25)$$

and:

$$v(x) = \sqrt{\frac{M}{\beta} \cdot g - \frac{K}{\beta} \cdot e^{-2x \cdot \frac{\beta}{M}}} \qquad (26)$$

The elimination of K is possible if equation (5) is valid for the complete trajectory of fall and the condition $v(o) = o$ for $x = o$ is satisfied.
In that case

$$\frac{M}{\beta} \cdot g - \frac{K}{\beta} = 0$$

or:

$$K = Mg$$

and (26) becomes

$$v(x) = \sqrt{\left(\frac{M}{\beta} g - \frac{M}{\beta} \cdot g \cdot e^{-2x\frac{\beta}{M}}\right)}$$

or:
$$v(x) = \sqrt{\frac{M}{\beta}}\, g \cdot \sqrt{(1 - e^{-2x\frac{\beta}{M}})} \qquad (27)$$

Equation (27) gives the fall velocity as a function of height of fall.

The terminal velocity under turbulent conditions becomes:

$$\lim_{x \to \infty} v(x) = \sqrt{(\frac{M}{\beta} \cdot g)} = v_f \qquad (28)$$

or may be derived directly from (5) for $M\frac{dv}{dt} = 0$.

3. EXPERIMENTAL SET–UP

Within a tower, variation of fall heights between 0.5 and 13 m was accomplished by placing a burette provided with a capillary at different elevations. Different capillaries produced drops with diameters between 1.6 and 6.0 mm. The time interval between the formation of drops was 1-2 seconds. At the lower end of their fall trajectory the drops pass through a 10 cm wide and 50 cm long tube. Within the tube, two horizontal infrared beams at a distance of 50 cm are interrupted by the faling drops. From the time interval between the interruption of the highest beam and the lower one measured by a timer-counter, the fall velocity was calculated.

The equivalent diameter of the drops defined as the diameter of a spherical drop with the same mass was determined using

$$M = (\rho_w - \rho_a)\, (1/6\ \pi\ d_{eq}^3) \qquad (29)$$

where ρ_w is the density of water (kg/m^3)
           ρ_a is the density of air (kg/m^3)
and M is the mass of the drops collected in a closable tube, immediately after sampling.

4. RESULTS

A review of results of measurement on fall velocity for different drop diameters at different fall heights is given in fig. 1.

For a specific capillary, differences in drop sizes were observed for different experimental runs. However, within one experimental run the variation in drop size for a specific capillary was less than 0.01 mm.

For each height of fall, the velocity of a drop with a specific size was determined out of 15 measurements. The values show a normal distribution. In the sample of n measurements with a mean value $\bar{x}$ and a variance of s^2, the standard error $s_{\bar{x}}$ is estimated as

$$s_{\overline{x}} = \left(\frac{s^2}{n}\right)^{1/2} \tag{30}$$

In all cases $s_{\overline{x}}$ appeared to be less than 0.01 m sec.$^{-1}$.

Systematic errors can originate from the timer-counter and from deviations in the trajectory of velocity measurement (i.e. the distance of 50 cm between the infrared beams).

The timer-counter was tested with the aid of an oscilloscope and is considered as a neglectable source of error.

Deviations in the trajectory of measurement are mainly caused by a non-parallelism of the infrared beams. This error was estimated as $\leqslant$ 0.02 m.sec.$^{-1}$.

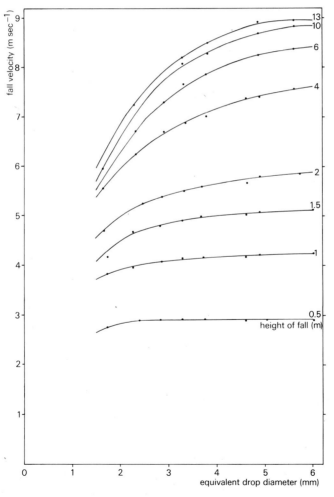

Fig. 1:   Fall velocity of several sizes of raindrops after heights of fall from 0.5 to 13.0 meters.

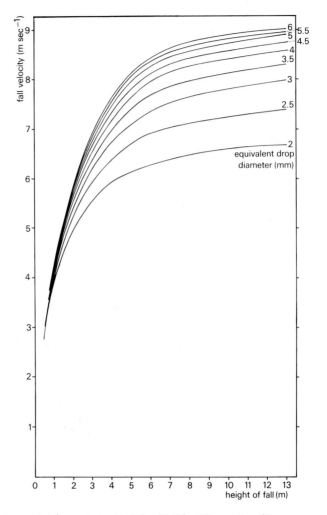

Fig. 2:　Relation between fall velocity and height of fall for different drop diameters.

The height of fall was defined as the distance between the capillary tip and the midpoint between the infrared beams. The error in the measurement of this distance is estimated to affect the fall velocity values to a maximum of 0.01 m.sec.$^{-1}$.

At smaller heights of fall, drops are still accelerating in the trajectory between the two beams. Therefore the velocity values for smaller heights deviate slightly from the measured values. A graphical representation of the measured values permitted to estimate this error as less than 0.02 m.sec.$^{-1}$.

Using fig. 1, the relation between height of fall and velocity was determined for a number of equivalent diameters (Fig. 2 and table 1). Based on the discussion of the sources of error above it is estimated that in fig. 2 the maximum error in fall velocity is between 0.03 and 0.04 m.sec.$^{-1}$ for a given height of fall.

Tab. 1: FALL VELOCITIES OF WATERDROPS OF VARIOUS SIZES AFTER DIFFERENT FALL HEIGHTS

height of fall (m)	equivalent drop diameter (mm)								
	2.0	2.5	3.0	3.5	4.0	4.5	5.0	5.5	6.0
0.50	2.83	2.95	2.96	2.96	2.96	2.96	2.96	2.96	2.96
1.00	3.92	4.00	4.02	4.04	4.06	4.08	4.10	4.12	4.14
1.50	4.59	4.72	4.84	4.94	5.00	5.04	5.08	5.12	5.15
2.00	4.98	5.26	5.42	5.56	5.65	5.74	5.78	5.82	5.86
3.00	5.56	5.94	6.21	6.40	6.54	6.68	6.77	6.84	6.92
4.00	5.95	6.39	6.73	6.97	7.17	7.34	7.44	7.54	7.64
5.00	6.14	6.72	7.10	7.41	7.64	7.80	7.96	8.05	8.11
6.00	6.28	6.94	7.36	7.69	7.95	8.12	8.27	8.36	8.42
7.00	6.39	7.04	7.53	7.86	8.15	8.31	8.45	8.54	8.62
8.00	6.48	7.15	7.65	7.97	8.26	8.43	8.56	8.66	8.75
9.00	6.56	7.20	7.74	8.06	8.34	8.51	8.65	8.75	8.84
10.00	6.62	7.26	7.81	8.14	8.41	8.58	8.72	8.82	8.90
13.00	6.68	7.40	7.98	8.30	8.58	8.75	8.90	8.96	9.02
∞ *	6.68	7.41	7.99	8.46	8.75	8.96	9.08	9.13	9.24
∞ **	6.58	7.41	8.06	8.52	8.86	9.10	9.25	9.30	9.30
∞ ***	6.49	7.42	8.06	8.52	8.83	9.00	9.09	9.15	

* terminal velocities calculated by substitution of the derived constant value of $\frac{M}{\beta}$ in equation (28)
** terminal velocities after LAWS (1941)
*** terminal velocities after GUNN & KINZER (1949)

5. DISCUSSION

The movement of a falling drop through the air can be compared with the flow of air along a fixed spheroid. Assuming that a drop is a non-deformational spheroid, the transition between laminar and turbulent flow occurs at a REYNOLDS' number of 400 or 450 (BEARD, PRUPPACHER & KLETT 1978).

Following the fall trajectory where laminar flow conditions are present, the N_{Re} value of 400 or 450 will be exceeded and turbulent conditions occur over the rest of the fall.

Secondly, the drops are either in acceleration or have reached their terminal velocity. During the acceleration phase the movement of drops initially takes place under laminar flow conditions. After a certain distance of fall flow conditions change into turbulent whereas the drop is still accelerating. Finally, under turbulent conditions the terminal velocity will be attained.

From the measurements performed under the three conditions of flow being laminar accelerating, turbulent accelerating and turbulent uniform, the height of fall, the equivalent drop diameter and the fall velocity are known. The remaining important variable, being the friction coefficient, cannot be measured directly.

5.1. LAMINAR FLOW CONDITIONS

The distance over which laminar conditions occur was found to be approximately 2 m for drops of 1.6 mm diameter. For larger drops the distance over which laminar flow occurs

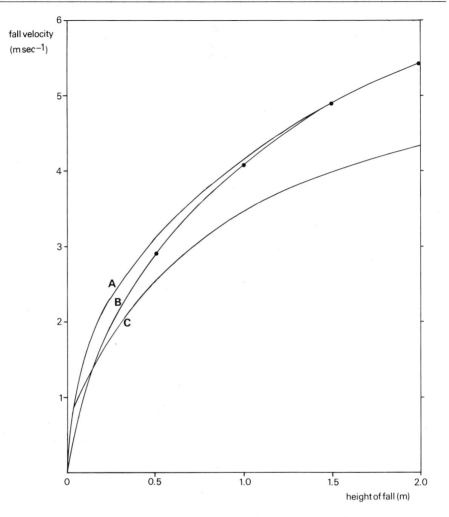

Fig. 3:   The relation between fall velocity and fall height for drops of an equivalent diameter of 3 mm.
A is according to the theoretically derived equation for turbulent flow at the constant value of $\frac{M}{\beta}$
B is according to the experimental results
C is according to the theoretically derived equation for laminar flow at a value of $\frac{M}{\alpha}$ of 1.6

decreases rapidly (35 cm for drops of 3 mm diameter; 15 cm for drops of 5 mm diameter).

    The equation for laminar flow (20) appears to apply to small heights of fall. That is, for these small distances a value for α can be found, using values of fall velocity and height of fall from fig. 2. To find a fall velocity of the drops over the first 50 cm of fall it was necessary to interpolate between a height of fall of 0 cm and 50 cm (see fig. 3). The value of $\frac{M}{\alpha}$ varies per drop and for each drop diameter, and this variation of $\frac{M}{\alpha}$ over the laminar distance implies that (20) cannot be applied for drop diameters used in the experiments.

    This may be due to observed changes in drop shape during their fall over the distance where laminar conditions are present. These changes result from difference between the initial form at the tip of the capillary tube (prolate) and the final equilibrium form which is spheroid or oblate (EDGERTON & KILLIAN 1939, EPEMA, in prep.).

Another possible explanation of the variation of $\frac{M}{\alpha}$ over the laminar distance can be found by taking into account that within the laminar flow conditions several flow regimes can be distinguished (PRUPPACHER & KLETT 1978). Each of these flow regimes has its own drag regime. The most important change in drag regime appears to occur at $N_{Re} = 20$ when a standing eddy starts to form (PRUPPACHER & STEINBERGER 1968, LE CLAIR et al. 1970).

In the derivation of the theoretical model for laminar flow conditions the frictionterm $\frac{M}{\alpha}$ was considered to be constant. It is therefore concluded that (20) is not valid under the experimental conditions.

5.2.   TURBULENT FLOW CONDITIONS

Considering the flow as turbulent when N_{Re} is over 400 or 450 equation (27) cannot be applied without restrictions. Implied in (27) is the assumption that (26) is valid for the whole trajectory of fall which includes the portion where laminar flow conditions are present. Only for this assumption the boundary condition can be used in (26) in order to eliminate the constant K.

It would be more appropriate however, to calculate the drop velocity at $N_{Re} = 400$ (450) and obtain from fig. 2 the height of fall where this velocity is attained. In this case K may be written as

$$K = \frac{Mg - \beta^{v} D^{2}}{e^{-2 \, ^{x}D \, \frac{\cdot \beta}{M}}} \qquad (31)$$

and combining (26) and (31)

$$v = \sqrt{\frac{M}{\beta} g - (\frac{M}{\beta} g - {}^{v} D^{2}) e^{2} \frac{\beta}{M} (x D - x)} \qquad (32)$$

where x_D and v_D are respectively the height of fall and the velocity at the beginning of the turbulent flowregime.

Although (32) is more appropriate than (27), the latter is still preferred since:

1. the N_{Re} – value defining the transition between laminar and turbulent flow is not known precisely: i.e. 400 o 450.

2. for the calculation of K according to (31) and hence the velocity, a point must be read from fig. 2. In doing so an experimental value is used to calculate K, after which K is used in the analytical derivation. This is not considered justified.

3. equation (27) is more simple and holds as much as (32) for fall trajectories over more .than about 50 cm.

Considering $\frac{M}{\beta}$ after a fall of more than about 1 m, the value appears to be constant for drops $\leqslant$ 3 mm.

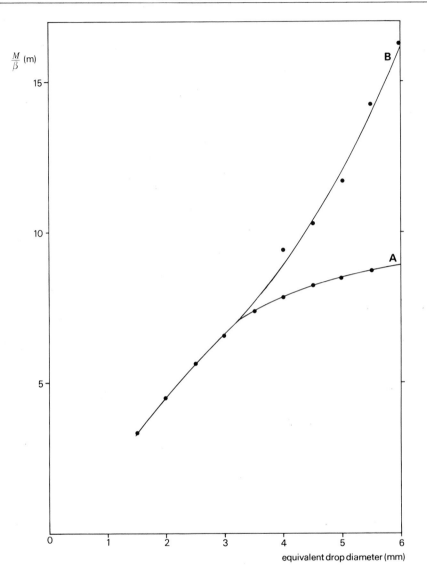

Fig. 4:   End value (A) and peak values (B) of $\frac{M}{\beta}$ for different drop diameters.

Substituting the constant value of $\frac{M}{\beta}$ in equation (27) the deviation of the calculated curve from the experimental curve is within the error of measurement after a fall of 0.5 m or more (fig. 3).

At fall heights of less than 0.5 m using the constant value of $\frac{M}{\beta}$, equation (27) gives an estimate of the fall velocity which is too high compared with the real velocity (fig. 3). This also is true for drop diameters over 3 mm. However, a final constant value of $\frac{M}{\beta}$ for drops larger than 3 mm is only attained after reaching a peak value between 1 and 3 m fall.

Final and peak values of $\frac{M}{\beta}$ as a function of drop diameter are given in fig. 4.

5.3. TERMINAL FALL VELOCITIES

Regarding terminal velocities in relation to drop diameters there is a rather extensive amount of literature (e.g. SPILHAUS 1948, WOBUS et al. 1971, DINGLE & LEE 1972, BEARD 1977a, 1980).

On the other hand there is relatively little known about the velocity of drops during the acceleration phase. Formulae describing the relation between terminal velocity and drop diameter take into account a drag index. Generally, theoretical derivations have the form

$$4/3 \ \pi \ r^3 \ (\rho_w - \rho_a) \ g \ = \ C_d \ \pi r^2 \ \rho_a \ v^2 \qquad (33)$$

or

$$4/3 \ \pi \ a^2 b(\rho_w - \rho_a) \ g \ = \ C_d \ \pi a^2 \ \rho_a \ v^2 \qquad (34)$$

where (33) and (34) assume the drop to be a sphere and an ellipsoid respectively. The elements πr^2 and πa^2 represent that part of the drop surface subject to friction.

Equation (33) and (34) are in fact special forms of equation (28) in which

$$\beta \ = \ C_d \ \pi \ \rho_a \ r^2 \ \text{ or } \ \beta \ = \ C_d \ \pi \ \rho_a \ a^2.$$

It is impossible to describe in one equation the terminal velocity as a function of drop diameter. For several drop diameter ranges the drops have different forms and are therefore subject to different drag regimes. In deriving the terminal velocity as a function of drop diameter the trajectory of fall is therefore divided into several parts. WOBUS et al. (1971) and DINGLE & LEE (1972) developed formulae in the form

$$v \ = \ + \ d \ + \ d^2 \ + \ d^3 \ ... \ d^n \qquad (35)$$

BEARD (1976) distinguished different flow regimes and thus drag regimes, based on physical conditions.

For drops between 1.07 and 7 mm diameter which are subject to deformation and $3.10^2 \leqslant N_{Re} \leqslant 4.10^3$, BEARD (1976) derived the following relations

$$y \ = \ B_0 \ + \ B_1 x \ + \ ... \ + \ B_5 x^5 \qquad (36)$$

$$x \ = \ \ln \ (16/3) \ N_{Bo} \cdot N_p^{\ 1/6} \qquad (37)$$

$$N_{Re} \ = \ N_p^{\ 1/6} \cdot e^y \qquad (38)$$

where N_p is the physical property number
and N_{Bo} is the Bond number

Nevertheless, it is emphasized that the behaviour of faling drops between 1.07 and 7.0 mm is still not physically understood. The relation between a friction coefficient on the one hand and N_{Re} and dropform on the other hand, has to be established experimentally even for the formulae of BEARD (1976). Therefore, at this stage of knowledge where the drag form is difficult to describe, a general equation like (28) seems as appropriate as equations (33) to (38). The basic problem remains the determination of the friction coefficient.

Using equation (28), the calculated terminal velocities are in accordance with the experimental results of LAWS (1941) and GUNN & KINZER (1949) (table 1).

For the calculation the constant value of $\frac{M}{\beta}$, valid for the terminal velocity, was used. In our experimental set-up where a fall height of 13 m is available, 98% or more of the terminal velocity can be attained.

5.4. FALL VELOCITIES DURING THE ACCELERATION PHASE

As with terminal velocities, the main problem in deriving equations for fall velocities in the acceleration phase is the establishment of the friction coefficient. Moreover, oscillations in drop form occur in this phase. The oscillations may affect the friction coefficient.

WANG & PRUPPACHER (1977) and BEARD (1977b) use friction data of terminal velocities for the acceleration phase. BEARD (1977b) derived a formula describing the relation between fall velocity and time, which was transformed into a relation between velocity and height of fall. BEARD (1977b) concludes that if there are oscillations in drop form at all, they do not influence the fall velocity. According to our experimental results and data of LAWS (1941) this may be true, but only for fall heights exceeding 1 à 2 m (see fig. 3). As observed, the main oscillations in drop form occur over heights of fall less than 2 m (EPEMA & RIEZEBOS, in prep.).

The variation in the value of $\frac{M}{\beta}$ is probably caused by these changes in drop form, where $\frac{M}{\beta}$ is at its maximum when drops are prolate.

Apart from the influence on fall velocity, changes in drop form may be important for the development of erosivity indices in which the drop impact area is taken into account as well as the time over which a drop impact exerts its influence on soil particles (GHADIRI & PAYNE 1979, IMESON et al. 1981).

In summary, it appears that equation (27) is an appropriate description of the relation between fall velocity and height, since for each change in drop shape a calculated value of $\frac{M}{\beta}$ can be substituted. By doing so it is possible to take into account a variation in drop form which influences the fall velocity.

The results of measurements in the acceleration phase deviate only slightly from those of LAWS (1941). The present observations however, have a smaller dispersion than those of LAWS (1941) and are therefore considered more accurate.

Although in both laminar and turbulent flow regimes drop shape changes are at the origin of changes in the friction term, two different considerations of the friction terms $\frac{M}{\alpha}$ and $\frac{M}{\beta}$ were necessary. The $\frac{M}{\alpha}$ values change continuously and more rapidly with height of fall than those of $\frac{M}{\beta}$ and could not be derived from measurements in the given experimental set-up.

6. CONCLUSIONS

Based on interruption of two infra-red beams, by individual, simulated raindrops, fall velocities at different fall heights could be measured accurately.

The results of fall velocities measured at different heights and for different drop diameters are generally in accordance with those given by LAWS (1941). However, slight differences can be observed. For terminal velocities the results are compared with those of LAWS (1941) and GUNN & KINZER (1949) in table 1.

Theoretically, two flow regimes may be distinguished. Lainar flow conditions at N_{Re} less than 400 or 450 occur in the upper section of the fall trajectory, followed by turbulent flow conditions at higher N_{Re} -values. The theoretically derived equation, describing the relation between fall velocity for laminar conditions (eq. 20) did not appear to be in accordance with our findings. It is suggested that this discrepancy between theory and measurement is the result of oscillations in drop shape. These oscillations cause changes in friction, which were not taken into account in the theoretical derivation where the friction term $\frac{M}{\alpha}$ was considered constant.

The oscillations in drop shape under laminar conditions which will be discussed in a forthcoming paper (EPEMA & RIEZEBOS, in prep.) may have major influences on the erosivity of simulated rain as generated from rainulators with restricted fall heights. Especially when the impact area and the time of impact are considered factors in an erosivity index, the drop shape oscillations may not be neglected.

For turbulent flow conditions, the theoretically derived relation between fall distance and fall velocity (eq. 27) was confirmed by the results of measurement. The friction coefficient $\frac{M}{\beta}$ attains a constant value after a fall of about 0.5 m. However, for drops > 3 mm in diameter $\frac{M}{\beta}$ reaches a peak value between 1 and 3 m fall. The variation in the value of $\frac{M}{\beta}$ is thought to be caused by changes in drop shape, where friction is smallest when drops are prolate.

ACKNOWLEDGEMENT

The authors are much indebted to Prof. Dr. J.H.J. Terwindt for his constructive critical remarks and to Dr. J.A. van Dooyeweert for his aid.

REFERENCES

BEARD, K.V. (1976): Terminal velocity and shape of cloud and precipitation drops aloft. Journal of the Atmospheric Sciences, 33, 851-864.

BEARD, K.V. (1977a): Terminal velocity adjustment for cloud and precipitation drops aloft. Journal of the Atmospheric Sciences, 34, 1293-1298.

BEARD, K.V. (1977b): On the acceleration of large waterdrops to terminal velocity. Journal of Applied Meteorology, 16, 1068-1071.

BEARD, K.V. (1980): The effects of altitude and electrical force on the terminal velocity of hydrometers. Journal of Atmospheric Sciences, 37, 1363-1374.

BUBENZER, G.D. (1979): Rainfall characteristics important for simulation. Proceedings of the Rainfall Simulatur Workshop. Tucson Arizona, 22-34.

DINGLE, A.N. & LEE, Y. (1972): Terminal fallspeeds of raindrops. Journal of Applied Meteorology 11, 877-879.

EDGERTON, E.K. & KILLIAN, J.R. (1939): Flash: seeing the unseen by ultra-high-speed photography. Hale Publishing Company.

EPEMA, G.F. & RIEZEBOS, H.Th. (in prep.): The shape of falling water drops.

GHADIRI, H. & PAYNE, D. (1977): Raindropimpact stress and the breakdown of soil crumbs. Journal of Soil Science 28, 247-258.

GHADIRI, H. & PAYNE, D. (1979): Raindrop impact and soil splash. In: Lal. R. and D.J. Greenland (eds). Soil physical properties and crop production in the tropics. J. Wiley, 95-104.

GUNN, R. & KINZER, G.D. (1949): The terminal velocity of fall for water droplets in stagnant air. Journal of Meteorology, **6**, 243-248.

HUDSON, N.W. (1971): Soil Conservation. Cornell University Press, New York.

IMESON, A.C., VIS, R. & DE WATER, E. (1981): The measurement of waterdrop impact forces with a piezo-electric transducer. CATENA, **8**, 83-96.

LAWS, J.O. (1941): Measurement of the fall-velocity of waterdrops and raindrops. Transaction American Geophysical Union, **21**, 709-721.

LeCLAIR, B.A., HAMIELIC, A.E. & PRUPPACHER, H.R. (1970): A numerical study of the drag on a sphere at low and intermediate Reynolds numbers. Journal of Atmospheric Sciences, **27**, 308-315.

MEYER, L.D. (1965): Simulation of rainfall for soil erosion research. Transactions of the ASAE, **8**, 63-65.

MORGAN, R.P.C. (1980): Conclusion Ch. 9. In: Soil Erosion ed. by Kirkby & Morgan, John Wiley and sons.

PRUPPACHER, H.R. & KLETT, J.D. (1978): Microphysics of clouds and precipitation. D. Reidel Publishing Company, Dordrecht.

PRUPPACHER, H.R. & STEINBERGER, E.H. (1968): An experimental Determination of the drag on a sphere at Low Reynolds Numbers (E). Journal Applied Physics, **39**, 4129-4132.

SPILHAUS, A.F. (1948): Raindrop size, shape and falling speed. Journal of Meteorology, **5**, 108-110.

WANG & PRUPPACHER, H.R. (1977): Acceleration to terminal velocity of cloud and raindrops. Journal of Applied Meteorology, **16**, 275-280.

WOBUS, H.B., MURRAY, F.W. & KOENIG, L.R. (1971): Calculation of the terminal velocity of waterdrops. Journal of Applied Meteorology, **10**, 751-754.

LIST OF SYMBOLS

a, b	major and minor semi-axes of the oblate spheroid [m]
A, B	constants
C_D	dragcoeffcient $[4 \triangle \rho \ g \ d_{eq} \ / \ 3 \rho_a \ v_f^2]$
d_{eq}	equivalent drop diameter [m]
E	erosivity
g	acceleration of gravity [m/sec^2]
K	constant
m	mass [kg]
n	number of samples
N_{Bo}	Bond number $[= \triangle \rho_a g \ d_{eq}^2/\sigma]$
N_P	physical property number $[= \sigma^3 \rho \ \alpha^2/\eta^4 \triangle pg]$
N_{Re}	Reynolds number $[\rho_a v \ d_{eq}/\eta]$
p, q	coefficients
r	radius [m]
s^2	variance
s_x	standard error
t	time [sec]
v	fall velocity [m/sec^2]
v'	$\dfrac{dv}{dt}$
v_D	fall velocity at the beginning of the turbulent flow regime [m/sec^2]
v_f	terminal fall velocity [m/sec^2]
x	height of fall [m]
x_D	height of fall at the beginning of the turbulent flow regime [m]
y, z	coefficients

α, β	constant for laminar $[\text{kg/sec}]$, resp. turbulent flow $[\text{kg/m}]$
$\triangle \rho$	difference between fluid properties of drop and air $[= \rho_w - \rho_a]$
η	dynamic viscosity $[\text{kg sec m}^{-2}]$
ρ_a	density of air $[\text{kg/m}^3]$
ρ_w	density of water $[\text{kg/m}^3]$
σ	surface tension $[\text{kg/sec}^2]$

Addresses of authors:
Gerrit F. Epema*, Hans Th. Riezebos, Department of Physical Geography, Geographical Institute,
State University of Utrecht, Heidelberglaan 2, P.O. Box 80.115, 3508 TC Utrecht, The Netherlands
* present address: Department of Soil Science and Geology, Agricultural University,
P.O. Box 37, 6700 AA Wageningen, The Netherlands

Jan de Ploey (Ed.):
Rainfall Simulation, Runoff and Soil Erosion
CATENA SUPPLEMENT 4, Braunschweig 1983

MEASUREMENTS OF SPLASH–SALTATION FLUXES UNDER OBLIQUE RAIN

J. **Moeyersons**, Tervuren

SUMMARY

This study deals with the problem of direct measurements of the net splash-saltation fluxes. On the base of theoretical considerations, a technique has been developed to measure the net splash-saltation flux under artificial oblique rains in laboratory conditions. This has been done for different slope inclinations, ranging from weather-side to lee-side conditions.

In most cases, the net splash saltation flux goes in the same sense as the velocity component of the raindrops, parallel to the soil surface, regardless its inclination.

Indirectly, the laboratory measurements show that splash-saltation can be considered as a pluvio-eolian process, except for the pure theoretical case of a vertical rain.

They also suggest that the measurement of splash-saltation fluxes in the field is a rather complex operation, because neither direction nor sense of the flux can be assumed beforehand on the base of the slope configuration alone. The design is made of a field set up enabling to measure an arbitrarily oriented splash-saltation flux.

RESUME

Cette étude traite le problème de la mesure directe du flux des particules de sol jaillissant sous l'effet des impacts des gouttes de pluie. Des considérations théoretiques ont mené au développement d'une technique pour mesurer le "flux de saltation", sous des pluies obliques artificielles, créées au laboratoire. Des pentes du côté du vent et du bas côté ont été simulées.

Dans la plupart des cas, le "flux de saltation" va dans le même sens que la composante de la vitesse des gouttes selon la surface du sol, quelle que soit la pente.

Indirectement, il découle des mesures que le jaillissement par le "splash" peut être considéré comme un processus pluvio-éolien, sauf pour le cas purement théorique d'une pluie verticale.

Les résultats indiquent que la mesure du "flux de saltation" sur le terrain est une opération compliquée, parce que la configuration seule de la pente ne permet pas d'estimer à l'avance ni sa direction ni son sens. Une installation de terrain, permettant de mesurer un flux quelconque, est proposée.

1. INTRODUCTION

The spatial redistribution of soil particles and aggregates as a result of saltation caused by raindrop impacts, has been recognized since a long time (ELLISON 1944). During the subsequent years the process of splash-saltation has been analysed in respect to factors as ejection angles, mean saltation distances, detachability and others. POESEN & SAVAT (1981) give an excellent review of this work, together with an extensive bibliography. With the years, there was a growing concern to provide means of measuring splash erosion and of finding mathematical equations for predictive or postdictive purposes. So, VAN HEERDEN

(1967), was the first to express splash-saltation erosion in the mathematical form:

$$E = \sum_{0}^{i} m_i \, x_i$$

where

E = total splash-saltation erosion
m_i = elementary soil mass
x_i = vectorial distance travelled by m_i

Other authors as MEYER & WISHMEIER (1969) and ROWLINSON & MARTIN (1971) provided mathematical models of splash-saltation erosion. One of the pioneers in the study of the process of splash-saltation is certainly J. DE PLOEY (1969,1972). He succeeded to derive from his analytical work a practical and general formula, describing splash-saltation transport as:

$$a = k. (\sin \alpha)^{0.75}$$

where

a = the discharge over a cross-section: m^2/year
k = a factor, function of rainfall and soil erodibility characteristics
α = slope angle in degrees,

whereby ranges of k-values are given (MOEYERSONS & DE PLOEY 1976). A further discussion of this formula can be found in SAVAT (1981). POESEN & SAVAT (1981) published experimental data which throw new light on the factors governing detachability and transportability. From these data they calculated mass distribution curves and saltation distances (SAVAT & POESEN 1981), on which they rely for the elaboration of a more sophisticated splash-saltation erosion formula, taking into account the granulometric composition of the sediment.

Thus, while analytical research has resulted in the elaboration of mathematical predictive formulae, the direct measurement of the net effect of splash-saltation seems still to be problematic. This is illustrated by MORGAN (1978), who correctly states that most methods to measure the net effect of splash erosion in the field have their disadvantages. He claims that the alternative method which he proposed provides a good indicator for splash erosion, but in the same time he admits that improvements in design are needed.

So, there seems to exist a certain need for a theoretically correct method of direct measurement of splash-saltation. Such a method could be used as a means of verification of the different splash-saltation erosion formulae. But more than a simple control is at stake. Recent investigations with artificial oblique rain have shown that the net resultant splash-saltation transport is highly influenced by the angle at which raindrops strike the inclined ground surface (MOEYERSONS 1982). This observation puts all formulae, proposed on the base of former experiments in their true perspective: they are correct for the theoretical case of a vertical rain. However, as vertical rain is a rather exceptional phenomenon, one can wonder to what extent they are usefull as tools of prediction or postdiction.

In the light of this observation there were two possibilities to continue the work. Experiments could be set up in order to evaluate the effect of the rainfall obliquity on ejection angles, projected saltation distances detachability and so on, to elaborate a mathematical equation. The objection was that this procedure would be very difficult and time consuming, leading to higher risks of errors. Therefore, we decided to develop a simple and theoretically correct method to measure directly the net splash-saltation flux.

2. THEORETICAL CONSIDERATION

The case can be considered of a bare slope with uniform soil cover, exposed to a uniform rain at constant intensity. When splash-saltation occurs, a snapshot should show the soil surface with a cloud of soil particles above, each particle situated on a point of its saltation trajectory. When the picture is moved forward, it should be seen that the cloud is permanently renewed: some particles jump in a direction with an upslope component, others in a direction with downward component. So, one can consider two fluxes over a cross-section: an upslope flux (φu) and a downslope flux (φd). Hereby a flux is simply defined as the amount of material passing within a unit time over the unit cross-section. The total net saltation flux can be defined as:

$$\emptyset \ = \ \varphi d - \varphi u. \tag{1}$$

It should be emphasised that the flux-concept is not new. The downward splash-saltation flux φd corresponds, in fact, to the term S_a used by DE PLOEY (1969), while φu corresponds with the term E'_a for the same cross-section, used by the same author.

In the theoretical case, presented here, detachability and transportability are constant over the entire slope. So, if the slope is considered infinite and rectilinear, $\emptyset$ is constant for the entire slope. In case the slope is delimited by cross-sections m and n (fig. 1A), then $\emptyset \ = \ -\varphi$u at n and $\emptyset \ = \ \varphi$d at m. The upward flux φu will attain its maximum value at a distance l upslope from m and remain the same higher up. In the same way φd reaches its maximum value at a distance L from n and remains constant till the foot of the slope. L stands for the maximum downward saltation distance and l for the maximum upward saltation distance. The net saltation flux $\emptyset$ takes the number of ejections per unit area and the mean saltation distances implicitly into account. This can intuitively be demonstrated on fig. 1A. There, φd through cross-section A clearly depends on the number of particle ejections in belt L. If it is assumed that a certain proportion of the total amount of ejections passes through A, a decrease of ejections per time unit, which means a decrease in detachability, will cause a lower flux φd in A. If, on the other hand, the detachability would remain constant with an increase of the mean saltation distance, φd in A will increase because more particles from zone L will pass. Moreover, in that case φd is not at its maximum value in A. This should be reached at a point situated downwards from A, at the maximum downward saltation distance from the crest.

From equation (1) it follows that $\emptyset$ can be defined by measuring φu and φd.

On fig. 1A, φd can be measured in m, φu in n. If we consider the case of φd measured in m, it will be shown that for a cross-section of limited length (a) in m, φd equals the amount of sediment caught in a rectangular recipient R, with length (L) and width (a) (fig. 1B).

Let φd through cross-section (a) be determined first. The lower part of the slope can arbitrary be subdivided in slope sections of the same dimensions as catching tray R. In the same time other catching trays, S, T ... are added. The total amount of material ejected within a certain time out of r over the line m can be called Ar. If the maximum lateral saltation distance equals s, Ar will then pass over cross-sections a, b, c, d and e.

Let us consider the case of a rain with a horizontal velocity component whose projection on the soil surface coincides with the slope line. As in the case of a vertical rain, the redistribution of particles from one impact point will become symmetric to a slope line passing through the impact point, if time is taken into account.

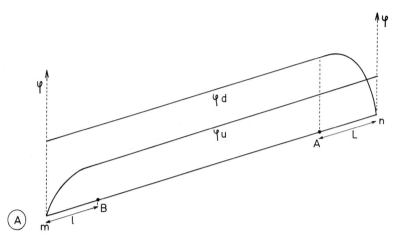

Fig. 1A: Rectilinear slope section m-n and the distribution of upward and downward oriented splash-saltation fluxes. L: maximum downward saltation distance; l: maximum upward saltation distance.

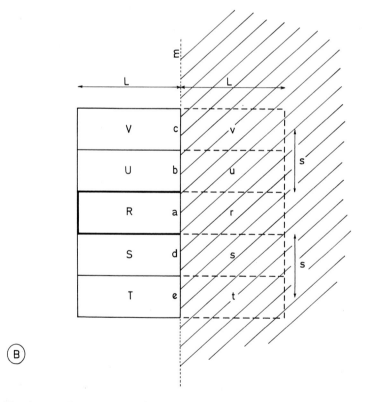

Fig. 1B: View in plan of the lower part of slope section m-n. R, S, T, U, V are sediment traps below the slope section, with cross-sections a = b = c = d = e. r, s, t, u, v are parts of the slope section, all of the same surface area as the traps. L: maximum downward saltation distance; s: maximum lateral saltation distance.

It can, therefore, be understood that the splash balance will be zero in the direction perpendicular to the slope. So, if an amount of material Ar/x from r traverses cross-section d, it should be compensated by the same amount passing within the same time through cross-section b. In the same time, an amount of material Ar/y will saltate through cross-sections c and e. In this case

$$Ar = 2\frac{Ar}{x} + 2\frac{Ar}{y} + \frac{Ar}{z} \qquad (2)$$

Where Ar/z equals the amount of material saltated out of r through cross-section a. For the same reason of symmetry, it should be accepted that the amount of material Ar/x, passing over cross-section d, will be compensated by the same amount of material ejected out of s, As/x, saltating within the same time over cross-section a.

Consequently, the amount of material (X), traversing cross-section (a) within a certain time can be defined as:

$$X = \frac{Ar}{z} + \frac{As}{x} + \frac{Au}{x} + \frac{At}{y} + \frac{Av}{y}$$

Because $\frac{As}{x} = \frac{Ar}{x}, \frac{Au}{x} = \frac{Ar}{x}, \frac{At}{y} = \frac{Ar}{y}, \frac{Av}{y} = \frac{Ar}{y}$

and because of (2),
$$X = Ar.$$

The very same reasoning can be made concerning the amount of material caught in tray R during the same time.

Consider Ar divided over $\frac{Ar}{p}$, going to R

$\frac{Ar}{q}$, going to S and to U

$\frac{Ar}{t}$, going to T and to V

than R will receive:
$$\frac{Ar}{p} + \frac{As}{q} + \frac{Au}{q} + \frac{At}{t} + \frac{Av}{t} = Ar$$

where As and Au stand for the material respectively ejected out of s and u, assuming that Ar = As = Au. So, it can be seen that, during the time considered, the amount of material collected in R, and the amount of the material traversing cross-section (a) equal both the amount of material splashed out of r over m. Hence, in fig. 1B, φd is defined by the amount of material collected in R divided by the time considered and by the width (a) of R.

It is needless to show that φu can be measured in the same way at the crest of the slope.

3. THE MEASUREMENT OF SPLASH–SALTATION FLUXES IN THE LABORATORY

3.1. PRINCIPLES

On the occasion of geomorphological research in Rwanda (MOEYERSONS 1978), it was decided to study the splash-saltation phenomenon under artificial oblique rain by means of the recently developed S.T.O.R.M.-1 rain simulator (MOEYERSONS 1982). This was done on small slope sections, representing weather-side and lee-side situations with respectively slope inward and slope outward rains.

The usable part of the impluvium of S.T.O.R.M.-1 is rather small. This makes direct measurements of the total splash-saltation fluxes impossible. So, a technique has been developed to measure saltation fluxes by fractions. Fig. 2A illustrates the principe of the experimental set up. The arrow represents the horizontal raindrop velocity component. The particles, ejected out of the source area S (22,5 × 15 cm), fall within the elliptic area as indicated by the dashed line. This area is filled up by sediment traps, with the same surface dimensions as the source recipient (22,5 × 15 cm) and arranged as indicated. Now, the case is considered of φl, in the opposite sense of the horizontal velocity component of the rain. Fig. 2B represents the end of a long rectilinar slope. A sediment trap, 22,5 cm wide and at least as long as the maximum saltation distance in the sense of φl can be imagined at the end of the slope. So, the splash saltation flux can be defined as: φl = material collected in T (gram)/22,5 cm · time.

From the weight of sediment, collected in the recipients on fig. 2A, the amount of material which should fall in sediment trap (T) in fig. 2B can easily be calculated. For convenience, the lower part of the slope is subdivided into imaginary rectangular sections, a to o, 22,5 cm long and 15 cm wide and arranged as indicated in fig. 2B. So, in the particular case of fig. 2, (T) in fig. 2B will receive the following amounts of sediment:
– from partial area a: the sediment caught in recipients 6, 7 and 8 in fig. 2A.
– from b: the sediment in 6 and 7.
– from c: the sediment in 6.

The enumeration can be further completed and the additional result will be: 22,5 cm × time xφl = the amount of material caught in I in fig. 2A (2, 5, 8, 11, 13)

$$+\ 2 \times \text{(sediment in II)}$$
$$+\ 3 \times \text{(sediment in III)}$$

In the same way φr, in the sense of horizontal velocity component of the rain is expressed as:

$$\varphi r = (\text{IV} + 2\,\text{V} + 3\,\text{VI})\ \text{time}^{-1} \cdot 22,5\ \text{cm}^{-1}.$$
$$\text{and}\ \Phi = \varphi l - \varphi r$$

From the theoretical point of view, the dimensions of the source area are of no importance. Nevertheless, the smaller they are, the bigger the "edge"–effects will be because the circumference of the source grows proportionally with decreasing area.

For reasons of symmetry, explained above, the elliptic field in fig. 2A possesses a symmetry axis, indicated by AB. Every sediment trap will receive the same amount of material as the corresponding trap on the other site of the axes (e.g. traps 5 and 11). This practical con-

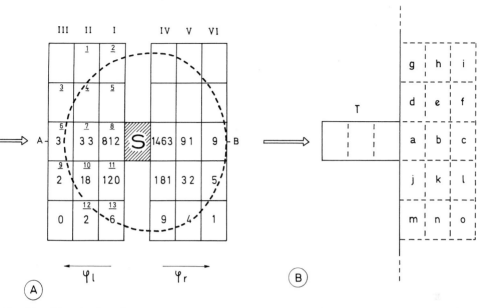

Fig. 2A: View in plan of experimental set-up. S = source area; other compartments are sediment traps. Double arrow: horizontal velocity component of the raindrops. φ_l and φ_r : saltation flux respectively to the left and the right. Further explanation: see text.

Fig. 2B: View in plan of the theoretical case of a sediment trap, T installed at the limit of a slope, a, b ... subdivisions of part of the slope surface in partial areas, with the same dimensions as in fig. 2A.

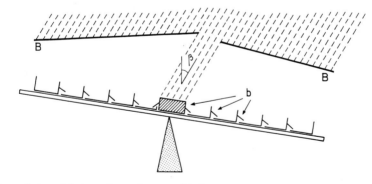

Fig. 2C: Lateral view of the experimental set-up with the source area and sediment traps, arranged on inclined screen. α: slope inclination in degrees, β: angle between vertical line and raindrop trajectory, in degrees; B: protection boards.

sideration allowed to use in the experiment only those sediment traps, which were in line with the source area and the horizontal raindrop velocity component together with the remaining traps on one side of the axis. It is clear that the dimensions of the elliptic area vary in function of slope inclination and rainfall obliquity. The number of recipients was therefore, adapted to every particular case, so that all or nearly all particles could be intercepted in that part of the elliptic catchment area considered.

3.2. SET UP, PROCEDURES AND RESULTS

Cardboard boxes, 22.5 cm long, 15 cm wide and 5 cm deep were varnished in order to make them water resistent. One of them, destinated to contain the sediment, was fortified at its inner side by small wooden boards, to avoid deformation when filled with sediment. The wooden boards remain 2 cm below the rim of the box, so that, when filled to the rim, only the 1 mm thick cardboard side remained visible. Perforations in the bottom permitted eventual drainage of the sediment. The soil material used, comes from the 50 cm thick humic A-hori- zon from Rwaza hill in Southern Rwanda. It is a dark-brown stony earth, containing about 4% of humic material. It is badly sorted and contains up to 20% of clay (less than 2 micron and colloids), about 40% of silt (63-2 micron) and about 30% of sand sized particles (2000-63 mi- cron). A variable amount of coarser particles is also present. Most of them are angular quartz grains between 2 and 3 mm diameter, but quartzite stones and iron nodules can occur.

For every measurement new sediment was used with an initial water content of about 3%. This sediment was manually compacted till a dry bulk density of about 1.30 gr/cm^3 was reached.

The source box with the sediment, together with the boxes used as sediment traps were fixed on a screen by means of thumbnails as shown in fig. 2A. Fig. 2C shows how the screen could be rotated, the rotation axis of the screen being in horizontal position and perpendicu- lar to the horizontal velocity component of the rain drops. The slope inclination is given by the symbol α. In the case of fig. 2C, α is arbitrarily considered as negative, because the slope is exposed to the rain, called a slope inward rain. When the screen is inclined to the other side, α is considered positive and the rain is slope outwards. The sediment traps were made from the cardboard boxes as indicated above. According to every particular position on the screen (fig. 2C), sides were cut off so that only one vertical face was left between every sediment trap. This was done to avoid splashed particles to fall between two boxes. Furthermore, the sides of the sediment traps were provided with small boards (b) for the same purpose. As shown on fig. 2C, the rainfall obliquity is expressed by the angle β between a vertical line and the rain- drop trajectory. Protection boards were suspended above the set up, so that the sediment traps could only receive material and water, splashed out of source S.

The experiment has been carried out for $\beta = 5°$ and $\beta = 20°$ with various slope in- clinations and a variable number of sediment traps, according to the size of the elliptic catch- ment area. Every rain shower took 30′ at a constant rainfall intensity of 50 mm/h. The mean drop diameter was close to 2.5 mm and the vertical velocity component of the drops was close to their natural vertical fall velocity. More technical information concerning the measurement of β, the mean drop diameter and the vertical velocity component of the drops, is given by MOEYERSONS (1982).

As an example, the net splash saltation flux is calculated for the first measurement for rain with $\beta = 5°$ on a horizontal surface ($\alpha = 0°$). Fig. 2A gives the set up of the source box and the sediment traps. The weight of sediment, caught by every individual sediment ttrap is indicated (in milligrams). The splash flux in opposite sense to the horizontal velocity com- ponent of the rain (φl) can be defined as:

$$\varphi l = \frac{2(6 + 120) + 812 + 2\lfloor 2(2 + 18) + 33 \rfloor + 3\lfloor 2(0 + 2)53 \rfloor}{22.5 \text{ cm} \times 30'}$$

$$= \frac{1.231\text{g}}{22.5 \text{ cm} \times 30'}$$

The opposite splash flux can be written as:

$$\varphi_r = \frac{2(181+9)+1463+2[2(4+32)+91]+3[2(1+5)+9]}{22.5\ cm \times 30'}$$

$$= \frac{2.232g}{22.5\ cm \times 30'}$$

and $\Phi = \varphi_r - \varphi_l = \dfrac{1.001g}{22.5\ cm \times 30'}$

what indicates that there is a net splash-saltation flux in the sense of the horizontal velocity component of the rain.

One could assume from fig. 2A that a small amount of soil has been splashed over a wider area than is occupied by the sediment traps. From the calculation above, it can easily be seen that this apparently small loss of sediment can hardly modify the result.

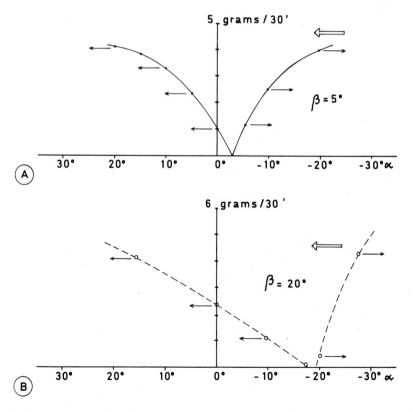

Fig. 3: Graphs, representing 22.5 cm $\times$ $\varnothing$, expressed in grams/30', in function of slope inclination. Double arrows indicate the sense of the horizontal velocity component of the rain. Single arrows indicate the sense of $\varnothing$ parallel to the slope lines. A: $\beta = 5°$, B: $\beta = 20°$.

The graphs on fig. 3 show the splash-saltation fluxes as calculated for the other cases of α and β. The results are significant and convincing: the net splash-saltation flux depends not only on slope inclination but also on slope orientation, when it concerns oblique rain.

One should be aware of the fact that the water content of the source sediment necessarily changes during every experiment. According to POESEN & SAVAT (1981), this might have resulted in changes in the detachability. Moreover as the degree of rainfall obliquity probably influences the infiltration capacity of the sediment in function of slope angle, it can be expected that the evolution of the surface water content of the sediment in time was different for every particular set up.

This situation is considered as opportune because it probably imitates the natural condition more closely than an imaginary experiment where the sediment water content would have been manipulated. On the other hand, the initial soil water content, the thickness of the source and the duration and intensity of the natural rain were calculated beforehand as in order to avoid percolation during the experiment and hence to maintain a realistic soil tension. This tension apparently sufficed to prevent noteworthy runoff.

3.3.   DISCUSSION OF THE RESULTS AND THEIR IMPLICATIONS

The results, presented here, cover only cases where the horizontal velocity component of the rain is perpendicular to the slope contours. In both cases of $\beta = 5°$ and $\beta = 20°$, the net splash-saltation flux equals zero for conditions of slope inward rains where the slope inclinations are a few degrees below the β-value. For $\beta = 20°$, the net flux $\varnothing$ equals zero for a slope inclination between 19° and 17°. For $\beta = 5°$, $\varnothing$ equals zero on a slope of about 3°. This result is important for two reasons. First, it shows that the splash-saltation flux can be oriented upslope in cases of slope inward rains for slopes between 0° and $(\beta - \pm 2)°$. This implicates that considerations concerning the effect of splash-saltation on the form of a hill are complex because the divide between upslope and downslope transport does not coincide with the hill summit. One can even go further and suppose a rather flat area where the steepest slopes are somewhat lower than the prevailing rainfall obliquity expressed by the angle β. The experiment indicates that in such landscape splash transport can become a meaningfull mechanism for long distance transport, if no natural barriers as rivers are involed and if there is a prevailing wind direction and hence a prevailing rainfall obliquity. Secund, the results are certainly an underestimation because S.T.O.R.M.-1 produces oblique rain without wind. As in nature oblique rain results from wind action, it is believed that the experimental results underestimate the fluxes in the sense of the horizontal velocity component of the rain and overestimate the opposite fluxes. So, the dissymmetry of the graphs, presented here, should still be more pronounced in nature. The point is that splash-saltation can be considered as a pluvio-eolian process, whereby the role of wind and water drops cannot be clearly distinguished. Indeed, even the detachment of particles from the ground under the impuls of raindrop impacts is function of wind direction and velocity, because this is the prime factor, determining the rain obliquity. So, pure rain splash-saltation only occurs under the rare, or maybe non existent, condition of rain without wind.

The experiment, described above, has been carried out as part of a program of erosion studies in Southern Rwanda. While it can be admitted as a general rule that splash-saltation erosion in that area is unimportant compared to other processes such as runoff erosion and even creep, it is probably of much more significance in the particular case of freshly cultivated field plots. Rain simulation on cultivated fields as well as simple observations during rain

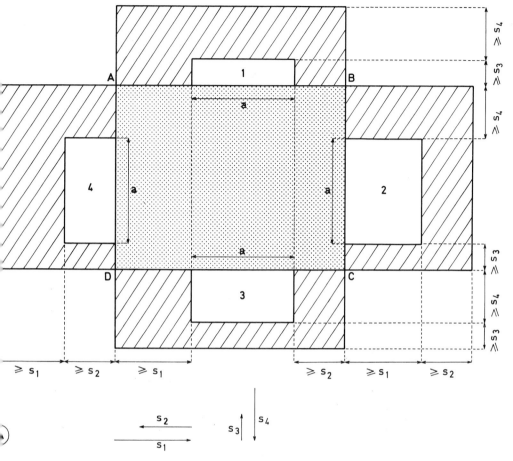

Fig. 4A: Schematic representation of field set up for the measurement of the splash-saltation flux. Dotted area: undisturbed slope section. 1, 2, 3, 4: sediment traps. Arched area: fixed soil surface s_1, s_2, s_3, s_4: maximum saltation distances, taken in the directions of the sides of the rectangular slope section.

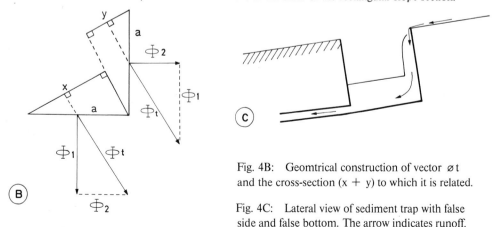

Fig. 4B: Geomtrical construction of vector $\varnothing t$ and the cross-section $(x + y)$ to which it is related.

Fig. 4C: Lateral view of sediment trap with false side and false bottom. The arrow indicates runoff.

storms have shown that runoff is not very important and often discontinuous. This follows from the high soil infiltration capacity as a result of hoeing. It seems therefore, that net upward oriented splash fluxes on fields upon the weather-side of a hill (where $\beta > \alpha$), might compensate for the restricted downward transport by runoff. So, as long as the soil infiltration capacity can be maintained high by reworking the field at regular times, the fields in question may have an advantage over other fields, where the net splash flux and runoff erosion both act in downslope direction.

Finally, the experimental results show that eventual direct measurements in the field are rather complicated, because the direction and sense of the splash-saltation flux are unknown. Indeed, while the experiments are only related to situations of slope inward and slope outward rain, in nature there exist also situations where the horizontal rain velocity component might be more or less parallel to the slope contours. There is no reason why such rains, called transverse rains, should not cause fluxes oblique to the local slope line. As it is stated above that there is a need for good field measurements, we present here a possible field set up. It consists of 4 sediment traps, with a width (a). They should be placed, one at every side of a square or rectangular undisturbed slope section, the orientation of which has no importance. Some dimensions, however, should be respected. This can be illustrated on fig. 4A. If the maximum saltation distances in the direction of the two pairs of sides of the slope section are known (s_1, s_2, s_3, s_4), trap 1 should be situated at a distance from A, at last equal to s_1 and at a distance from B equal or more than s_2. The length of the trap should at least be equal to distance s_3. In this way, the material, collected within a certain time in trap 1, will be the same as the amount of material passing over its side (a) out of the slope section, provided that the trap is protected against all material coming from the other parts of the slope around the trap. This last condition can be realized by fixing the soil surface in the shaded area (fig. 4A) by means of chemical fixatives, used as soil stabilizers (GABRIELS, HARTMAN & DE BOODT 1974) or lacquers used to take negatives from soil profiles. So, two splash fluxes can be defined. The first flux ($\varnothing 1$) is determined on the base of the material collected in sediment traps 1 and 3. The secund flux ($\varnothing 2$) can be calculated from the amount of material collected in sediment traps 2 and 4. The vectorial summation of $\varnothing 1$ and $\varnothing 2$ gives the total flux $\varnothing t$. On fig. 4B it can be seen that $\varnothing t$ is not related to a cross-section (a) but to a cross-section, perpendicular to t, composed of line sections x and y. If t has to be known, the length of the cross-section should be calculated. In the case of fig. 4B

$$x + y = a. \cos \left(\text{arc tg } \frac{\varnothing 1}{\varnothing 2} \right) + a. \cos \left(\text{arc tg } \frac{\varnothing 2}{\varnothing 1} \right)$$

The field set up, presented here, is theoretically correct in respect to the calculation of the total net splash-saltation flux over a section perpendicular to it. Two practical problems, however, remain to be resolved. First of all, there is the problem of runoff water which may fill the traps and add not splashed material, and/or may cause overflow of the traps and disappearance of collected material. More solutions exist for this problem, but the type of solution depends on local field factors as slope and type of soil material. Anyway, runoff coming from the sealed surface around the traps can be deviated by small gutters. Runoff, coming out of the slope section on which splash-saltation is masured can be collcted by the traps if they have a false side and false bottom as shown in fig. 4C. Enough perforations should be provided to permit the collected water to infiltrate quickly into the soil. If runoff is too high, the lower chamber of the trap could be provided with an outlet, coming at the surface downslope the installation. The second problem is the possibility that material should be splashed out of the trap. This simply can be avoided by making the trap deep enough.

REFERENCES

DE PLOEY, J. (1969): L'erosion pluviale: expériences à l'aide de sables traceurs et bilans morpho-génétiques. Acta Geographica Lovaniensia, **VII**, 1-28.

DE PLOEY, J. (1972): Enkele bevindingen betreffende erosieprocessen en hellings-evolutie op zandig substraat. Tijdschr. Belg. Ver. Aardr. Studies, **XLI**, **1**, 43-67.

ELLISON, W.D. (1944): Studies in drop erosion. Agricultural Engineering, **25**, 53-55.

GABRIELS, D., HARTMANN, R. & DE BOODT, M. (1974): Soil splash and runoff from untreated and chemically treated silt loam aggregates. Mededelingen Fakulteit Landbouwwetenschappen, State Univ. Ghent, **39**, 1971-1977.

MEYER, L.D. & WISHMEIER, W.H. (1969): Mathematical simulation of the process of soil erosion by water. Transactions Am. Soc. Agricult. Engineers, **12**, **6**, 754-758.

MOEYERSONS, J. (1978): Een geomorphologisch en kwartair-stratigrafisch studieprojekt in Rwanda. Africa–Tervuren, Koninklijk Museum voor Midden-Africa, Belgium, **XXIV**, **1**, 6-14.

MOEYERSONS, J. (1981): S.T.O.R.M.-1: a device for the simulation of oblique rain. First applications. Geo. Eco. Trop., **5**, 163-180.

MOEYERSONS, J. & DE PLOEY, J. (1976): Quantitative data and splash erosion, simulated on un-vegetated slopes. Zeitschr. Geomorph. NF **25**, 120-131.

MORGAN, R.P.C. (1978): Field studies of rainsplash erosion. Earth Surface Processes, **3**, 295-299.

POESEN, J. & SAVAT, J. (1981): Detachment and transportation of loose sediments by raindrop splash. Part II: detachability and transportability measurements. CATENA, **8**, 19-41.

ROWLINSON, D.L. & MARTIN, G.L. (1971): Rational model describing slope erosion. Journ. Irrigation and Drainage Div., Am. Soc. Civ. Eng.

SAVAT, J. (1981): Work done by splash: laboratory experiments. Earth Surface Proc. and Landforms, **6**, 275-283.

SAVAT, J. & POESEN, J. (1981): Detachment and transportation of loose sediments by raindrop splash. Part I. The calculation of absolute data on detachability and transportability. CATENA, **8**, 1-17.

VAN HEERDEN, W.M. (1967): An analysis of soil transportation by raindrop splash. Transact. Am. Soc. Agr. Eng. **10**, 166-169.

Address of author:
Jan Moeyersons, Koninklijk Museum voor Midden-Africa
B–1980 Tervuren, Belgium

Jan de Ploey (Ed.):
Rainfall Simulation, Runoff and Soil Erosion
CATENA SUPPLEMENT 4, Braunschweig 1983

COMPARABILITY OF SOIL EROSION MEASUREMENTS WITH DIFFERENT LABORATORY RAINFALL SIMULATORS

R.B. **Bryan**, Ontario
J. **de Ploey**, Leuven

SUMMARY

Results of comparative measurement of erosion from twelve soil samples from Canada, Belgium and Israel under simulated rainfall in two laboratories are presented. The erodibility ranking from the two laboratories under a variety of simulated storm sequences is shown to be in general agreement, but a number of discrepancies in ranking appear. These are analyzed in detail in relation to minor variations in test procedures, in simulator or flume design, or in sample properties, and test procedures are recommended which will minimize discrepancies. It appears that minor variations in test design are significant only when soils have a very high sand content or poor aggregation. For other soils laboratory testing of disturbed samples under simulated rainfall appears to produce valid, comparable results, encouraging confidence in the value of the technique as a rapid, economic means of assessing soil erodibility in widely separated areas. Finally the results are used to evaluate the use of two sample properties, the WSA > 0.5 aggregation index and the C_{5-10} consistency index, as potential indices of erodibility.

RESUME

L'article présente les résultats issus de deux laboratoires différents, Toronto et Leuven, où on a examiné l'érodibilité de douze échantillons de sols en provenance du Canada, de la Belgique et d'Israel, tout en utilisant des simulateurs de pluies différents. En général, les résultats obtenus sont assez comparables malgré qu'apparaissent certaines divergences dans les deux classifications des érodibilités. Celles-ci sont examinées en détail. Elles sont provoquées par des variations, parfois minimes, du protocole, par des différences de construction du simulateur de pluies et des bacs expérimentaux, et par des propriétés variables des échantillons. On discute l'amélioration de techniques afin de réduire ces divergences, qui sont particulièrement frappantes pour des sols sablonneux ou des matériaux de faible aggrégation. Pour les autres types de sols les deux laboratoires offrent des résultats comparables et encourageants puisqu'il semble bien que le laboratoire ouvre des possibilités pour une étude rapide et économique de l'érodibilité des sols. Finalement l'article évalue les indices d'aggrégation WSA > 0.5 mm et de consistence C_{5-10} comme indices d'érodibilité.

Rainfall simulators have been used extensively in field and laboratory research on soil erosion in many countries during the past sixty years. Many techniques have appeared which reflect differences in objectives, in technologic, logistic and financial capacity and in the local climatic conditions whose simulation is desired. No comprehensive review of simulators and procedures exists but many of the basic techniques, and associated problems, have been discussed in PARR & BERTRAND (1960), BRYAN (1970), HALL (1970) and HUDSON (1971). Much of our understanding of the soil erosion process and of the geomorphologic evolution of hillslopes is based on simulated rainfall studies. In view of this it is surprising that little attention has been paid to the comparability of data acquired using different simulators or to the way in which the results obtained might differ from the situation under natural rainfall. If the comparability can be established, or the appropriate measures for correction identified, the potential value of rainfall simulation in a wide range of studies would be greatly enhanced.

As a first stage in establishing comparability a research project was designed, based on erosion research facilities available in laboratories in Toronto and Leuven. Identical soil samples from Canada and Belgium were tested under closely similar preparation and test procedures. Major rainfall parameters such as intensity and duration were maintained contant and the only differences were those caused by different techniques of rainfall simulation, and minor differences in the size and shape of the erosion plots used.

1. CHARACTERISTICS OF RAINFALL SIMULATORS

The two rainfall simulators used have been described elsewhere (BRYAN 1974a, DE PLOEY 1981a), and therefore only the major characteristics are outlined. The simulator used in the Toronto laboratory was the Edmonton-pattern simulator (Photo 1), which has been used in several earlier studies (BRYAN 1973, 1974b, 1979, BRYAN & LUK 1981, LUK 1977, 1979, MORGAN 1979). Rainfall is simulated by two upward-pointing spray arcs from jets set in a moveable carriage which passes to and fro across the erosion plot, providing intermittent rainfall application. The on:off time ratio is 1:1 and the interval between applications is 1.1 seconds. Raindrops produced range from 0.2 to 6 mm in diameter, approximately the same as in natural rainfall, but the median diameter is somewhat smaller than in equivalent natural rainfall. Fall-height from the spray apex to the erosion plot surface is 2.2 m. The kinetic energy reproduction varies somewhat with the rainfall intensity used, but is typically about 65 per cent. The erosion plot measures 30.5 × 30.5 cm. Soil transported from the plot by wash is collected in one container, while that transported by splash is separated by a carefully constructed shield (Photo 2), splashed material being collected only from the downslope side of the plot.

The simulator used in the Leuven laboratory comprises a drop-former and a splash-screen (Photo 3). The drop-former is suspended at a height of 7.1 m and releases, at the end of capillary tubes, 4.1-4.2 mm drops which achieve 90% of their terminal fall velocities. The faling drops hit a splash-screen, suspended at 5.4 m, composed of 0.4 mm wires constituting 3.07 mm square meshes. At the given suspension height, this splash-screen "reworks" the 4.1-4.2 mm drops to give the following drop size distribution: 0-1 mm (2.2%); 1-2 mm (29.4%); 2-3 mm (41.4%); 3-4 mm (23.2%); 4-5 mm (3.85%). The modal drop diameter is 2.3-2.4 mm and there is a good simulation of a representative type of natural rainfall.

The Leuven erosion plots are 20 × 100 cm flumes (Photo 4), with a depth of 5 cm. The base of these flumes is perforated and covered with floor-cloth pieces, meaning that porewater at this level is at atmospheric, neutral pressure. Therefore the infiltration capacity in the flumes is lower than in a continuous, non-saturated profile with field soil suction.

Although similar rainfall intensity and duration were used on both simulators, there are several important differences in the units which may affect erosional data. These are the differences in fall-height and size range of drops, which result in a higher level of kinetic energy reproduction in the Leuven simulator. The employment of intermittent rather than continuous rainfall in the Toronto simulator may also affect results, particularly on sandy soils. This is discussed in detail below.

Photo 1:
General view of the Edmonton-pattern rainfall simulator used in the Toronto laboratory.

Photo 2:
Erosion plot in the Toronto laboratory, showing separation of splash and wash transport. (Note that the shield protecting the wash transport slot was subsequently lowered to 1 cm height to provide more complete separation).

Photo 3:
General view of the drop-forming apparatus in the Leuven simulator.

Photo 4:
Erosion flume for the Leuven simulator with Milliken sample undergoing testing.

Differences in the size and structure of the erosion plots also present some difficulties. The Leuven plot is longer and narrower that the Toronto plot and is somewhat less freely-drained. The relative plot areas are 2000 cm^2 and 930 cm^2. In the discussion throughout the paper, results have been adjusted to a common basis of one metre square. The implicit assumption is that eroded soil comes from the complete plot area. In fact recent work by MORGAN (1979) suggests that most of the soil eroded by sheetwash comes from within 15 cm of the lower edge of the plot. While the reasons are not fully understood, this appears to be a microscale version of the partial area contribution model now generally accepted in hydrology. The implications of this observation are twofold. Firstly, if virtually all soil eroded comes from immediate vicinity of the plot-edge, the validity of adjusting erosion values to a unit area basis is highly questionable. Provided the plot is large enough to include the complete contributing area, then area should be irrelevant, and the only valid basis for comparison would be the unit length of plot edge. Although the Leuven plot has a larger area, the plot edge is only 66% of that in the Toronto plot. The second implication is that as the Leuven plot is less freely-drained, and as in nature partial area contributions are primarily controlled by subsurface water relations, the actual contributing area in the Leuven plot would be higher. It must be stressed, however, that the localization of the source of eroded soil close to the flume edge does not apply to soil samples on which rilling occurred, such as the Perwez-9, Everberg-7, Everberg-5 and Milliken. These problems are not addressed again specifically in the paper, but are a focus for continuing research.

One further potential source of divergence is the recording of material transported by splash. In the Leuven tests splashed material was collected off a lateral splash board as an index of splash detachment. In the Toronto tests splashed material was collected off a board at the downslope edge of the plot, which under identical conditions would give slightly higher splash figures. In any case, both sets of data are only indices of splash erosion, as no allowance is made for variable distances of splash transport, and no possibility exists for return of splashed particles.

2. CHARACTERISTICS OF SOIL SAMPLES AND TEST PROCEDURES

The samples used in the test included five from Canada, six from Belgium and one from the Northern Negev, Israel, which both authors happened to have in their laboratories. The basic characteristics of the samples used are given in Table 1. With one exception sub-samples used in each laboratory were taken from the same bulk sample. In the case of the Pontypool samples were collected from two field profiles, located within 2-3 metres of one another. The Pontypool is developed over heterogeneous outwash deposits in a kame moraine, in which texture is particularly variable. Four of the five Canadian samples were collected from Southern Ontario. The Milliken and the Lockport are lessivé soils of the grey-brown luvisol group. The Milliken is developed over glacial tills with some lacustrine inter-mixture; the samples were collected from the Ap horizon of soil which had been in continuous cropping for maize for many years, and which is subject to sheet and rillwash, and to crusting (Photo 5). The Lockport is developed over stiff red shale bedrock which weathers to provide a deep regolith. Once the surface soil is exposed on hillslopes it is vulnerable to rill-wash and gullying, forming areas of typical badland erosion (Photo 6). Samples come from the Bt and C horizons. The Farmington is a thin soil with some rendzina characteristics developed over limestone, all samples coming from the A horizon in a wooded area. The final Canadian sample comes from the foothills of the Rocky Mountains in Alberta, from a striking palaeo B horizon developed in thick accumulations of calcareous aeolian silt.

Photo 5:   Surface crusting, rill and sheetwash and deposition on Milliken soil under continuous maize cultivation.

Photo 6:   Intense gullying and "badland" dissection of Lockport soil and underlying regolith.

Photo 7:
Heavy crusting, rill and sheetwash in the Everberg area at the end of the winter.

Photo 8:
Comparatively stable, structured topsoil in the Stabroek area at the end of the winter.

Photo 9:   Soil development on the Shivta limestone at Sde Boqer, with limestone blocks and loamy crack infillings.

The Belgian samples come from Ap horizons of soils, located on the central loess plateau and in the northern coversand area. An exception is the Tongrian sample which is a pure Oligocene marine sand. Perwez-9 was collected in the full loess area with lessivé soils, between Leuven and Namur. The Everberg-5 and Everberg-7 samples are from nearly Leuven where the loess mantle becomes more sandy (Photo 7). Lier is a loamy sandy topsoil, from the coversand area, southeast of Antwerp. Stabroek, finally, is the most clayey sample and obviously a well aggregated topsoil, from the Scheldt polderland, north of Antwerp (Photo 8).

The Negev sample comes from the experimental drainage basin of A. YAIR set on the barren limestone hills near Sde Boqer in the northern Negev (YAIR et al. 1978). The soil is, at last in part, of aeolian origin, and is found as infilling in cracks between and beneath massive blocks of Shivta limestone (Photo 9) which creep slowly downhill by so-called "dry block-creep" on pedestals with a very low water content (YAIR & DE PLOEY 1979). The soil is calcareous and rich in sand and silt, with very poor aggregation (Table 1).

Several different test procedures were followed in each laboratory. The initial standard procedure involving pre-sieving all samples through a 10 mm aperture square-hole sieve to remove coarse rock and organic debris. Samples were placed loosely in the erosion plot and levelled but not compacted. In the Leuven test the samples were placed in the drained plot to a depth of 4-5 cm; in the Toronto test sample were placed on a bed of glass beads over the perforated plot base, probably ensuring better drainage than in the Leuven test. Erosion plots were set to a constant inclination of 10°, and were subjected to two periods of rainfall at an intensity of 50 mm/hr. The first rainfall period of 30 min fell on soil in initially air-dry condition and was followed by a 60 min period of drainage and drying, before the second 30 min

Tab. 1: BASIC CHARACTERISTICS OF SOIL SAMPLES USED IN COMPARATIVE RAIN-FALL TESTING

Soil Type	Location	Particle Size (%)*			Organic Matter (%)	WSA (%)*** > 0.5 mm	C_{5-10}**	pH
		Sand	Silt	Clay				
Perwez-9	Belgium	10.1	75.8	14.1	2	11.65	1.7	7-7.5
Orchard Creek	Alberta, Canada	6.8	80.3	12.9	0.7	2.00	2.0	7.8
Everberg-7	Belgium	17.7	72.5	9.8	2.7	9.50	2.0	7-7.5
Sde Boqer	Negev, Israel	48.2	33.3	18.5	0.0	43.65	2.0	n.a.
Stabroek	Belgium	49.2	33.9	16.9	5.2	34.17	3.0	6.5-7.0
Lier	Belgium	57.7	38.9	3.4	4.0	6.46	2.5	6.5-7.0
Pontypool	Ontario, Canada	70.0	22.5	7.5	1.3	3.92	1.7	6.5
Everberg-5	Belgium	15.9	72.3	11.8	2.7	34.78	2.1	7-7.5
Lockport	Ontario, Canada	5.9	41.7	35.8	6.0	41.77	3.5	5.5
Tongrian	Belgium	94.0	2.0	4.0	0.0	0.00	0.0	n.a.
Milliken	Ontario, Canada	52.5	36.8	15.7	2.6	8.77	1.8	6.5
Farmington	Ontario, Canada	25.8	53.4	20.8	12.8	78.80	3.2	8.0

* Belgian and Negev samples dispersed with sodium oxalate + sodium carbonate; Canadian samples dispersed with sodium hexametaphosphate + sodium carbonate.

** The C_{5-10} index $= W_5 - W_{10}$, in which W_5, W_{10} are the water content, in % dry weight for which the groove in the Casagrande cup test closes over 1 cm after 5 and 10 blows respectively.

*** The WSA(%) > 0.5 mm = weight of aggregates retained on a 0.5 mm diameter sieve after 20 minutes wet-sieving at 60 cycles per minute, expressed as a percentage of the original sample weight.

Tab. 2: RESULTS OF RAINFALL TEST SERIES B

Toronto: 4 hour continuous test with rainfall intensities ranging from 45 to 56.9 mm/h^{-1}. Air-dry bare, sieved soil on 10° slope.

Leuven: 5 hour continuous test with rainfall intensities of 75 mm/h^{-1}. Sieved bare soil on 10° slope pre-wetted for 60 min by 75 mm of rainfall.

Sample	Splash	TORONTO Wash (g/m^{-2}/mm^{-1})	Total	LEUVEN TOTAL (g/m^{-2}/mm^{-1})	% Difference
Lier	0.99	13.12	14.11	31.7	+ 124.7
Everberg-5	0.47	9.77	10.24	26.6	+ 159.8
Perwez-9	0.96	5.98	6.94	50.7	+ 630.6
Everberg-7	1.03	5.55	6.58	35.0	+ 431.9
Stabroek-2	0.67	5.65	6.32	32.3	+ 411.1
Sde Boqer	0.65	4.71	5.36	37.9	+ 607.1
Orchard Creek	1.08	3.66	4.74	45.0	+ 849.4
Lockport	0.39	4.24	4.63	21.5	+ 364.4
Tongrian	1.92	1.91	3.83	23.2	+ 505.7
Milliken	0.71	1.45	2.16	15.2	+ 603.7
Pontypool	0.74	1.24	1.98	27.0	+ 1263.6
Farmington	0.22	0.19	0.41	14.2	+ 3363.0

rainfall period. In the Leuven test each sample was tested once, while in the Toronto five replicate tests were carried out using identical subsamples.

A second set of tests were carried out in Leuven in which sieved, air-dried samples were pre-wetted for one hour, and then subjected to five continuous hours of rainfall at an intensity of 75 mm/hr, wash and splash erosion being recorded at the end of the 5 hour period. Each test was repeated and the data in Table 2 are the mean of two results. In Toronto somewhat comparable tests were carried out, but samples were not pre-wetted, the average rainfall intensity was 50 mm/hr, and because of equipment malfunction with the moveable simulator carriage, tests were continued only for 4 hours. Wash and splash erosion was recorded at 10 minute intervals for the first half-four, and thereafter at 30 minute intervals until the end of the test.

In addition to the tests under simulated rainfall standard sample analyses were also carried out for particle size distribution, organic matter content (loss on ignition at 650°C for 6 hours), percentage-weight of water-stable aggregates > 0.5 mm diameter (by wet-sieve analysis) and Atterberg consistency limits. In the latter case the liquid limit curve was extended to provide information suitable for calculation of the C_{5-10} consistency index (DE PLOEY 1979, 1981b, DE PLOEY & MUCHER 1981).

3. DISCUSSION OF RESULTS

The basic data collected during simulated rainfall tests are shown in Tables 2-4. Not only does the magnitude of soil-loss recorded in the two laboratories differ considerably, but so does the relative erodibility ranking. Most of the soil erosion figures from Leuven are substantially higher than those from Toronto, the discrepancy for total soil-loss for series B tests (Table 2) ranging from $+ 124.7\%$ for the Lier to $+ 3363\%$ for the Farmington. Higher soil-loss in the Leuven tests was predicted because of the influence of four factors: kinetic energy of rainfall, continuity of rainfall, length of the erosion plot and drainage of the erosion plot.

Although comparatively few measurements have been made of the kinetic energy of natural rainfall numerous experimental studies using calculated values (discussed by e.g. SMITH & WISCHMEIER 1962, HUDSON 1971) have shown an almost direct relationship between soil-loss by splash or wash and kinetic energy levels. On this basis one would expect the Leuven results to be approximately 30% higher than those in Toronto.

The effect of continuity of rainfall is more difficult to estimate. In theory intermittent rainfall will allow some drainage of the immediate soil surface, increasing infiltration and therefore both the amount and direction of rainfall necessary to generate runoff. Intermittent drainage will also reduce pore-water pressure in the immediate soil surface, thereby increasing effective normal stress and resistance to entrainment. The magnitude of the effect would vary with the soil type, depending on the rate of drainage and the significance of the frictional component of entrainment resistance. The existence of these effects has been demonstrated experimentally by SLONEKER & OLSON (1974) and SLONEKER et al. (1974, 1976). Rainfall also retards thin sheetwash, so intermittent application should produce slightly higher mean flow velocities, but SAVAT's (1977) experimental data indicate that this effect is probably quite insignificant in these tests. The results of SLONEKER et al. concern intervals of 5 to 40 seconds; as the interval for the Toronto simulator is only 1.1 seconds it is felt that the potential for drainage and the effect on soil-loss is probably insignificant, except perhaps during the early stages of tests on air-dry soils.

The length of the erosion plot is potentially significant as it affects the depth and velocity of runoff, and therefore the hydraulic characteristics and the shear stress generated. No direct measurements of either depth or velocity of runoff are available. SAVAT (1977) carried out tests with a similar rainfall simulator and rainfall intensity in Leuven, using an impermeable runoff plot. He found that steady state conditions were established with a flow distance of 40 cm. Interpolating from his data, the maximum potential flow velocity over impermeable surfaces in the Leuven plot would be almost 50 cm/s. and for the Toronto plot, slightly less. The actual conditions during the tests were, of course, much more complex, with varying infiltration capacities and time to equilibrium flow, and surfaces of varying roughness subject to differing patterns of change during the test. In both cases flow velocities must have been substantially below the maximum potential, and, at least for the Toronto plot, probably well below the theoretical critical threshold velocity for particle entrainment. There was no indication of incipient rill development in any of the Toronto tests, while in the Leuven tests minor rills appeared on the Milliken and Sde Boqer samples and major rills on the Everberg-5, Everberg-7 and Perwez-9 samples.

In view of the apparent incompetence of sheetflow on the Toronto plot it is notable that in all tests and for all samples but the Tongrian and Farmington by far the largest amount of soil was carried off the plot in sheetwash. This agrees with earlier observations on Alberta soils (BRYAN 1974). It is difficult to identify entrainment mechanisms precisely but it is believed that most of this material must be entrained by rainsplash, though transported by sheetwash, and constitutes rainwash erosion (DE PLOEY et al. 1976). In the later stages of the Series B tests some soil may also have moved by solifluction, particularly on samples with low liquid limits. It is believed that the Tongrian and Farmington samples are protected from rainwash erosion because very little runoff is generated. In the case of the Tongrian this reflects an extremely high sand content, and in the case of the Farmington stable, well-developed aggregation associated with strong flocculation in calcareous soils.

While differences in kinetic energy and in velocity of sheetflow are unquestionably significant, it seems that the most important factor influencing the discrepancy of data is the storage and drainage capacity of the erosion plots. Although the Leuven plot is 115% larger than the Toronto plot, the relative sample depths are 5 and 8 cm, so maximum storage capacity per unit area for the Leuven samples is 37% less. If drainage differences are ignored and storage capacity is assumed to control runoff generation, the Leuven samples would yield runoff earlier than the Toronto samples. This would apply even in the Series A tests where rainfall intensities were the same, but the discrepancy would be much larger in Series B tests where the Leuven intensities were 25 mm h^{-1} higher and storage capacity was largely satisfied before the tests by prewetting with 75 mm water. This discrepancy would apply only if all the storage capacity is readily available. This is probably nearly true for sandy soils like the Tongrian or well-aggregated soils like the Farmington, but on finer, or less-stable soils where surface crusts or seals tend to form, very much less than the theoretical capacity may actually be available. In the absence of actual measurements of void ratios, wetting depths and crust behaviour the discussion cannot be rendered much more precise. It does suggest, however, that there are good theoretical grounds to expect the maximum discrepancy between the results of the two laboratories for sandy soils and for well-aggregated soils, and these discrepancies would be more apparent in the Series B that the Series A tests. In fact the different ranking in the two laboratories is largely due to the divergent classification of the sandy Lier and Pontypool samples.

It is impossible in a limited series of tests to reproduce all possible erosional situations, but the series used covers most common situations, and gives some indication of response in extreme rainstorm events. Series A with two short, intense storms with a brief interval of drainage represents conditions which recur at least annually in Ontario, Canada, but only once every 10 years in Belgium. The Series B storm greatly exceeds any normal conditions

Tab. 3:   RESULTS OF RAINFALL TEST SERIES A

1 hour test; 30 min rainfall at 50 mm/h^{-1}; 60 minutes drying; 30 min rainfall at 50 mmh^{-1}; 10° slope; air-dry, bare sieved soil.

Soil	TORONTO						LEUVEN		
	Splash	Wash		Total			Splash	Wash	Total
	$\overline{x}$	(cv%)	$\overline{x}$	(cv%)	$\overline{x}$	(cv%)			
		($g/m^{-2}/mm^{-1}$)						($g/m^{-2}/mm^{-1}$)	
Everberg-5	1.21	(21.5)	9.01	(31.1)	10.22	(28.1)	3.92	62.80	66.72
Everberg-7	0.80	(13.8)	6.15	(22.6)	6.95	(21.4)	0.89	2.36	3.25
Stabroek-2	1.38	(1.5)	5.96	(29.7)	6.82	(26.8)	2.72	30.01	32.72
Pontypool	1.73	(30.1)	4.39	(12.8)	6.12	(3.8)	3.99	3.28	7.27
Perwez-9*	0.97	(24.7)	4.16	(4.8)	5.13	(7.8)			
Lier	1.07	(20.6)	4.02	(59.0)	5.10	(50.0)	4.30	26.55	30.85
Lockport	0.67	(26.9)	4.22	(16.1)	4.89	(12.1)	1.88	7.39	9.27
Orchard Creek	1.58	(26.6)	2.55	(71.4)	4.13	(40.2)			
Tongrian	1.20	(20.8)	1.05	(37.1)	2.25	(27.1)			
Milliken	0.94	(13.8)	0.91	(17.7)	1.85	(13.0)			
Farmington	0.74	(15.5)	0.61	(14.8)	1.34	(13.4)	0.86	0.0	0.86

$\overline{x}$ = mean of 5 replicates

cv = coefficient of variation (%) = $\frac{\hat{\delta}}{\overline{x}} \times 100$

* = mean of 4 replicates

and represents a catastrophic occurrence comparable to the Hurricane Hazel storm which caused widespread damage in Ontario in 1955. It may also give some indication of response patterns during intense spring storms on soils already saturated by snowmelt. One reason for simulating such a severe event was related to the use of air-dry sieved samples. This procedure was originally adopted by BRYAN (1969) to reduce the effect of sample disturbance during transport; in this study it was essential because of transportation of large bulk samples across the Atlantic. Air-dry sieved samples provide conditions analogous to those found on ploughed, harrowed agricultural soils, but does not, of course, give any indication of the response pattern of the coherent, massive, undisturbed soil. When a disturbed soil is subjected to rainfall, coherence is eventually re-established, although the time required differs greatly between soil types. The Series B test was prolonged to permit this to occur, and the later stages therefore provide some indication of the behaviour of undisturbed soils under extreme rainfall. The Series A test should give a reasonable indication of the behaviour of disturbed soils under more normal conditions.

It is easier to compare results during Series A tests as test conditions were similar, but unfortunately complete data are available only for seven samples (Table 3). These show several discrepancies with Leuven values both below and above those for Toronto. In comparing the results it is important to note that the Toronto results are the mean of five replicates while the Leuven results are from single tests. The inherent variability of soil loss under controlled conditions has not been extensively studied but BRYAN & LUK (1981) have shown its significance in judging the validity of data, in a study using three of the soil types used in this study, the Lockport, Pontypool and Milliken. The inherent variability essentially represents the degree to which soil loss values assessed from a single sample may be expected to differ from the true mean value, and is calculated as the coefficient of variation = $\frac{\hat{\delta}}{\overline{x}} \times 100$ where δ is the standard deviation and $\overline{X}$ the sample mean. Inherent soil-loss variability differs between soil types, depending on factors such as the percentage aggregation and the size, shape and stability of aggregates. The data in Table 3 show a range for total soil-loss from 3.8% for the Pontypool to 50% for the Lier. It should be stressed that these coefficients of variation are based only on five replicates; BRYAN & LUK's (1981) data show that although the mean of 5 replicates will lie much closer to the true mean than the value from a single sample, the divergence can still be considerable. Accurate establishment of the true mean may require many more replicate tests.

The significance of the inherent variability of soil-loss must be borne in mind when considering the relative ranking of soil samples on the basis of soil-loss in Series A and Series B tests (Table 4). Despite the similarity of test procedures, agreement in the Series A tests is not good, only the Everberg-5 and the Farmington being similarly ranked in both laboratories. The rank correlation coefficient at 0.570 is just below the 5% significance level. If the Leuven values are adjusted by the maximum amount indicated by coefficient of variation, the range of soil-loss values is, of course, reduced, but the ranking is not altered. When the Series B tests are considered, the range of soil-loss values is very similar, but the ranking appears somewhat better with the Everberg-7, Stabroek-2, Tongrian and Farmington ranked similarly in both laboratories. The rank correlation coefficient is only slightly higher (0.588) but as more samples were involved it is significant at the 5% level. The potential significance of inherent soil-loss is more apparent when the Series B Leuven data are adjusted by the same procedure. This gives a new ranking which is very similar to that in the Toronto laboratory, with a rank correlation coefficient of 0.920, which is, of course, highly significant.

The adjustment and re-ranking procedure must be treated with caution. The actual coefficient of variation may not be accurate as it is based only on five replicates and because it was assessed in Series A tests. The coefficient of variation in the longer Series B tests should be smaller (BRYAN & LUK 1981). The main problem, however, is the use of the full range of the coefficient in the direction necessary to diminish discrepancy. It is very unlikely that all the individual Leuven observations will differ from the mean by the full amount, and the divergence may be in the other direction. If the full adjustment is made in the opposite direction the rank correlation coefficient is reduced to 0.290. The significance of the coefficient of variability is therefore that the actual discrepancy between the rankings in the two laboratories may be either very much smaller or greater than indicated in Table 4.

Two types of discrepancies in the data must be considered: those between the two tests in one laboratory and those between laboratories for one test. In the Toronto laboratory the greatest discrepancy between Series A and B tests affects the Lier and Pontypool. The Lier can be explained in part by inherent variability of soil-loss, as it has the highest coefficient of variation. It is also a result of continuity of rainfall. In the Series B test soil-loss during the first 30 minutes was negligible ($1.75 \text{ g/m}^{-2}/\text{mm}^{-1}$), but thereafter it accelerated rapidly to 16.09 $\text{g/m}^{-2}/\text{mm}^{-1}$ for the second 30 minutes, and this rate was maintained throughout the remainder of the test. In the Series A test, the intervention of 60 minutes drainage after the first 30 minutes of rainfall would prevent moisture contents in the surface soil reaching the threshold level necessary to trigger this rapid soil-loss rate. The Pontypool is more problematic as the coefficient of variation is extremely low. It would be tempting to suggest that this discrepancy represents a real difference in response to storms of different duration and intensity due, perhaps, to rapid removal of erodible particles and development of an erosion pavement. The data do not support this, however, as soil-loss in the Series B test is equally distributed throughout the storm. In the Series B test soil loss in the first 30 minutes of rainfall is at only $0.69 \text{ g/m}^{-2}/\text{mm}^{-1}$ compared with a rate of $4.46 \text{ g/m}^{-2}/\text{mm}^{-1}$ for the Series A test. It is believed that this discrepancy has risen because of inadequate location control dur-

Tab. 4:   COMPARATIVE RANKING OF SAMPLES IN TORONTO AND LEUVEN TESTS BY
MAGNITUDE OF TOTAL SOIL LOSS

| 1 hour tests (Series A) | | 4 and 5 hour tests (Series B) | |
Toronto	Leuven	Toronto	Leuven
Everberg-5	Everberg-5	Lier	Perwez-9
Everberg-7	Stabroek-2	Everberg-5	Orchard Creek
Stabroek-2	Lier	Perwez-9	Sde Boqer
Pontypool	Lockport	Everberg-7	Everberg-7
Lier	Pontypool	Stabroek-2	Stabroek-2
Lockport	Everberg-7	Sde Boqer	Lier
Farmington	Farmington	Orchard Creek	Pontypool
Rank correlation coefficient 0.570*		Lockport	Everberg-5
*Not significant at 5% level		Tongrian	Tongrian
		Milliken	Lockport
		Pontypool	Milliken
		Farmington	Farmington
		Rank correlation coefficient 0.588*	
		*Significant at 5%-level	

ing sampling. The Pontypool soil is developed on a kame moraine with extremely variable textural and aggregation characteristics, so a very small error in sampling location can influence sample properties dramatically. Although samples were collected by the same worker from within several metres of the same location, the behaviour under rainfall is quite different.

In the Leuven laboratory four samples showed marked discrepancies between the Series A and B tests: the Lockport, Pontypool, Everberg-5 and Everberg-7. The two Everberg samples showed the most major change: the Everbeg-5 was the most highly erodible sample in the Series A test with a soil loss rate of 62.80 $g/m^{-2}/mm^{-1}$ but in the Series B test was ranked only 8 with a soil loss rate of 26.60 $g/m^{-2}/mm^{-1}$. The Everberg-7 showed a soil-loss rate of 3.25 $g/m^{-2}/mm^{-1}$ in Series A and 35 $g/m^{-2}/mm^{-1}$ in Series B. The two soils are virtually identical in all the properties measured except the percentage-weight of water-stable aggregates > 0.5 mm (Table 1). The most plausible explanation of the discrepancy concerns detailed processes of crusting at the soil surface. In the Toronto Series B test the most rapid rate of soil-loss on the Everberg-5 occurred during the second 30 minutes of rainfall, and thereafter declined slightly as the surface was increasingly dominated by residual stable aggregates. This effect was less noticeable on the Everberg-7 where aggregation is poor and the maximum soil-loss rate was delayed until the third 30 minute period. The timing of this effect in relation to the onset of rainfall appears particularly critical; in the case of the Leuven Series B test, pre-wetting the samples with 75 mm of water would move the transition towards the start of the test, and reverse the relative positions of the two soils. In the Toronto test with no pre-wetting and much lower rainfall kinetic energy, the reversal was not complete before the end of rainfall. The pre-wetting period also probably accounts for the discrepancy between tests for the Lockport sample. Although shown by particle-size analysis to contain 41.7% silt, this soil behaves as a heavy, cohesive, plastic clay with strong blocky aggregates coated by clay skins. It seems likely that as in some other soils with high ferric oxide contents, it is difficult to disperse clays adequately during particle size analysis. In any case the soil aggregates are strong and resistant in a dry state, but gradually soften and disperse on prolonged wetting. The use of a pre-wetting period would enhance aggregate break-down and increase the rate of soil-loss.

As noted in Tables 2, 3 and 4, there are considerable discrepancies in the results and the ranking of soils in the two laboratories. These result from very complex and detailed interactions during the tests and the precise treatment of the samples prior to rainfall. The main samples involved are the Everberg-5, Lier, Lockport and Pontypool, which have been discussed above, and the Orchard Creek and Sde Boqer samples. In both cases the pre-wetting employed in the Leuven tests appears to be a critical factor for it permitted runoff to start almost immediately, rather than after a considerable delay as in the Toronto tests. The result was probably also affected by the higher kinetic energy of the Leuven simulator which accentuates any discrepancies related to the formation of surface crusts. In general it is perhaps surprising not that there is divergence between the two laboratories, but that there results agree so well, considering the significance of precise variations in test procedures and simulator characteristics. It seems that the major problems arise in assessing accurately the erodibility of sandy soils with very poor aggregation, such as the Pontypool or Lier, and fine-grained soils vulnerable to surface crusting and sealing. In the first case the moisture relations at the soil surface are critically important in particle detachment and any differences brought about by variations in drainage, in continuity of rainfall or in pre-test wetting will result in marked discrepancies in measured soil-loss rates, particularly during rainstorms of fairly short duration. In the second case, the development of the surface crust and its subsequent effect on both infiltration capacity and entrainment resistance are greatly affected not only by moisture content but also by the kinetic energy of rainfall and also the stability of aggregation. Again major discrepancies tend to occur, which would be enhanced by the use of pre-sieved soils, and which therefore could be expected to diminish as the duration of the rainstorm increases.

4. INDICES OF SOIL ERODIBILITY

The main objective of the study was comparison of the relative assessment of soil erodibility under controlled conditions in the Toronto and Leuven laboratories and consideration of discrepancies in erodibility ranking. Inevitably this raises the relationship between soil loss rates and soil properties and the potential for isolating some properties as indices of soil erodibility. Textural properties which affect runoff generation and entrainment resistance are potentially significant, but the relationship is usually far from direct. In Figures 1 and 2 a general negative relationship between erodibility and combined clay and organic matter content is apparent, but the influence of high sand content is also significant in the behaviour of Lier, Pontypool and Tongrian samples, particularly in the Leuven tests.

Many soil properties have been proposed as erodibility indices, most of which have been discussed by BRYAN (1968). In comparative tests in this and a subsequent study (BRYAN 1974b) it was found that most indices are highly unreliable when applied to more than a very limited range of soils. The only indices which gave promising results were those based on soil aggregation, and in particular, the percentage-weight of water-stable aggregates > 0.5 mm diameter. This index has been used with good results on a wide range of soils from brown chernozemic soils of the western Canadian prairies to humus-iron podzols of the British Isles. It shows a general negative correlation between percentage-weight WSA > 0.5 mm and soil loss by splash or wash. In Belgium, however, BOLLINNE (1978) found that soils with good surface aggregation suffered more severe erosion and therefore felt that aggregation

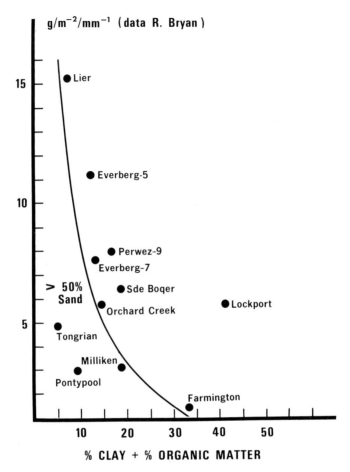

Fig. 1:   Erosion data of Toronto Series B test compared with percent clay and organic matter.

indices are not entirely reliable indices of erosion for Belgian soils. It should be noted that in BOLLINNE's study a visual assessment of structural characteristics was used and not a controlled measurement of aggregate stability. Nevertheless it was felt that the apparent contradiction between the studies cited justified testing the performance of the WSA > 0.5 index against soil-loss data in this study (Figure 3).

Soil-loss data were also tested against another index, the C_{5-10} consistency index, based on the Atterberg liquid limit consistency test. DE PLOEY (1979, 1981a) found this to be a good index for the vulnerability of Belgian soils to surface crusting and it may also have potential as an index of erodibility. Although crusting has frequently been linked with erosion in the literature, it is not yet clear whether the relationship is always positive and direct. Crusting will frequently result in reduced infiltration, particularly if accompanied by sealing (McINTYRE 1958, BRYAN 1973). The resulting increase in runoff will enhance erosive capacity, but it is possible that this is more than offset by the increased resistance of the coherant crusted surface. Further research on the precise influence of crusting on erosion

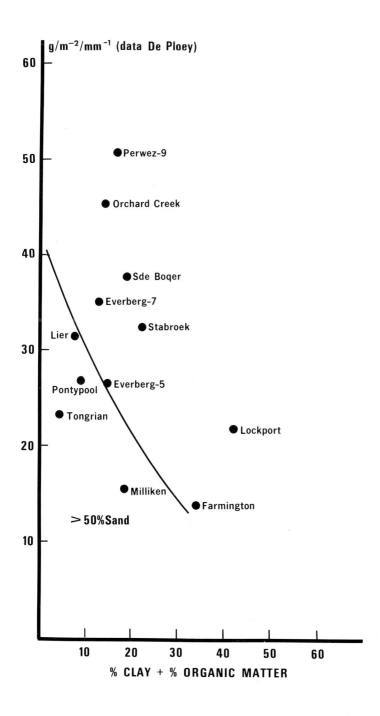

Fig. 2:   Erosion data of Leuven Series B test compared with percent clay and organic matter.

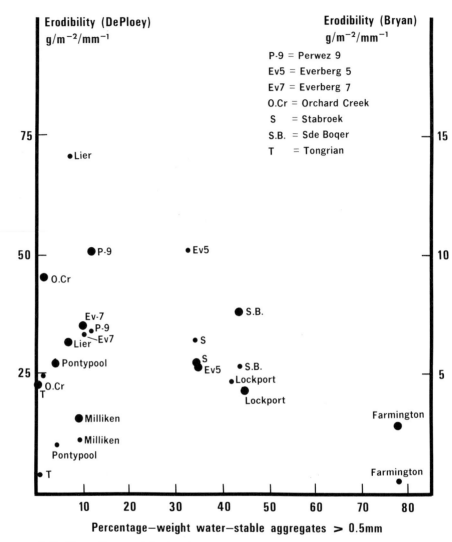

Fig. 3:   Soil-loss in Toronto and Leuven Series B tests compared with WSA > 0.5 mm index.

is necessary before the C_{5-10} index can be relied on as an index of erodibility. One possibility that seems worth investigation is that crust formation will tend to shift the dominant entrainment processes from rainsplash and sheetwash to rillwash.

Even if the C_{5-10} index can be used directly as an index of erodibility it probably should not be compared directly with the WSA > 0.5 index. Any erosional response to crusting would result from enhanced runoff and would therefore be somewhat delayed. The C_{5-10}

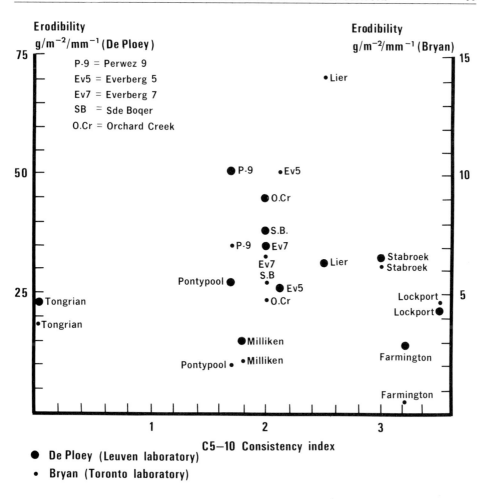

Fig. 4: Soil-loss in Toronto and Leuven Series B tests compared with C_{5-10} consistency index.

index should therefore perform best as an index of soil-loss during fairly prolonged rainfall as in the Series B tests. The WSA > 0.5 index, on the other hand, assumes that the soil is in a non-coherent condition in which entrainment is determined by the size, shape and specific gravity of individual particles as aggregates. It is therefore most appropriate as an index for disturbed, sieved samples, or for soils recently affected by agricultural tillage. This index could be expected to perform best during short rainstorms as in the Series A tests, in which there is little opportunity for the soil to regain coherence. It should also be noted, however, that index effectiveness depends not only on aggregate stability but also on the aggregation level of the soil. If only a small percentage of the soil is aggregated, the stability of aggregates will have little influence on erosional behaviour. By contrast with the WSA > 0.5 index, the effect of crusting on erosion would be somewhat delayed as increased soil-loss would follow increase in runoff.

In theory both indices should show negative correlation with soil-loss. In Figure 3 and 4 index values are plotted against total soil-loss in the Series B test. In fact no clear trend appears in Figure 4, though there is some indication of a polynomial relationship with sandy samples at the lower end and clay and organic-rich samples at the upper end. The index does separate the most and least erodible samples in the Leuven test, the Perwez-9 and Farmington, satisfactorily, but if the top six and bottom six samples are separated (Table 4) the average C_{5-10} values are 2.20 and 2.05 respectively. This suggests that although the C_{5-10}^0 index predicts crusting satisfactorily it cannot be used as a reliable index of erodibility for the sample soils. The same pattern is shown by similar groupings in the Toronto test with values of 2.22 and 2.03 respectively. Again, however, the most and last erodible soils (Lier and Farmington) are satisfactorily separated with values above and below a value of 3 which DE PLOEY (1979) found to be a significant threshold for crusting resistance.

In Figure 3 a general clear negative relationship is apparent between the WSA > 0.5 index and soil-loss, except for poorly aggregated sandy soils and the Orchard Creek samples. This is in accord with the discussion above and it appears that if less than 10 per cent of the soil is aggregated the index is not an efficient measure. The index performed reasonably well for the Leuven tests with average values of 17.91 and 28.01 for most and least erodible samples respectively. It was not, however, satisfactory for the Toronto tests where the values were 23.37 and 22.54 respectively. Following the preceding discussion it could be expected to perform better for Series A results. When compared with data from Table 3 the average value for the six mosts erodible soils is 16.75 compared with 23.62 for the four least erodible (Sde Boqer sample not included).

5. CONCLUSION

For reasons already discussed in some detail the precise erodibility ranking differs between the two laboratories, with discrepancies noted particularly for sandy, poorly aggregated soils. Nevertheless, despite differences in equipment design and in detailed test procedures, there is a fair measure of agreement on a broad classification. In general the Belgian samples are considerably more erodible than those from Canada, and the Sde Boqer sample from the Negev Desert ranks amongst the more erodible soils. One clear hiatus is the lack of objective consistent field measurements and observations against with which these experimental data can be compared. There is no question that severe erosion can occur on loamy and silty soils in Belgium. BOLLINNE (1978) measured erosion rates up to 103 t/ha/yr^{-1} on erosion plots on loamy soils in Hesbaye, and GABRIELS et al. (1977) recorded rillwash denudation rates of 1.3 mm in two months on loamy sands in southern Flanders. Comparable measurements have not been made on soils involved in this study but field observations show that after exposure during rainy winters the Lier, Everberg-5 and Everberg-7 soils show evidence of rainwash and basal colluviation, and crusting over 50% of the surface (DE PLOEY 1979). The Perwez-9 and the Stabroek do not show evident surface wash and are less than 50% crusted and are regarded as "stable". It is interesting that these observations accord more closely with the Toronto ranking in Series B tests than the Leuven ranking (Table 4).

No quantitative field data exist for the Canadian soils, but field observations suggest that the Orchard Creek soil is subject to rapid rill and gully erosion when subjected to intense rainfall or snowmelt. This agrees with the Leuven ranking (Table 4). The Lockport, although not ranked as highly erodible by either laboratory, does suffer severe and apparently rapid erosion in the field (Photo 6). This may be related to clay softening and dispersion by intense,

Photo 10a

and 10b:

Photo 10a and 10b: The appearance of laboratory samples of Lockport soil before and after 60 minutes of rainfall at 50 mm $^{-1}$ in the Toronto laboratory.

prolonged wetting during snowmelt rather than rainfall. The main reason for the discrepancy between laboratory measurements and field data, however, appears to be the importance of the impermeable, overconsolidated field structure which was impossible to preserve during sampling or to recreate in the laboratory. Photo 10 shows the dramatic difference between the Lockport sample in the laboratory after 60 minutes of rainfall and the appearance of the surface in situ in the field (Photo 6). Amongst the other Canadian samples, laboratory results for the Farmington conform well with field evidence. The Pontypool offers frequent examples of deflation hollows and general lack of resistance to wind erosion, but water erosion is not significant, probably due to exceptionally high infiltration capacities. Perhaps the most surprising result is the Milliken soil. In the field this is subject to severe crusting and rillwash and abundant deposition of transported soil on gentle footslopes indicates rapid soil-loss. Nevertheless both laboratories agreed on its low ranking in the Series B test where rill-wash tendencies would be developed to the maximum. This underlines the difficulty of correlating precise controlled laboratory tests with generalized field observations. A most useful extension of the present study would be comparative testing of soil samples in the laboratory which have already been monitored extensively in field erosion plots such as those maintained by the United States Soil Conservation Service. In this connection it is worth noting that test results were compatible with values for the Universal Soil-Loss Equation K factor calculated from the nomograph (SMITH & WISCHMEIER 1978) which were 0.31-0.32 for Canadian samples and 0.38-0.40 for Belgian samples.

One aspect of the tests of potential interest is the optimal rainfall simulator design and test procedure. Clearly the simulator which approaches the conditions of natural rainfall most closely is preferable. Where space permits the Leuven simulator with its closer approach to natural kinetic energies and its continuous rainfall is preferable. Choice of the optimal test procedure is more problemmatic. In one sense the Series A tests most closely approximate frequently recurring storm events, and the ranking produced, particularly in the Leuven laboratory, conforms quite closely with field observations. On the other hand the variability of results is maximal in these tests, and duration of rainfall is insufficient for samples to redevelop the coherent structures of undisturbed soils. For these reasons a more prolonged test, preferably accompanied by pre-wetting and consolidation is desirable. It does appear from Figures 1 and 2, however, that the Leuven Series B test is too prolonged and severe. It causes excessive surface breakdown on most soils and tends to produce an almost random scatter of results, rather than the fairly well developed relationship seen in Figure 1. It seems therefore that the optimal test procedure would involve approximately one hour of pre-wetting, a period of consolidation (1-2 hours?) and finally a two-hour duration rainstorm using the Leuven simulator. It is worth re-emphasizing the point made in preceding discussion that erodibility ranking is not independent of the duration of the test, and quite different results may be obtained from tests of differing duration.

Most of the literature on soil erodibility (e.g. BRYAN 1968) implicitly assumes that soil behaviour in any erosional process is more or less constant and that an erodibility ranking for any process will not change with process intensity. In HUDSON (1971, 59) this assumption is explicitly stated. The results of this study suggest strongly that the assumption is not correct. Soil-loss figures and erodibility rankings are predictably influenced by the varying imperfections of the rainfall simulation technique used, but they are also artifacts of the test procedure adopted. In most erosion studies an attempt is made to relate this closely to local climatic conditions, and in this sense soil erodibility is a unique product of the pedogenic environment. While it is certainly of academic interest to know how soils from widely disparate areas behave under identical test conditions, it is perhaps more important to recognize that there is no such thing as an objective, absolute ranking of erodibility, but only a local and relative ranking applicable only under clearly defined circumstances. The results of this study do indicate, however, that provided care is used in interpretation, erodibility rankings based on laboratory simulated rainfall tests can provide a rapid and economic means of assessing erosion hazard on soil samples from widely separated areas.

ACKNOWLEDGEMENTS

The research reported in this paper was in part supported by operating grants to R.B. Bryan from the Natural Scienes and Engineering Research Council, Canada, which are gratefully acknowledged.

REFERENCES

BOLLINNE, A. (1978): Study of the importance of splash and wash on the cultivated loamy soils of Hesbaye (Belgium). Earth Surface Processes, 3, 71-84.

BRYAN, R.B. (1968): The development, use and efficiency of indices of soil erodibility. Geoderma, 2, 5-26.

BRYAN, R.B. (1969): The relative erodibility of soils developed in the Peak District of Derbyshire. Geografiska Annaler, 51, 145-149.

BRYAN, R.B. (1979): An improved rain simulator for use in erosion research. Canadian Research of Earth Sciences, 7, 1552-1561.

BRYAN, R.B. (1973): Surface crusts formed under simulated rainfall on Canadian soils. Consiglio Nazionale delle Richerche Laboratorio per la Chimica del Terreno, Pisa, Conferenze 2, 30 pp.

BRYAN, R.B. (1974a): A simulated rainfall test for the prediction of soil erodibility. Zeitschrift für Geomorphologie, Supp.Bd., 21, 138-149.

BRYAN, R.B. (1974b): Water erosion by splash and wash and the erodibility of Albertan soils. Geografiska Annaler, 56, 159-180.

BRYAN, R.B. (1976): Considerations on soil erodibility indices and sheetwash. CATENA, 3, 99-111.

BRYAN, R.B. (1979): The influence of slope angle on soil entrainment by sheetwash and rainsplash. Earth Surfaces Process, 4, 43-58.

BRYAN, R.B. & LUK, S.H. (1981): Laboratory experiments on the variation of soil loss under simulated rainfall. Geoderma, 26, 245-265.

DE PLOEY, J. (1979): A consistency index and the prediction of surface crusting on Belgian loamy soils. Colloque: Erosion Agricole des Sols en Milieu Témperé Non-Méditerranean, ed. H. Vogt and T. Vogt, Université Louis Pasteur, Strasbourg, 133-137.

DE PLOEY, J. (1981a): Crusting and time-dependent rainwash mechanism on loamy soil. In: Soil Conservation, ed. R.P.C. Morgan, Wiley-Interscience, Chichester, 139-154.

DE PLOEY, J. (1981b): Some laboratory techniques for investigating land erosion. In: Erosion and Sediment Transport Measurement. IAHS Publication 133, 423-431.

DE PLOEY, J. & MÜCHER, H.J. (1981): A consistency index and rainwash mechanisms on Belgian Loamy soils. Earth Surface Processes and Landforms, 6, 319-330.

DE PLOEY, J., SAVAT, J. & MOEYERSONS, J. (1976): The differential impact of some soil loss factors on flow, runoff creep and rainwash. Earth Surface Processes, 1, 151-161.

GABRIELS, D., PAUWELS, J.M. & DE BOODT, M. (1977): A quantitative rill erosion study on loamy sand in the hilly region of Flanders. Earth Surface Processes, 2, 257-260.

HALL, M.J. (1970): A critique of methods of simulating rainfall. Water Resources Research, 6, 1104-1114.

HUDSON, N.W. (1971): Soil Conservation. Batsford, London.

LUK, S.H. (1977): Rainfall erosion of some Alberta soils: a laboratory simulation study. CATENA, 3, 295-320.

LUK, S.H. (1979): Effect of soil properties on erosion by wash and splash. Earth Surface Processes, 4, 241-255.

McINTYRE, D.S. (1958): Permeability measurements of soil crusts formed by raindrop impact. Soil Science, 85, 185-189.

MORGAN, C.L. (1979): Field and laboratory examination of soil erosion as a function of erosivity and erodibility for selected hillslope soils in Southern Ontario. Unpublished Ph.D. thesis, University of Toronto.

MÜCHER, H.J., DE PLOEY, J. & SAVAT, J. (1981): Response of loess materials to simulated translocation by water: micromorphological observations. Earth Surface Processes and Landforms, **6**, 331-336.

PARR, J.F. & BERTRAND, A.R. (1960): Water infiltration into soils. Advances in Agronomy, **12**, 311-363.

SAVAT, J. (1977): The hydraulics of sheet flow on a smooth surface and the effect of simulated rainfall. Earth Surface Processes, **2**, 125-140.

SMITH, D.D. & WISCHMEIER, W.H. (1962): Rainfall erosion. Advances in Agronomy, **14**, 109-148.

SMITH, D.D. & WISCHMEIER, W.H. (1978): Predicting Rainfall Erosion Losses. A guide to Conservation Planning. United States Department of Agriculture Handbook **537**.

SLONEKER, L.L. & MOLDENHAUER, W.C. (1974): Effect of varying on-off time of rainfall simulator nozzles on surface sealing and intake rate. Soil Science Society of America Proceedings, **38**, 157-159.

SLONEKER, L.L., OLSON, T.C. & MOLDENHAUER, W.C. (1974): Soil water pressure during intermittent simulated rain application measured with a new rapid response tensiometric technique. Soil Science Society of American Proceedings, **38**, 985-987.

SLONEKER, L.L., OLSON, T.C. & MOLDENHAUER, W.C. (1976): Effect of pore water pressure on sand splash. Soil Science Society of America Proceedings, **40**, 948-951.

YAIR, A., SHARON, D. & LAVEE, H. (1978): An instrumented watershed for the study of partial area contribution of runoff in an arid area. Zeitschrift für Geomorphologie, Supp.Bd., **29**, 71-82.

YAIR, A. & DE PLOEY, J. (1979): Field observations and laboratory experiments concerning the creep process of rock blocks in an arid environment. CATENA, **6**, 245-258.

Addresses of authors:
Rorke B. Bryan, Department of Geography, Scarborough College, University of Toronto, 1265 Military Trail, West Hill, Ontario, M1C 1A4, Canada
Jan de Ploey, Laboratorium voor Experimentele Geomorfologie, Instituut voor Aardwetenschappen, Katholieke Universiteit te Leuven
Redingenstraat 16bis, 3000 Leuven, Belgium

Jan de Ploey (Ed.):
Rainfall Simulation, Runoff and Soil Erosion
CATENA SUPPLEMENT 4, Braunschweig 1983

A PRELIMINARY SURVEY OF THE HYDRAULIC PROPERTIES OF RAINFOREST SOILS IN TROPICAL NORTH–EAST QUEENSLAND AND THEIR IMPLICATIONS FOR THE RUNOFF PROCESS

M. **Bonell**, Townsville
D.A. **Gilmour** & D.S. **Cassells**, Gympie

ABSTRACT

Tropical rainforests cover some 600,000 ha in north east Queensland. Little is known about the hydraulic properties of their soils though a number of studies in the South Creek experimental catchment near Babinda report the widespread occurrence of saturation overland flow during monsoonal rainfall events. This paper reports the results of a preliminary survey of the hydraulic conductivity and bulk density characteristics of the major rainforest soil types in this area. The survey was undertaken as an initial test of the relevance of hydrological process models developed in the South Creek catchment in terms of describing the hydrology of the northern rainforest zone.

Thirteen sites were selected to cover a range of rock and soil types and annual rainfalls. Two of the sites were associated with intensively instrumented runoff plots in the South Creek catchment on red podzolic soils. One of the plots was located on the upper slopes of the experimental catchment. The second was located in the incised area which differs from the upper slope plot in that there are large areas of weathered rock and rock floaters in the subsoil. The known hydrological behaviour of these intensive plot sites was used to infer the likely hydrological response of the other eleven sites based on a knowledge of their soil hydraulic properties.

The top 0.2 m of all the soils tested is highly permeable offering virtually no impedence to even the highest rainfall intensities encountered. Analysis of profile data below 0.2 m suggests that the sites can be divided into three groups. The first group included all of the yellow podzolics and some of the red podzolics, including the upslope runoff plot of South Creek. This group has the least permeable subsoils and evidence from South Creek suggests that saturation overland flow is probably the dominant storm runoff path. The second runoff plot located in the incised area of South Creek is included in the group with the most permeable subsoils along with krasnozems and red earths. It seems likely that subsurface flow becomes an important storm runoff source although saturation overland flow could still occur during periods of high intensity rainfall. The third soil group contained the remainder of the red podzolics and occupies an intermediate position in terms of hydraulic conductivity and runoff response.

The underlying geology seems to be an important influence in determining the hydraulic conductivity of soils derived from basalts and colluvium. However for soils derived from granite and metamorphic rock, soil colour (which is a reflection of a number of soil forming factors) appears to be a better indicator of hydraulic conductivity. There was no obvious separation of the soils into groups on the basis of different annual rainfall.

1. INTRODUCTION

Tropical rainforest covers some 600,000 ha in north-east Australia. In common with rainforest areas elsewhere (UNESCO 1978, LAL 1980), the hydraulic properties of rainforest soils in northern Australia are poorly documented. However, a number of studies in the South Creek experimental catchment near Babinda report the widespread occurrence of saturation overland flow during the high intensity rainfall events associated with summer monsoon conditions (GILMOUR et al. 1980, BONELL et al. 1981). Other studies in the catchment have indicated the importance of the relationship between vertical changes in saturated hydraulic conductivity and short term rainfall intensity in determining the disposition of rainfall between storm runoff and deeper infiltration into the soil profile (GILMOUR et al. 1980, BONELL et al. 1981).

This paper reports the results of a preliminary survey of the hydraulic conductivity and bulk density characteristics of the major soil types that support rainforests in north Queensland. The survey was undertaken as an initial test of the relevance of hydrological process models developed in the South Creek catchment in terms of describing the hydrology of the northern rainforest zone. It is significant that the combination of high rainfall, most of which is concentrated in a few months of the year, and fully wetted soil profiles makes hydraulic conductivity near saturation a meaningful parameter in this area.

Thirteen sites were selected to cover a range of rock and soil types and annual rainfalls. Two of the sites were associated with two intensively instrumented sites in the South Creek catchment. Statistical and numerical analyses of the hydraulic conductivity data from all sites were then undertaken to evaluate the differences between each of these two catchment sites and the other eleven sampling sites. The known hydrological behaviour of the two catchment sites was then used to infer the likely hydrological response of the other sites based on a knowledge of their soil hydraulic properties. The results of this survey are also compared with the literature on the hydraulic properties of rainforest soils in other areas of the humid tropics.

2. THE STUDY SITES

The location of the study sites and their respective physical properties are summarised in Figure 1 and Table 1. The runoff plots in the South Creek catchment at Babinda were studied in detail.

2.1. THE SOUTH CREEK CATCHMENT

South Creek ($17°20'S$, $145°58'E$) is a 25.7 ha experimental catchment which has been instrumented since 1969. The vegetation cover is mesophyll vine forest (TRACEY & WEBB 1975) which is typical of much of the rainforest vegetation on the wet tropical lowlands of north Queensland. In common with many other tropical areas, the forest floor in this catchment has only a thin, discontinuous layer of rotting leaf and twig litter as a result of high litter decomposition rates in this hot, humid environment. A conspicuous feature of the forest floor in this catchment is the mass of exposed tree roots which suggests the presence of widespread surface wash.

The catchment soils are derived from basic metamorphic rocks. Classified as red podzolics (STACE et al. 1968, Gn 3.11, 3.14, NORTHCOTE 1979), they are deeply weathered to a depth of six metres. The kaolin dominant clay content increases gradually from about 38% at the surface to about 51% between 0.4 and 0.5 metres depth.

Runoff plot 1a (site 1) was located in the lower reaches of the catchment where the

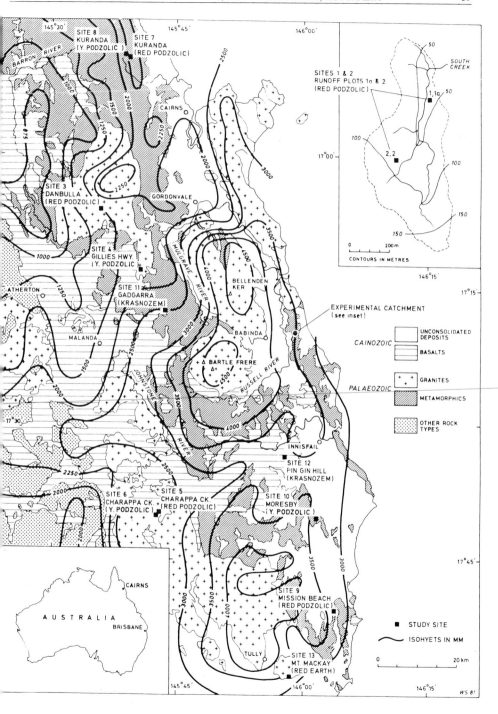

Fig. 1:   The location of the study sites in relation to the geology and 30 year mean annual rainfall (1926-1955) of the wet tropical coast hinterland.

Tab. 1:   THE GEOLOGY, SOILS, SLOPE ANGLES AND RAINFALL AT EACH SITE

Site No	Name	Geology[1]	Great Soil Group/ Soil Order[2]	PPF[2]	Soil Series[3]	Solum Depth
1	The Babinda Catchment lower slope runoff plot 1a	Devonian or Lower Carboniferous Metamorphics	Red Podzolic* Ultisol-Inceptisol	Gn3.14	Galmara	1.50 m
2	The Babinda Catchment upper slope runoff plot 2	)evonian or Lower Carboniferous Metamorphics	Red Podzolic* Ultisol-Inceptisol	Gn3.14	Galmara	1.20 m
3	Danbulla	Lower Permian to Middle Carboniferous Granite	Red Podzolic Ultisol	Gn3.14		2.10 m
4	Gilles Highway	Lower Permian to Middle Carboniferous Granite	Yellow Podzolic Ultisol-Inceptosil	Gn3.74		1.50 m
5	Charappa Creek	Lower Permian to Middle Carboniferous Granite	Red Podzolic Ultisol	Gn3.14		> 2.00 m
6	Charappa Creek	Lower Permian to Middle Carboniferous Granite	Yellow Podzolic Inceptisol	Gn3.74		1.40 m
7	Kuranda	Middle Palaeozoic Metamorphics	Red Podzolic* Inceptisol	Um4.41	Galmara	1.00 m
8	Kuranda	Middle Palaeozoic Metamorphics	Yellow Podzolic* Inceptisol	Um4.43	Bicton	0.80 m
9	Mission Beach	Middle Palaeozoic Metamorphics	Red Podzolic* Inceptisol	Gn3.14	Galmara	1.20 m
10	Moresby	Middle Palaeozoic Metamorphics	Yellow Podzolic* Inceptisol	Gn3.71	Bicton	0.90 m
11	Gadgarra	Pliocene to Recent Basalt	Krasnozem Oxisol	Gn3.11	Eubenangee	> 2.00 m
12	Pin Gin Hill	Pliocene to Recent Basalt	Krasnozem Oxisol	Gn3.11	Pin Gin	> 4.00 m
13	Mt. Mackay	Quaternary (?) Colluvium	Red Earth Ultisol	Gn2.14	Tyson	1.80 m

1   Derived from 1:250,000 Geological Series, 1964, Sheets SE55-2 (CAIRNS) and SE55-6 (INNISFAIL).
2   Principal profile forms (PPF) of NORTHCOTE (1979) and great soil groups of STACE et al. (1968) or Soil Order (SOIL SURVEY STAFF 1975) have been assigned by R.F. ISBELL and G.G. MURTHA, CSIRO, Div. Soils, Townsville. Those soils marked * are not typical members but no more appropriate great soil group is available.
3   Where possible the sites have been assigned to the soil series of MURTHA (1982).
4   This project was carried out in co-operation with C.S.I.R.O., Division of Soils, Townsville; with the present authors being responsible for the hydraulic properties.
5   Annual rainfall estimated from the 30 year mean isohyetal map (1926-1955), Water Resources Commission, Queensland (1956) and from observations within the Babinda catchment 1970-1977 (GILMOUR et al. 1980).

Tab. 1 continued:

Surface Soil[4]	Sub Soil[4]	Slope Angle	Annual Rainfall[5] (mm)
Grey-brown or brown clay loam A1 over weakly developed brown light clay A2 horizon. Strong granular of fine blocky structure. On steeper slopes the A1 may be severely eroded.	Yellowish red light medium clay with moderate fine blocky structure. Diffuse change to weathered parent material from about 95 cm.	32° (Lower slope)	4239
as above	Red medium clay with moderate fine blocky structure. Diffuse change at about 75 cm to friable strongly weathered parent material.	23° (Upper slope)	4239
Dark grey-brown clay loam, strong granular A1 to 20 cm over slightly paler gritty light clay A2.	Dark Red, gritty medium clay; moderate fine blocky structure.	19.5° (Mid slope)	1750
Dark grey-brown loam A1 over slightly paler gritty clay loam A2; strong granular or medium blocky structure. Total thickness 20 cm.	Yellowish brown gritty light clay or sandy clay; moderate medium blocky; some weathered parent material from 90 cm.	16° (Upper slope)	1750
Dark reddish brown sandy clay loam A1 over yellowish red gritty clay loam A2. Moderate to strong granular structure. Total thickness 20 cm.	Dark red light to medium clay; moderate medium blocky structure; some weathered rock from 150 cm.	18° (Midslope)	2600
Dark greyish brown sandy clay loam A1 over light yellowish brown clay loam A2. Moderate granular grading to moderate fine blocky structure. Total thickness 30 cm.	Yellowish brown medium clay; moderate medium blocky structure. Grades to clayey grit weathered granite from about 130 cm.	1° (On top of crest between creeks)	2600
Reddish brown loam, moderate to strong fine granular structure A1 horizon 20 cm thick.	Red loam to clay loam, weak to moderate fine blocky structure. Grades to weathered parent material from 60 cm.	19° (Midslope)	2300
Dark greyish brown silty clay loam A1 over pale brown loam to light clay A2. Strong fine granular structure throughout. Total thickness 20 cm.	Brownish yellow clay loam to light clay, moderate medium blocky structure. Grades to weathered parent material from 60 cm.	10.5° (Midslope)	2300
Dark reddish brown clay loam A1 with strong granular structure over yellowish red clay loam to light clay A2. Total thickness 40 cm.	Red light medium clay; weak to moderate fine blocky structure. Some weathered parent material throughout.	7.5° (Midslope	3250
Dark greyish brown clay loam; strong medium crumb structure.	Mottled yellowish brown and light yellowish brown fine sandy clay; weak medium blocky structure; increasing weathered parent material from 70 cm.	5° (Upper slope)	4239
Dark reddish brown clay loam A horizon with moderate fine granular structure.	Dark red light to medium clay; strong fine polyhedral structure; trace of weathered basalt from 180 cm.	9.5° (Upper slope)	2400
Dark reddish brown clay loam A horizon with strong fine granular structure.	Dark red medium clay; strong fine polyhedral structure; some weathered basalt from 210 cm.	2.5° (Upper slope)	3400
Very dark grey brown sandy loam A1 over weakly developed dark yellowish brown light sandy clay loam A2 horizon; weak blocky structure throughout. Total thickness 30 cm.	Red sandy clay loam; massive and very porous; grading to alluvial granitic grit from 180 cm.	2° (At the base of Mt. Mackay)	3700

stream is most incised, and runoff plot 2 (site 2) represented the upslope areas where first order streams are prevalent. In the incised area, unweathered boulders and zones of partially weathered rock are abundant in the deep clay profiles and result in near saturated, hydraulic conductivity values (at a depth of 0.5 m) an order of magnitude higher than those measured in upslope locations. The significance of this in terms of runoff response from the individual plots has been described elsewhere (GILMOUR et al. 1980, BONELL et al. 1981). Consequently only those aspects necessary for the present discussion are described here.

The runoff process is greatly influenced by the distribution of annual rainfall and variations in rainfall intensity. Average annual rainfall is 4239 mm (1970-77) with a marked concentration (63.5%) in the summer months (December – March). At this time the intertropical convergence zone moves southward into the area and frequently produces daily rainfall totals in excess of 250 mm from well organised tropical lows or cyclones which develop in this trough. The equivalent hourly rate of maximum 6 minute rainfall intensities in this period ranges from 70-150 mm (GILMOUR & BONELL 1979, BONELL & GILMOUR 1980).

During this same period, large amounts of saturation overland flow (KIRKBY 1978) occur despite high surface hydraulic conductivity in the A horizon. This type of flow is considered to be a mixture of "surface stormflow" and "subsurface stormflow", as defined by HEWLETT (1974), and is attributed to the high rainfall intensities in relation to the marked decline of hydraulic conductivity with depth (BONELL et al. 1981).

Sample estimates of the available water storage capacity in the top 0.2 m of the soil matrix range from 24 mm on the upper slope site to 52 mm in the incised area sites (unpublished data). However, under summer monsoon intensities, this available water capacity is quickly exceeded which causes a temporary perched water table to reach the surface and generate saturation overland flow. Thus the subsoil below 0.2 m m acts as an 'impeding' layer despite the relatively high hydraulic conductivity values associated with the medium-fine blocky structure of this horizon (Table 1). However, the duration of saturation overland flow was found to depend on the temporal variations in rainfall intensity, the upper soil store capacity and the spatial variation of saturated hydraulic conductivity of the subsoil below 0.2 m.

In this context, the fundamental factor determining runoff response is the seasonal decline in rainfall intensity from the summer monsoon to the post-monsoon 'transitional' season. This change occurs in early April and continues until mid-June and a further 23.5% of mean annual rainfall occurs during this time.

In this period, daily rainfall totals can still exceed 100 mm with the heavier rainfall events usually resulting from disturbances in the upper westerlies which are accentuated by orographic uplift of low level moist easterlies from a coastal ridge of high pressure. This combination of meteorological factors produces lower maximum 6 minute intensities (25-65 mm hr^{-1}) than those that occur during the summer season (BONELL & GILMOUR 1980). Thus saturation overland flow occurs throughout storms on the upper slopes, but is confined to the highest rainfall intensities in the incised area during the post-monsoon 'transitional' season. It is only under summer monsoon intensities that the upper soil store of the incised area is persistently full, allowing saturation overland flow to occur for the most part of these storms. Volumes of subsurface flow are much larger in the incised area and this is attributed to the higher subsoil hydraulic conductivity (BONELL et al. 1981).

The remaining 13% of mean annual rainfall occurs during winter and spring and the pre-monsoon seasons. Rainfall in this period comes largely from low intensity events associated with S.E. stream showers. Maximum 6 minute intensities are usually less than 20 mm hr^{-1} (BONELL & GILMOUR 1980). During this period, the soils below 0.2 m depth only occasionally act as an impeding layer (GILMOUR et al. 1980).

The foregoing conditions cause stream hydrographs in the summer monsoon and post-monsoon 'transitional' seasons to show sharp peaks to rainfall with often more than 45% of total rainfall occurring as quickflow. Statistical analysis has shown the lag response between rainfall and saturation overland flow, 0.25 m subsurface flow and stream discharge as being about 6, 12 and 24 minutes respectively (BONELL et al. 1981).

2.2. THE REPRESENTATIVE SOIL SITES OUTSIDE THE SOUTH CREEK CATCHMENT

It is evident there is a need to investigate the pertinent soil physical characteristics of a range of soil and parent material types before any generalisations can be made regarding the hydrological behaviour of rainforest ecosystems elsewhere in the area. For example metamorphic rocks have a varied origin and contain different minerals therefore some diversity in soil hydraulic properties amongst this group might be expected.

Reconnaissance soil investigations in the area have indicated that two of the major parent materials which occur in the northern zone, granites and metamorphics, develop both red and yellow soils (ISBELL et al. 1968). An attempt was made to sample the climatic/-pedology spectrum by selecting both red and yellow soil phases of the granites and metamorphics at both the drier and wetter end of the rainfall range (Fig. 1, Table 1). A basalt site was also chosen at each end of the rainfall range. An additional site in a granitic colluvial material was sampled because of the common occurrence of such areas on the eastern edge of the coastal ranges. The sites were selected in collaboration with C.S.I.R.O., Division of Soils.

3. EXPERIMENTAL METHODS

3.1. HYDRAULIC CONDUCTIVITY, K

An infiltrometer ring (0.3 m dia, 0.1 m deep) and a constant head permeameter (TALSMA 1969, DUNIN 1976) were used to give estimates of the near-saturated hydraulic conductivity of the 0-0.1 and 0.1-0.2 m layers. The 'impeding' subsoil layer (0.2-1.0 m) was initially measured within the experimental catchment using the 'shallow-well pump-in' or 'well permeameter' (BOERSMA 1965, BOUWER & JACKSON 1974). The method is time consuming and restricts the number of test holes that can be conveniently measured, since it normally took 5-8 hours to achieve steady state infiltration rates in the initially very moist catchment soils.

For these reasons, use was made of a simplified well permeameter (TALSMA & HALLAM 1980) with which a steady state could be attained for three dimensional flow within 8 minutes in wet soils. The field procedure in this work involved a pre-wetting phase of 20 minutes in newly augered holes before the constant head permeameter was placed over the cavities and measurements taken. This fairly long pre-wet period was considered necessary to achieve sufficient saturation in these soils which have hydraulic conductivty values in the order of 0.1-0.9 m day^{-1} (TALSMA 1977 pers. comm.). The depths 0.2-0.5 and 0.5-1.0 m were considered in the impeding layer to check for variations of K.

At each of sites 3 to 13, ten samples were taken randomly for the depths 0-0.1 and 0.1-0.2

m and five samples were taken for the horizons 0.2-0.5 and 0.5-1.0 m. The catchment samples for the top 0.2 m were taken close to each of the runoff plots whilst measurements for the deeper layers were made on sites 1 and 2 when records were terminated in 1978. The intensive catchment programme means that the sample sizes for the catchment runoff plots are much larger than those for te remaining sites.

The ring infiltrometer favours primarily the vertical as against both horizontal and vertical components of hydraulic conductivity combined in the well permeameter method. However, in the latter case BOUWER & JACKSON (1974) noted that the technique measured K mostly in a horizontal direction. The well permeameter K values are normally 50%-85% of the true saturated hydraulic conductivity (K_S) as measured by the auger hole method (TALSMA 1960, WINGER 1960). The underestimation is due to clogging of the pores on the sidewalls of the auger hole.

4.   FORMULAE FOR CALCULATION OF HYDRAULIC CONDUCTIVITY

4.1.   RING PERMEAMETER

Using Darcy's Law, the calculation of hydraulic conductivity from the ring infiltrometer is based on a constant head of 0.04 m of water over a sample 0.1 m deep.

$$K = Q \cdot \frac{dz}{d\phi} \qquad (1)$$

where K = hydraulic conductivity (cm min^{-1})

$$\frac{dz}{d\phi} = \frac{\text{sample length}}{\text{total head}}$$

Q = flow rate through the sample (cm min^{-1}).
This is calculated from:

$$\frac{\Delta\chi \text{ x scale factor}}{\text{Area of ring}}$$

$\Delta\chi$ is the rate of fall in head in the perspex permeameter and the scale factor is the volume of water (cm^3) between the inner and outer perspex tubes for each cm head of water.

4.2.   WELL PERMEAMETER (TALSMA & HALLAM 1980)

The formula for calculating hydraulic conductivity was developed by ZANGER (1953):

$$K = \frac{Q|\sinh^{-1}(H/r - 1)|}{2\pi H^2} \qquad (2)$$

where Q = rate of water flow into auger hole (cm^3 min^{-1}).
This is calculated from:

$$\frac{\triangle\chi \text{ x scale factor}}{\text{Time}}$$

with $\triangle\chi$ and the scale factor measured in the same way as for equation (1).

H = constant water depth in the auger hole
r = radius of hole

The conditions for use of equation (2) are that $H/r \geqslant 10$ (WINGER 1960) and the depth (S) to the water table or impermeable layer below the hole exceeds 2H (ZANGER 1953). Both these assumptions were valid in this work.

The mean auger hole radius (r) was 0.025 m and constant water depths (H) in the auger hole were maintained at 0.30 and 0.50 m for the depth increments 0.2-0.5 and 0.5-1.0 m respectively.

ZANGER's (1953) formula is expanded to the following which is slightly different from that used by BOERSMA (1965) and BOUWER & JACKSON (1974):

$$K = \frac{Q}{2\pi H^2} \left[\ln(\frac{H}{r} + \sqrt{\frac{H^2}{r} + 1)} - 1 \right] \qquad (3)$$

4.3. BULK DENSITY

At each site, five bulk density samples were taken from each of the following depths: 0-0.05, 0.05-0.1, 0.125-0.175, 0.325-0.375 and 0.725-0.775 m. The last three layers correspond with the mid-points of the depth ranges adopted for K determination.

5. STATISTICAL AND NUMERICAL ANALYSES

Exploratory data analysis (TUKEY 1977) indicated that the K data frequency distributions are closely approximated by the log – normal function. This finding is in agreement with other field investigations (ROGOWSKI 1972, NIELSEN et al. 1973, BAKER 1978). Consequently the use of log means for inter-layer comparison of K is a more appropriate measure than the use of arithmetic means (TALSMA 1965, NIELSEN et al. 1973). The antilog of the standard deviation of the log transformed K data (antilog S_1) is also included as an index of variability (BAKER 1978). A value of 2 was suggested by ROGOWSKI (1972) as the upper limit of uniformity of K in soil series.

With regard to bulk density, the arithmetic means have been reported (NIELSEN et al. 1973).

The use of further statistical and numerical analysis on the K data is confined to the 'impeding' layers as these control the runoff process. It became apparent that the analysis had to be approached in different ways as no one method is entirely valid. The first step was to test the transformed data for the 0.2-0.5 m and 0.5-1.0 m layers using one way analysis of variance. Both F tests were significant (F < 0.001) and the least significant difference (LSD) test was used between individual pairs of means (SNEDECOR & COCHRAN 1967). A significance level of 0.01 was used to test differences between specific pairs of sites. The next stage was the application of hierarchical clustering techniques to establish possible groupings amongst the sites (EVERITT 1980, WEBSTER 1977, WILLIAMS 1971, 1976). A preliminary step was to plot a scatter diagram of the log means of K for the impeding layers at each site to detect any groupings and also to indicate the population structure. In the latter case, this can be helpful in the selection of suitable strategies for cluster analysis (WEBSTER 1975). In this study several techniques were used and the results compared in line with recommendations elsewhere (EVERITT 1980, WEBSTER 1977).

Squared Euclidean Distance was used as the similarity measure, after standardisation using the method proposed by BURR (1968). This was followed by the application of the following strategies, minimum incremental sums of squares (BURR 1970), error sums of squares (WARD 1963), flexible sorting, $\beta = -0.25$ (LANCE & WILLIAMS 1967) and group-average (SOKAL & MICHENER 1958). The first two techniques are strongly space dilating whereas the remander are described as slightly space dilating or space conserving respectively (WEBSTER 1977, WILLIAMS 1976). These measures were undertaken using the computer programs CLUSTAN (WISHART 1978) and MULCLAS in the C.S.I.R.O. TAXON library (DALE et al. 1980).

6.   RESULTS AND DISCUSSION

6.1.   HYDRAULIC CONDUCTIVITY FOR SPECIFIC LAYERS

The hydraulic conductivity data for the specific layers are presented in Table 2. The rapid decline in K with depth cannot be entirely attributed either to underestimation of this variable by the well permeameter method (TALSMA & HALLAM 1980) or anisotropy (CHILDS 1969, MAASLAND 1957); but instead reflects mainly the biological influences in the surface layers.

Tab. 2:   HYDRAULIC CONDUCTIVITY AT EACH SITE

Site No	Geology	Depth Interval (m)	Numbers of Samples	Arithmetic Mean	Log Mean	Range	Antilog S_1
Transmissive layers							
1	Babinda Catchment	0-0.1	46	35.68	23.81	2.95-183.3	2.57
2	– Metamorphics		9	18.12	9.94	3.1-85.75	2.84
3	Granites		10	103.5	96.48	50.59-170.96	1.51
4	"		10	29.95	27.15	10.67-56.42	1.62
5	"		10	51.09	46.27	16.67-96.72	1.64
6	"		10	77.81	58.76	16.79-236.7	2.20
7	Metamorphics		10	52.11	36.33	12.89-170.96	2.30
8	"		10	86.22	65.33	24.14-307.73	2.07
9	"		10	106.99	102.68	53.73-138.48	1.37
10	"		10	39.45	35.07	17.84-85.88	1.65

Hydraulic Conductivity (metres/day)

). 2   continued:

Geology	Depth Interval (m)	Numbers of Samples	Hydraulic Conductivity (metres/day)			Antilog S_1
			Arithmetic Mean	Log Mean	Range	
Basalts		10	40.58	36.76	18.84-79.13	1.59
"		10	102.83	97.42	54.59-144.81	1.43
Colluvium		10	57.91	55.04	22.79-93.66	1.43
Babinda Catchment	0.1-0.2	45	2.09	1.36	0.08-11.17	2.69
– Metamorphics		5	1.73	1.43	0.5-2.98	2.09
Granites		10	24.78	22.93	10.84-38.91	1.54
"		10	7.68	7.16	3.69-10.92	1.50
"		10	17.63	16.58	8.31-27.59	1.47
"		10	15.13	12.26	1.56-27.35	2.29
Metamorphics		10	8.47	7.11	2.8-24.39	1.81
"		10	6.22	4.78	1.73-15.86	2.79
"		10	9.87	9.83	7.69-12.35	1.20
"		10	2.96	2.43	1.16-7.96	1.84
Basalts		10	9.13	8.59	5.1-17.1	1.44
"		10	13.46	13.09	8.7-21.12	1.28
Colluvium		10	9.33	8.4	2.66-15.39	1.69
peding layers						
Babinda Catchment	0.2-0.5	13	0.38	0.18	0.009-2.160	3.80
– Metamorphics		14	0.09	0.03	0.004-0.540	5.23
Granites		5	0.20	0.14	0.037-0.380	2.65
"		5	0.09	0.08	0.024-0.170	2.15
"		5	0.05	0.04	0.012-0.087	2.35
"		5	0.09	0.08	0.046-0.179	1.65
Metamorphics		5	0.29	0.25	0.068-0.510	2.13
"		5	0.02	0.02	0.020-0.028	1.14
"		5	0.20	0.19	0.140-0.260	1.30
"		5	0.02	0.02	0.012-0.031	1.43
Basalts		5	0.58	0.52	0.253-1.089	1.68
"		5	1.46	1.37	0.840-2.450	1.48
Colluvium		5	0.76	0.44	0.020-1.140	5.63
Babinda Catchment	0.5-1.0	6	0.99	0.26	0.050-4.520	5.88
– Metamorphics		11	0.03	0.02	0.003-0.110	2.88
Granites		5	0.08	0.06	0.023-0.210	2.47
"		5	0.02	0.02	0.007-0.060	2.23
"		5	0.01	0.01	0.004-0.018	1.87
"		5	0.03	0.03	0.013-0.061	1.83
Metamorphics		5	0.08	0.07	0.036-0.160	1.75
"		5	0.03	0.03	0.020-0.034	1.21
"		5	0.07	0.06	0.030-0.120	1.64
"		5	0.02	0.02	0.009-0.023	1.49
Basalts		5	0.16	0.13	0.057-0.270	2.04
"		5	0.17	0.17	0.136-0.272	1.33
Colluvium		5	0.66	0.61	0.370-1.100	1.56

The log mean values of K for the 0-0.1 m layers indicate that these surface soils are all highly pervious to the rainfall intensities experienced in the Babinda catchment. The K values for sites 3, 9 and 12 are particularly high and can be partly explained by the strong crumb structure in these surface soils (Table 1). It is noteworthy that sites 1 and 2 in the Babinda catchment are at the low end of the range. The density of treè roots and biopores is likely to be another factor accounting for K differences between sites. However, when within site variability is considered many locations have standard deviation of the log mean (S_1) values less than 2. These are low for the principal layer of biological activity. The greatest variability is found in the Babinda catchment soils, even allowing for differences in sample size.

Some of the above characteristics are also evident in the 0.1-0.2 m layer. In terms of the runoff process, most sites have a hydraulic conductivity that can accommodate even the highest rainfall intensities recorded on the wet coast (150 mm hr^{-1}). The exceptions are the Babinda catchment sites 1 and 2 and site 10 where some impedence to vertical fluxes would develop. Under these circumstances, the available water storage capacity in the soil matrix would be reduced and confined to the top 0.1 m. The corresponding figures for the catchment upper slope and incised area would be 13 mm and 30 mm respectively. Nevertheless it is important to recognise that the top 0.2 m of the profile is an important water storage in all these rainforest soils under most conditions.

The term 'impeding layer' referring to the impeding nature of the soil to the prevailing maximum 6 min. rainfall intensities of 25-150 mm hr^{-1} (GILMOUR & BONELL 1979, BONELL & GILMOUR 1980) is appropriate to most sites between December and mid-June in line with the Babinda catchment. The exception is the krasnozem, site 12 at 0.2-0.5 m whose log mean K ($\leqslant 57$ mm hr^{-1}) would accomodate most events that occur in the post-monsoon 'transitional' season. This site has a sizeable upper soil storage capacity for water. However, the hydraulic conductivity is much lower, like the other soils, below 0.5 m. Saturation overland flow is not likely to occur so frequently at this site. It is recognised that the basis of this comparison is on the reasonable assumption that similar rainfall intensities to those measured in the Babinda catchment prevail at the representative sites.

At this point it is interesting to compare these K values with the limited evidence available from other rainforest areas. In doing this, however, several problems must be recognised. There is a lack of standardisation in the determination of hydraulic conductivity, size of the sample and the depths of the soil profile tested; all of these will affect the results (BOUWER & JACKSON 1974, KIRKHAM 1955, LAL 1980). However the comparison remains useful to determine whether other soils differ markedly from those reported here.

PLA (1978) quoted by LAL (1980) reported saturated hydraulic conductivity of coarse textured Ultisols in Venezuela in the range 0.36-1.44 md^{-1}. The colluvium site 13 is possibly the equivalent soil type (ISBELL 1981 pers. comm.) in which case the K log means below 0.2 m depth are within PLA's range. The remaining finer textured Ultisols in the present data are an order of magnitude lower with one exception (site 3, 0.2-0.5 m depth). EL–SWAIFY (1980) noted measurements of saturated K of 1.2-2.2 md^{-1} taken from "undisturbed" cores in selected Oxisols in Hawaii, with little difference between the surface and oxic horizons. On the other hand, FOOTE et al. (1972) gave "estimates" of saturated K for most of Hawaii's Oxisols as being in the range 0.38-3.84 md^{-1}. The results at 0.2-0.5 m depth in the krasnozem sites 11 and 12 are within the range quoted by FOOTE et al. but the layers below 0.5 m depth are less than 0.38 md^{-1}. However the order of magnitude remains the same. Below 0.2 m depth only site 12 (0.2-0.5 m) is within EL–SWAIFY's range. There is also a marked difference between the surface and subsoil K at sites 11 and 12 in contrast with EL–SWAIFY's observations. This factor was also noted in Amazonas Oxisols near Manaus by NORTCLIFF & THORNES (1981). They reported an average surface K of 22.11 md^{-1} (0-0.15 m depth) which is lower than in sites 11 and 12 (0-0.10 m depth). But in comparison with the north Queensland krasnozems, remarkably high K values persist down the Amazonas profile to 0.90 m depth (3.76 md^{-1}, 0.15-0.60 m; 1.47 md^{-1}, 0.60-0.90 m) before the next change in the order of magnitude of K (0.52 md^{-1}, 0.90-1.15 m). A consequence of this high subsoil K is that the occurrence of overland flow is rare on these Amazonas soils (NORTCLIFF & THORNES 1981). Short term rainfall intensities are not reported but maximum daily totals are significantly lower than those experienced in the Babinda catchment, due to the absence of tropical cyclonic activity near the Equator. This factor combined with a deep upper soil store probably explains NORTCLIFF & THORNES' observation and only emphasises the variability of tropical rainforest environments.

6.2. THE BULK DENSITY FOR SPECIFIC LAYERS

The mean bulk density for each of the layers is shown in Table 3. However, these data do not totally explain the measured differences in hydraulic conductivity. This is because total porosity (a direct reflection of bulk density) does not relate in a functional way to hydraulic conductivity (HILLEL 1980). The pore size distribution is one of the important criteria in this regard. The intensive biological activity in the surface of these soils is reflected in the very low bulk density values (LAL 1980) which in turn are associated with exceedingly high hydraulic conductivity values. Most of the pore space in the surface soils is composed of large pores which are conducive to rapid translation of water. In the case of the two basalt sites 11 and 12, remarkably low bulk density values persist down the profile. This is a feature of these soils and the causes are still under investigation (MURTHA 1981 pers. comm.).

EL–SWAIFY (1980) and LAL (1980) quoted bulk densities in the range from 0.7-1.7 g cm^{-3} and 0.5-1.2 g cm^{-3} for selected Oxisols and west African Ultisols respectively. With the

Tab. 3: THE BULK DENSITY STATISTICS (ARITHMETIC MEANS OF 5 SAMPLES, g cm^{-3}) OF SOILS AT EACH SITE

Site No.	Depth intervals (m)				
	0-0.05	0.05-0.10	0.12-0.17	0.325-0.375	0.725-0.775
1	0.72	0.68	1.02	1.16	1.17
2	0.97	1.07	1.08	1.20	1.34
3	0.58	0.79	0.88	1.02	1.09
4	0.55	0.89	0.98	1.19	1.31
5	0.93	1.08	1.14	1.58	1.40
6	0.46	0.90	0.99	1.00	1.05
7	0.78	1.04	1.22	1.26	1.41
8	0.58	0.85	0.92	1.30	1.32
9	0.66	0.80	0.89	1.30	1.53
10	0.68	1.05	1.18	1.37	1.20
11	0.59	0.70	0.74	0.73	0.74
12	0.67	0.73	0.78	0.94	0.99
13	0.81	0.88	1.03	1.37	1.43

Tab. 4: THE SIGNIFICANCE LEVELS OF THE LEAST SQUARED DIFFERENCE BETWEEN PAIRS OF LOG MEAN HYDRAULIC CONDUCTIVITY, 0.2-0.5 m INTERVAL

	The Babinda Catchment (Metamorphics) 1. Lower slope runoff plot 1a, Red Podzolic	2. Upper slope runoff plot 2, Red Podzolic	Granites 3. Danbulla, Red Podzolic	4. Gilles Highway, Yellow Podzolic	5. Charappa Creek, Red Podzolic	6. Charappa Creek, Yellow Podzolic	Metamorphics 7. Kuranda, Red Podzolic	8. Kuranda, Red Podzolic	9. Mission Beach, Red Podzolic	10. Moresby, Yellow Podzolic	Basalts 11. Gadgarra, Krasnozem	12. Pin Gin Hill, Krasnozem	Colluvium 13. Mt. Mackay, Red Earth
The Babinda Catchment (Metamorphics)													
1. Lower slope runoff plot 1a, Red Podzolic		0.01						0.01		0.01		0.01	
2. Upper slope runoff plot 2, Red Podzolic	0.01		0.01				0.01		0.01		0.01	0.01	0.01
Granites													
3. Danbulla, Red Podzolic		0.01								0.01		0.01	
4. Gilles Highway, Yellow Podzolic											0.01	0.01	
5. Charappa Creek, Red Podzolic							0.01				0.01	0.01	0.01
6. Charappa Creek, Yellow Podzolic											0.01	0.01	
Metamorphics													
7. Kuranda, Red Podzolic		0.01			0.01			0.01		0.01			
8. Kuranda, Yellow Podzolic	0.01						0.01		0.01		0.01	0.01	0.01
9. Mission Beach, Red Podzolic		0.01						0.01		0.01		0.01	
10. Moresby, Yellow Podzolic	0.01		0.01				0.01		0.01		0.01	0.01	0.01
Basalts													
11. Gadgarra, Krasnozem		0.01		0.01	0.01	0.01		0.01		0.01			
12. Pin Gin Hill, Krasnozem	0.01	0.01	0.01	0.01	0.01	0.01		0.01	0.01	0.01			

CONDUCTIVITY, 0.50-1.0 m INTERVAL

Site	1	2	3	4	5	6	7	8	9	10	11	12	13
The Babinda Catchment (Metamorphics)													
1. Lower slope runoff plot 1a, Red Podzolic			0.01	0.01	0.01	0.01	0.01	0.01	0.01	0.01			
2. Upper slope runoff plot 2, Red Podzolic			0.01	0.01	0.01		0.01	0.01			0.01	0.01	0.01
Granites													
3. Danbulla, Red Podzolic	0.01	0.01			0.01								0.01
4. Gilles Highway, Yellow Podzolic	0.01	0.01			0.01	0.01					0.01		0.01
5. Charappa Creek, Red Podzolic	0.01	0.01	0.01	0.01			0.01	0.01			0.01		0.01
6. Charappa Creek, Yellow Podzolic	0.01			0.01			0.01	0.01					0.01
Metamorphics													
7. Kuranda, Red Podzolic	0.01	0.01			0.01	0.01					0.01		
8. Kuranda, Yellow Podzolic	0.01	0.01			0.01	0.01							0.01
9. Mission Beach, Red Podzolic	0.01										0.01		0.01
10. Moresby, Yellow Podzolic	0.01										0.01	0.01	0.01
Basalts													
11. Gadgarra, Krasnozem		0.01		0.01	0.01		0.01		0.01	0.01		0.01	0.01
12. Pin Gin Hill, Krasnozem		0.01								0.01	0.01		0.01
Colluvium													
13. Mt. Mackay, Red Earth		0.01	0.01	0.01	0.01	0.01		0.01	0.01	0.01	0.01	0.01	

exception of site 11 (0-0.5 m), the basalt soils are located at the lower end of EL–SWAIFY's range. The Ultisols at sites 3 and 6 have bulk densities similar to those reported by LAL but site 5, in particular, exceeds the upper figure of 1.2 g cm^{-3} below 0.2 m.

6.3. COMPARISON BETWEEN THE CATCHMENT RUNOFF PLOTS AND REPRESENTATIVE SITES

Tables 4 and 5 summarise the results of the LSD test between pairs of sites.

The upper slope plot (site 2) shows similarities (P > 0.01) in both the layers 0.2-0.5 m and 0.5-1.0 m with all the yellow podzolics (sites 4, 6, 8, 10) and the red granitic soils at Charappa Creek (site 5). The runoff plot (site 1) in the incised area shows no clear relationship with any particular group at 0.2-0.5 m. At this depth the significant differences (P < 0.01) are with the nearby site 2 and sites 8, 10 and 11. However, at 0.5-1.0 m site 1 is closely identified (P > 0.01) with the basalt and colluvium soils (sites 11, 12, 13). It would seem that this is the result of the large areas of weathered rock and rock floaters giving additional structure to the soils in this area of the experiment catchment.

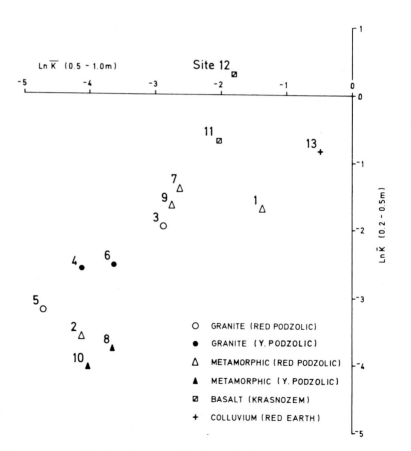

Fig. 2:   The scatter plot of the log$_e$K means of the impeding layer.

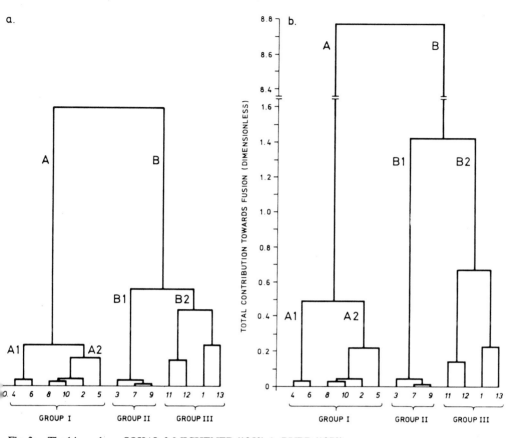

Fig. 3: The hierarchy a. SOKAL & MICHENER (1958), b. BURR (1970)

These comparisons can be extended to the runoff process if for the convenience of discussion similar slope angles, as well as short term rainfall intensities, found in the experimental catchment apply at all sites. Thus saturation overland flow could be regarded as the predominant storm flow component at locations identified with site 2. On the other hand, subsurface flow becomes more important at sites similar to site 1. Saturation overland flow will occur only under prolonged monsoonal intensities or the highest intensities in the post-monsoon 'transitional' season in line with the description for runoff plot site 1 (BONELL et al. 1981). The lowest frequency of saturation overland flow should be at site 12 on basalt due to the deep upper soil store.

The scatter plot and cluster analysis provide further insight into this description. The scatter plot of the $\log_e K$ means (Fig. 2) shows a nearly continuous distribution grading from predominantly yellow soils at one end of the spectrum, through a cluster of three red soils, into the higher hydraulic conductivity sites of the basalt, colluvium and runoff plot site 1. The within Babinda catchment differences are particularly emphasised. However, the near continual system makes it difficult to erect boundaries between groups and thus validates the application of cluster analysis. All four strategies produced the same groups and two dendrograms representing space dilating (BURR 1970) and space conserving (SOKAL &

MICHENER 1958) techniques are shown in Figure 3. Figure 3 suggests that all the yellow soils, the Babinda catchment site 2 and the Charappa Creek red (site 5) should be included in group I. Both dendrograms indicate a marked difference in hydraulic conductivity between this group and the remainder; even allowing for any inflation in the fusion levels resulting from group-size dependence in the space dilating techniques, as discussed by CLIFFORD & WILLIAMS (1973) and WILLIAMS (1976). The three red soils (sites 3, 7, 9) occupy group II which eventually fuses with group III that includes soils of the basalts, colluvium and runoff plot site 1. Those red podzolic soils represented in the cluster analysis group II (sites 3, 7, 9) occupy an intermediate position in the runoff process already described for soils in groups I and III.

6.4. COMPARISONS OF THE IMPEDING LAYER BETWEEN ALL SITES

The preceding analyses raises some other points which deserve comment. These are the effect of the factors geology, soil colour and annual rainfall on the overall K results.

It is evident that the geological factor explains some of the differences in selected cases. The two basalt sites 11 and 12 are closely identified with each other (P > 0.01, Tables 4 and 5, Figs. 2 and 3), despite a substantial difference in the annual rainfall. The colluvium site 13 shows significant differences from other sites except for the more permeable sites 1, 11 and 12 at 0.5-1.0 m depth (Tables 4 and 5). However, the analysis suggests that soil colour may be a more important criterion for comparing the soils of the granite and metamorphic rocks than underlying rock itself. There was a marked clustering of all the yellow soils from both granites and metamorphic in group I (Fig. 2 and 3). Table 2 shows that the yellow podzolic K values are generally an order of magnitude lower than K values for most of the red podzolics. The principal exceptions are the red soil sites 2 and 5 which are also included in group I. In fact the red podzolics are represented in all the three groups, however, most members are in group II. The macromorphology in Table 1 does not offer any significant reason for this pattern as the structure of both the yellow and red podzolics on the granites and metamorphics is very similar.

There is no obvious separation of the soils into groups on the basis of the drier and wetter end of th annual rainfall range. For example neither the basalt (11, 12) nor the yellow podzolic sites (4, 6, 8, 10) show any significant differences (P > 0.01, Tables 4 and 5) at both depths across the climatic spectrum. This is despite considerable variation in mean annual rainfall. The red podzolics are not so consistent, but even so the effect of different annual rainfalls is not obvious.

7. CONCLUSION

This work has demonstrated that the intensive biological activity in the top 0.1 m of these soils makes them capable of accepting the prevailing rainfall intensities. Similar conditions apply to the 0.1-0.2 m layer despite a decline in the log mean values of hydraulic conductivity. The possible exceptions are the two Babinda catchment runoff plots (sites 1 and 2) and a yellow podzolic (site 10) where some impedence to vertical fluxes would develop. However, in all cases the hydraulic conductivity and bulk density data suggest that the top 0.2 m is an important water store in these rainforest soils.

Most of the soil profiles below 0.2 m act as 'impeding layers' to the prevailing short term rainfall intensities. The results from the statistical and numerical analyses on the impeding layer K data have many features in common. This is despite cautionary remarks regarding the reliability of these methods.

In the light of these findings, any differences in hydraulic conductivity between sites is not considered significant under conditions of prolonged monsoonal intensities. Such situations occur frequently during the summer months due to tropical lows or cyclones or the persistance of an active monsoonal trough in the area (BONELL & GILMOUR 1980). At these times saturation overland flow is regarded to be an important storm flow component everywhere. Any temporary decline in rainfall intensities in summer storms, or more generally in the post-monsoon 'transitional' season, will allow the impeding layer K to control differences in the dominant storm flow components between sites. Saturation overland flow is thought to still prevail on all the yellow podzolics and the red podzolic site 5 (group I) in conformity with runoff plot site 2. On the other hand, subsurface flow becomes more important at sites in group III except at the highest intensities when saturation overland flow will develop in line with the description for runoff plot 1a (site 1) (BONELL et al. 1981). Saturation overland flow is thought to be not so frequent at site 12, on basalt, due to the deep upper store. The red podzolics on the granites and metamorphics in group II occupy an intermediate position in the runoff process between these two extremes. During the period of lowest rainfall intensities associated mainly with SE stream shower activity, the Babinda catchment work suggests that the soil below 0.2 m only occasionally acts as an impeding layer. At these times sites in group I are the most likely to generate slope runoff, however, the volumes concerned would be very small.

Other findings from this work suggest that the geological factor influences hydraulic conductivity of the impeding layers directly in terms of soils derived from the basalts and colluvium and indirectly when considering soil colour of the granites and metamorphics. There is some element of agreement with the generally held notion that the yellow colour in soils is attributed to poor drainage and aeration properties (SOIL SURVEY STAFF 1951). However, the converse applying to red soils is not evident in this work as two red podzolics closely identify with the yellow podzolics. The effect of spatial variability of annual rainfall did not cause any obvious separation into 'dry' and 'wet' soil groups for sites of similar geology or soil colour.

Despite the limited nature of the comparisons made with other work, it seems likely that there will be some differences between the present results and results from locations elsewhere in the humid tropics. This explains why the runoff generation processes can vary between tropical rainforest areas (WALSH 1980), particularly when the prevailing rainfall intensities are different from those described for the Babinda catchment.

The results of this initial study demonstrate the relevance of the detailed studies within the South Creek catchment to the development of a regional description of the rainforest's hydrology. Equally, they illustrate the limitations of the catchment studies as technically, they only relate to the eleven external sites as representatives of each soil system. At present, no allowance can be made for the variability within each soil system, including the effects of changing slope angles. In addition much of the discussion of runoff response has depended on the assumption that rainfall intensities experienced in the Babinda catchment prevail throughout the region. Clearly, there is a need for a much greater understanding of the spatial variation in soil types, in soil physical characteristics within soil types and in the rainfall intensity regimes within the region before anything approaching a complete understanding of the regions hydrology is developed.

ACKNOWLEDGEMENTS

The field work for this project was carried out with the assistence of M.J. Devery whose help is gratefully acknowledged. Additional advice and assistence was given by R.J. Coventry, R.F. Isbell, G.G. Murtha and J. Williams, CSIRO, Division of Soils, Townsville; and R. John, CSIRO, Division of Mathematics and Statistics, Townsville.

REFERENCES

BAKER, F.G. (1978): Variability of hydraulic conductivity within and between nine Wisconsin soil series. Water Resources Research 14, 103-108.

BOERSMA, L. (1965): Field measurement of hydraulic conductivity above a water table. In: Methods of Soil Analysis. Ed. C.A. Black, Agronomy Vol. 9, 234-252, American Society of Agronomy, Madison, Wisconsin.

BONELL, M. & GILMOUR, D.A. (1980): Variations in short-term rainfall intensity in relation to synoptic climatological aspects of the humid tropical north-east Queensland coast. Singapore Journal of Tropical Geography 1 (2), 16-30.

BONELL, M., GILMOUR, D.A. & SINCLAIR, D.F. (1981): Soil hydraulic properties and their effect on surface and subsurface water transfer in a tropical rainforest catchment. Hydrological Sciences Bulletin 26, 1-18.

BOUWER, H. & JACKSON, R.D. (1974): Determining soil properties. In: Drainage for Agriculture. Ed. J. van Schilfgaarde, Agronomy Vol. 17, 611-66, American Society of Agronomy, Madison, Wisconsin.

BURR, E.J. (1968): Cluster sorting with mixed character types I. Standardisation of character values. Australian Computer Journal 1, 97-99.

BURR, E.J. (1970): Cluster sorting with mixed character types II. Fusion strategies. Australian Computer Journal 2, 98-103.

CHILDS, E.C. (1969): An Introduction to the Physical Basis of Soil Water Phenomena. Wiley, London. 493 pp.

CLIFFORD, H.T. & WILLIAMS, W.T. (1973): Classificatory dendrograms and their interpretation. Australian Journal of Botany 21, 151-162.

DALE, M.B., HAIN, D., LANCE, G.M., MILNE, P., ROSS, D., THOMAS, M. & WILLIAMS, W.T. (1980): TAXON Users Manual. Edition 2, C.S.I.R.O., Division of Computing Research.

DUNIN, F.X. (1976): Infiltration: Its simulation for field conditions. In: Facets of Hydrology. Ed. J.C. Rodda, 199-227, Wiley – Interscience. London.

EL–SWAIFY, S.A. (1980): Physical and mechanical properties of Oxisols. In: Soils with Variable Charge. Ed. B.K.G. Theng, 303-324, New Zealand Society of Soil Science, Soil Bureau, Department of Scientific and Industrial Research, Lower Hutt, New Zealand.

EVERITT, B. (1980): Cluster Analysis. 2nd Edition, Social Science Research Council – Heinemann, London, 136 pp.

FOOTE, D.E., HILL, E.L., NAKAMURA, S. & STEVENS, F. (1972): Soil Survey of the Islands of Kauai, Oahu, Maui, Molokai, and Lanai, State of Hawaii. U.S. Department of Agriculture, Soil Conservation Service. 130 pp.

GILMOUR, D.A. & BONELL, M. (1979): Six-minute rainfall intensity data for an exceptionally heavy tropical rainstorm. Weather 34, 148-158.

GILMOUR, D.A., BONELL, M. & SINCLAIR, D.F. (1980): An Investigation of Storm Drainage Processes in a Tropical Rainforest Catchment. Australian Water Resources Council, Technical Paper 56, Australian Government Publishing Service, Canberra, 93 pp.

HEWLETT, J.D. (1974): Comments on letters relating to "Role of subsurface flow in generating surface runoff, 2 Upstream source areas" by R. Allan Freeze. Water Resources Research 10, 605-607.

HILLEL, D. (1980): Fundamentals of Soil Physics. 413 pp. Academic Press, New York.

ISBELL, R.F., WEBB, A.A. & MURTHA, G.G. (1968): Atlas of Australian Soils. Sheet 7, North Queensland with explanatory data, C.S.I.R.O. and Melbourne University Press, Melbourne.

KIRKBY, M.J. (ed.) (1978): Hillslope Hydrology. Wiley, Chichester. 389 pp.

KIRKHAM, D. (1955): Measurement of the hydraulic conductivity of soil in place. Symposium on permability of soils. American Society for Testing Materials, Special Technical Publication 163, 80-97.

LAL, R. (1980): Physical and mechanical composition of Alfisols and Ultisols with particular reference to soils in the tropics. In: Soils with Variable Charge. Ed. B.K.G. Theng, 253-279. New Zealand Society of Soil Science, Soil Bureau, Department of Scientific and Industrial Research, Lower Hutt, New Zealand.

LANCE, G.N. & WILLIAMS, W.T. (1967): A general theory of classificatory sorting strategies: 1 Hierarchial Systems. Computer Journal **9**, 373-380.

MAASLAND, M. (1957): Factors causing anisotropy and evidence of anisotropy in soils. In: Drainage of Agricultural Lands. Ed. J.N. Luthin, Agronomy Vol. 7, 240. American Society of Agronomy, Madison, Wisconsin.

MURTHA, G.G. (1982): Soils of the Tully Innisfail Area – Soil Series and Maping Units. C.S.I.R.O. Division of Soils, Divisional Report, in press.

NIELSEN, D.R., BIGGAR, J.W, & ERH, K.T. (1973): Spatial variability of field-measured soil-water properties. Hilgardia **42**, 215-260.

NORTHCLIFF, S. & THORNES, J.B. (1981): Seasonal variations in the hydrology of a small forested catchment near Manaus, Amazonas, and the implications for its management. In: Tropical Agricultural Hydrology. Ed. R. Lal and F.W. Russell. 37-57. Wiley.

NORTHCOTE, K.H. (1979): A Factual Key for the Recognition of Australian Soils. 4th Edition, Rellim Technical Publications, Glenside, South Australia, 124 pp.

ROGOWSKI, A.S. (1972): Watershed physics: soil variability criteria. Water Resources Research **8**, 1015-1023.

SNEDECOR, G.W. & COCHRAN, W.G. (1967): Statistical Methods. 6th Edition. Iowa State University Press, Iowa, U.S.A., 593 pp.

SOIL SURVEY STAFF (1951): Soil Survey Manual. U.S. Department of Agriculture Hand book No. 18, Government Printer, Washington, D.C., 189-191.

SOIL SURVEY STAFF (1975): Soil Taxonomy. A basic system of soil classification for making and interpreting soil surveys. U.S. Department of Agriculture Handbook No. 436, 754 pp.

SOKAL, R.R. & MICHENER, C.D. (1958): A statistical method for evaluating systematic relationships. University of Kansas Scientific Bulletin **38**, 1409-1438.

STACE, H.C.T., HUBBLE, G.D., BREWER, R., NORTHCOTE, K.H., SLEEMAN, J.R., MULCAHY, M.J. & HALLSWORTH, E.G. (1968): A Handbook of Australian Soils. Rellim Technical Publications, Glenside, South Australia, 435 pp.

TALSMA, T. (1960): Comparison of field methods of measuring hydraulic conductivity. International Commission on Irrigation and Drainage, 4th Congress, Madrid, C11, 145-156.

TALSMA, T. (1965): Sample size estimates in permeability studies. Proceedings of American Society of Civil Engineers **91**, 76-77.

TALSMA, T. (1969): In situ measurement of sorptivity. Australian Journal of Soil Research **7**, 269-276.

TALSMA, T. & HALLAM, P.M. (1980): Hydraulic conductivity measurement of forest catchments. Australian Journa of Soils Research **18**, 139-148.

TRACEY, J.G. & WEBB, L.J. (1975): A key to the vegetation of the humid tropical region of north Queensland – Bartle Frere 1:100,000 sheet C.S.I.R.O. Rainforest Ecology Unit, Division of Plant Industry, Long Pocket Laboratories, Indooroophilly, Brisbane, Queensland.

TUKEY, J.W. (1977): Exploratory Data Analysis. Addison-Wesley, Reading, Massachusetts, U.S.A., 688 pp.

U.N.E.S.C.O. (1978): Tropical Forest Ecosystems: a state of knowledge report. U.N.E.S.C.O., Paris, 258-261.

WALSH, R.P.D. (1980): Runoff processes and models in the humid tropics. Zeitschrift für Geomorphologie N.F. Supplement Band **36**, 176-202.

WARD, J.H. (1963): Hierarchical grouping to optimize an objective function. Journal of the American Statistical Association **58**, 491-501.

WEBSTER, R. (1975): Intuition and rational choice in the application of mathematics to soil systematics. Soil Science **119**, 394-404.

WEBSTER, R. (1977): Quantitative and Numerical Methods in Soil Classification and Survey. Clarendon, Oxford. 269 pp.

WILLIAMS, W.T. (1971): Principles of clustering. Annual Review of Ecological Systematics **2**, 303-326.

WILLIAMS, W.T. (Ed.) (1976): Pattern Analysis in Agricultural Science. C.S.I.R.O. – Elsevier, Melbourne – Amsterdam, 331 pp.

WINGER, R.J. (1960): In-place permeability tests and their use in subsurface drainage. International Commission on Irrigation and Drainage, 4th Congress, Madrid, 48 pp.

WILSHART, D. (1978): CLUSTAN User Manual. 3rd Edition, Program Library Unit, Edinburgh University.

ZANGER, C.N. (1953): Theory and problems of water percolation. Engineering Monographs No. **8**, Bureau of Reclamation, Denver, Colorado, U.S.A., 48-71.

Addresses of authors:

M. Bonell, Department of Geography, James Cook University of North Queensland, Townsville Qld 4811, Australia

D.A. Gilmour, Queensland Forestry Department, Forestry Training and Conference Centre, Gympie Qld 4570, Australia

D.S. Cassells, Forest Research Branch, Queensland Forestry Department, Gympie Qld 4570, Australia

Jan de Ploey (Ed.):
Rainfall Simulation, Runoff and Soil Erosion
CATENA SUPPLEMENT 4, Braunschweig 1983

STUDIES OF EROSION THRESHOLDS IN SEMI–ARID AREAS: FIELD MEASUREMENTS OF SOIL LOSS AND INFILTRATION IN NORTHERN MOROCCO

A.C. **Imeson**, Amsterdam

SUMMARY

Infiltration measurements and erosion plot data are described for a semi-arid area in the Rif Mountains of Northern Morocco. Infiltration envelopes were constructed from sorptivity measurements to indicate the relative frequency of ponding at the erosion plot sites. Actual amounts of soil loss were only partially related to ponding thresholds due to the effects of slope and surface storage. In general the infiltration envelopes were greatly influenced by the presence of a surface crust but the effect of antecedent precipitation was relatively short-lived. Other factors, which are also related to soil loss and infiltration, need to be considered if the erratic response of erosion to rainfall in semi-arid areas is to be explained. These are the chemical conditions which influence the dispersion of clay particles and the effect of the depth of the ponded water film on sediment entrainment.

ZUSAMMENFASSUNG

Infiltrationsversuche und Ergebnisse von Erosionsmeßparzellen werden aus einem semiariden Gebiet im Rif-Gebirge Nord-Marokkos beschrieben. Es wurden Versickerungsmodelle anhand von Infiltrationsmessungen aufgestellt, um die relative Häufigkeit von Oberflächenstau auf den Probeflächen zu erklären. Für die Erklärung des Bodenverlustes ist neben dem Schwellenwert für den Oberflächenstau aber auch die Hangneigung und das Volumen von Oberflächendepressionen wichtig. Die Infiltrationsparameter werden sehr stark durch die Anwesenheit einer Oberflächenkruste beeinflußt, aber die Auswirkungen von Vorregen waren nur recht kurz. Um die überraschenden Erosionsbeträge in semiariden Gebieten erklären zu können, müssen sowohl die chemischen Bedingungen untersucht werden, die die Dispersion der Tonfraktion beeinflussen, als auch die Schichtdicke des Oberflächenabflusses in ihrer Auswirkung auf die Sediment-Mobilisierung.

1. INTRODUCTION

In a recent paper BRYAN & CAMPBELL (1980) highlighted the problem of interpreting erosion plot and sediment yield data from semi-arid environments. It was pointed out that because infiltration capacities vary immensely, the response of runoff to rainfall is highly erratic and that further, due to irregular sediment contributions from overland flow, the relationship between sediment yield and discharge is highly variable. Even for controlled experimental conditions, BRYAN & LUK (1981) reported considerable variability in the amount of soil loss from replicated laboratory experiments.

This paper reports sediment loss data from a number of small plot experiments in a semi-arid area of Northern Morocco and describes the infiltration characteristics of the sampling sites related to threshold amounts of rainfall required to produce ponding. Two other conditions related to sediment entrainment are the thickness of the ponded waterfilm and the chemistry of the soil solution and runoff. These last two aspects of the sediment entrainment problem will be treated more fully in a subsequent publication.

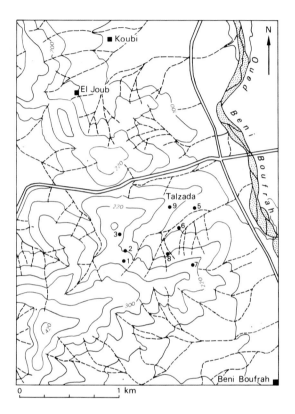

Fig. 1:   Location of the fieldwork area near Beni Boufrah, Morocco, and the location of the erosion plots.

1.1.   THE FIELD AREA

The study area is located in the Rif Mountains of northeast Morocco, close to the Mediterranean coast and the small town of Beni Boufrah (Fig. 1). The highly variable annual precipitation averages about 300 mm and falls mainly during the winter. The runoff plots and infiltration sites are located near the villages of El Joub and Talzda in a steeply sloping area of flysch rocks. The soils of this area have been mapped and described by JUNGERIUS (1982). On the north facing slopes usually reddish soils (Calcaric fluvisols) are found in red slope deposits, while elsewhere thin, brown, calcic cambisols are present. At a few sites particularly on marine deposits near Koubi, sodic and saline soils locally occur.

The observation points and sampling sites were selected on the basis of a pedogeomorphological survey, which had as its objective the recognition of landscape units which were relatively homogeneous with respect to slope, terrain position and soil type. This part of the Rif Mountains is an area of dry farming whereby predominantly barley is sown after the first winter rains in November and December. The remoter and poorer soils are not cultivated and support a maquis vegetation, often degraded and grazed by goats and sheep.

1.2. RAINFALL AND PONDING

If the intensity of rainfall (i) is higher than the prevailing saturated hydraulic conductivity (k_s) of the soil and if rainfall continues long enough, the soil surface will eventually become ponded. Several authors have discussed the relationship between rainfall intensity and ponding described by the infiltration envelope in some detail (RUBIN 1968, SMITH 1972, PARLANGE & SMITH 1972, SMITH & PARLANGE 1978, MOORE, LARSON & SLACK 1980). The time to ponding (t_p), apart from a rainfall characteristic, is also a reflection of a number of soil parameters related to the storage and transmission of water (AHUJA et al. 1976) in and through the soil. Although ponding does not imply the actual occurrence of surface runoff, due to surface storage, the ponding point represents an important threshold above which runoff is possible. Ponding times have been used in runoff and erosion studies, for example, by AHUJA et al. (1976) in Hawaii, by SCOGING & THORNES (1979) and THORNES (1980) in Southern Spain and by LI (1979) in a simple method for modelling on site soil erosion. SMITH & PARLANGE (1978) describe simple relationships which enable ponding times to be estimated from values of k_s and sorptivity (s). In Morocco it was found by IMESON & KWAAD (1980) that the amount of rain required to pond the soil (p_r) could be predicted reasonably well with one of these equations, namely

$$\int_{0}^{t_p} p_r \, dt = \frac{A}{k_s} \ln \frac{r_p}{r_p - k_s} \tag{1}$$

where $A = \dfrac{s^2}{2}$ and r_p the rainfall intensity.

1.3. FIELD MEASUREMENTS AND LABORATORY PROCEDURES

Field measurements of infiltration were made at sites located in the area of Talzda and Joub (Fig. 1) using a rainfall simulator described by IMESON (1977) and IMESON & KWAAD (1980). To obtain infiltration envelopes directly an apparently homogeneous sample area of about 40 m^2 was selected and at various locations within this, the ponding time (t_p) was recorded for different intensities. For each measurement the simulator had to be moved. Ponding was arbitrarily considered to be reached when approximately 40 per cent of the surface had attained this state. Due to microtopographic irregularities and the resulting redistribution of rainfall, a value of 40 per cent seemed from experience to be appropriate. A value of 100 per cent ponding occurred a relatively long time after ponding and overland flow had commenced in the microtopographic depressions. A disadvantage of this procedure is that the sample area is never completely homogeneous and that slight differences in soil moisture, crust development and stoniness can have a large effect on the value of t_p.

7

Nevertheless, in most cases very good infiltration envelopes were obtained with this procedure. The greatest drawback was the time required to complete the measurements.

The second type of measurement consisted of recording the accumulated infiltration at 30 second intervals when the ground surface was kept ponded over 40 per cent of its surface. This was achieved by continually reducing the rainfall intensity during the test. Measurements of this type were highly reproducible (IMESON & KWAAD 1981) and were used to calculate values of sorptivity required for constructing the infiltration envelopes with equation 1. The initial gradient of the cumulative infiltration curve plotted against $\sqrt{t}$ gives the value of the sorptivity (DUNIN 1976).

Small microplots were established in the winter of 1978/1979 in an attempt to establish the relative erodibility of the soils on the different geomorphological units. It was also hoped that data could be collected to examine the degree to which ponding relationships were related to runoff amounts and soil losses measured under natural rainfall. Due to problems of installation, maintenance and vandalism, reliable measurements were not obtained until February 1979, and thereafter only until July 1979. During this period, only ten rainfall events were recorded, none of which were extreme. Because of disturbances and other uncertainties, only data from five of the plots are considered reliable, even for this short period. Another limitation was the small area of the plots, averaging 4 m^2.

At sites where infiltration measurements were made the soil moisture content was determined at the surface and at a depth of 10 cm. Soil samples were collected and in the laboratory determinations made of grainsize distributions (without pretreatment to remove carbonates), pH, organic matter and saturated hydraulic conductivity. The pH was measured using a 1:25 soil 0.01 M CaCl$_2$ solution or H$_2$O ratio. Aggregate stability was determined by a procedure similar to that described by LOW (1954) whereby here the number of impacts from 2.7 mm waterdrops, allowed to fall 1 m, required to break 4-5 mm diameter aggregates sufficiently for them to pass through a 3 mm wire sieve, was counted. The dispersion index was determined by using the procedure of LOVEDAY & PYLE (1974). The soil erodibility factor of the Universal Soil Loss Equation was estimated from the nomogram in WISCH-MEIER & SMITH (1978) without correcting for permeability or soil structure.

2. INFILTRATION MEASUREMENTS

The threshold rainfall amounts required to produce ponding at the plot sites were calculated from measurements made during April and May 1979 using equation 1. The dry antecedent conditions are reflected in the soil moisture contents of the top 10 cm of soil, which ranged from 0.9 to 2.5 per cent. It proved impossible to use laboratory values of k_s in equation 1 as these were too unreliable. Instead appropriate values were found by fitting the calculated data, using measured values of sorptivity, to measured infiltration envelopes. For the soils considered here the infiltration envelopes were not very sensitive to the range of k_s values encountered in the field, for values of $t_p < 30$ min. Infiltration envelopes calculated for the different plot sites at k_s values of 1 cm h^{-1} are shown in Fig. 3.

Apart from plot sites 1 and 7, which would appear to be easily ponded and plot 9 where the rate of water acceptance is high, the infiltration envelopes appear rather similar. The high rate of infiltration at this last site is possibly a reflection of the coarse texture of the soil (50% > 2 mm) and the high aggregate stability.

There do not appear to be any obvious explanations for the low rates of infiltration at sites 1 and 7. As at all sites the soil surface was crusted and this is thought to be one ex-

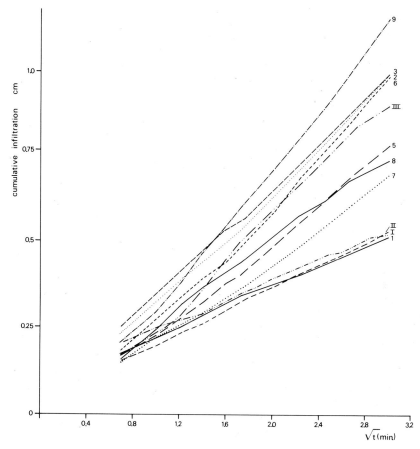

Fig. 2:   Measurements of cumulative infiltration rates at the plot sites and under degraded maquis (I, II & III)

planation for the relative similarity of most measurements.

The effect of both the initial soil moisture content and surface sealing on infiltration rates are well known (see for example DUNIN 1976). The effect of surface sealing is clearly indicated in Fig. 4, where cumulative infiltration rates are shown for sites having an intact crust and a crust which was broken. The effect of antecedent precipitation is also indicated in Fig. 4, showing infiltration measurements made during a period of wet weather. It was found that even during the winter the influence of antecedent rainfall on the sorptivity was relatively shortlived.

For comparison with the cultivated plot sites infiltration measurements made during the same period are also shown for a site near Talzda, under degraded shrubland ("parcours") used intensively for grazing. The parcours has a variable cover of 30-80 cm high shrubs separated by many animal pathways. The soil is everywhere trampled, usually has a surface crust and many stone and root capped pedestals indicating recent soil erosion. Three infiltration measurements are shown (Fig. 2) for a humus-rich soil at a protected site beneath a shrub (I), for a site on one of the pathways (II) and for a site on a pathway where the crust

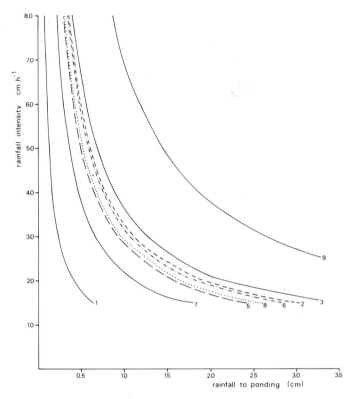

Fig. 3:   Infiltration envelopes calculated with equation 1 for the different plot sites.

was deliberately broken (III).

In spite of the contrasting cover types, curves I and II resemble the sorptivity measurements at plot 1. The third site III has a much higher rate of infiltration but this is nevertheless similar to the average rate of infiltration recorded at the cultivated plots. It would seem from these and other measurements that soils under a degraded maquis vegetation usually have lower rates of water acceptance than soils under cultivation.

3.   PLOT MEASUREMENTS

Surface conditions recorded during April 1979 in the plots are described in Table 1. Values of roughness refer to point measurements and indicate the average amplitude of the relief (cm). Also shown is the storage parameter (S_y) SEGINER (1971) which indicates the combined effect of slope and roughness. When $S_y > 1.5$ no storage is possible. All of the plots had a surface covered by a crust or by stones.

From a summary of the soil analyses of the Ap horizons (Table 2) it is clear that the cover of stones on the surface, estimated by using charts describing mottling, is greater than indicated by the laboratory analysis of the Ap horizons.

The rainfall events occurring during the observation period and the amount of sediment

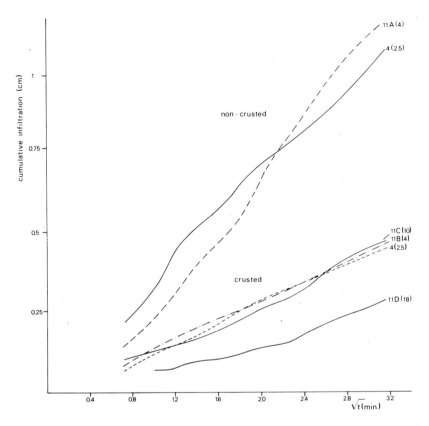

Fig. 4:   Effect of the presence of a surface crust on cumulative infiltration at sites 4 and 11. The figures in parenthesis indicate the volumetric soil moisture content.

collected are indicated in Tables 3 and 4. It can be seen that overland flow was not always verified, even though sometimes relatively large amounts of sediment were collected. Nevertheless, the largest soil losses did coincide with the ascertained occurrence of plot run-off. When the plots are compared, a relatively consistent pattern emerges with plot 2, general-ly losing the most soil and recording most overland flow. Conversely plots 1, 7, and 8 suffered relatively little erosion, except when overland flow occurred on plot 8. Plot 7 was clearly the plot recording the lowest soil loss. The totals collected for each rainfall event were ranked and the average rank number for each plot calculated.

Comparing the plot results with the soil properties at each site (Table 2, 3 and 4), the almost complete lack of relationship between soil loss and soil conditions is at first surprising. For example, there is no apparant relationship between on the one hand soil loss and on the other k_s, erodibility, the dispersion index or sorptivity. The lower the sorptivity the more fre-quently overland flow might be expected but this is not the case. Plot 1 should have been pon-ded most frequently but overland flow was never recorded. Plot 2, where runoff occurred most frequently, is the least likely to be ponded.

The seemingly contradictory relationships can partly be explained by the plot charac-

Tab. 1: SOME SURFACE CHARACTERISTICS RECORDED IN THE PLOTS DURING APRIL 1979

plot no.	slope (degrees)	roughness cm	Sy	stoniness	% crust covered surface	vegetation
1	17.5	5-15	0.46	25	70	poor cover of barley
2	25	5	1.41	7	93	poor cover of barley
3	19.5	1-2	3.5	100	–	no cover
5	5	7	0.12	35	65	good cover of barley
6	17.5	10	0.23	5	95	moderate cover of wheat
7	9	12	0.198	35	65	good cover of barley
8	15	3-4	0.268	90	10	no cover
9	10	10	0.26	40	60	good cover of barley

The percentage of the surface covered by stones and crust were estimated by using the Munsell charts for describing % of mottles. Sy is the storage parameter described by SEGINER (1971).

Tab. 2: PARTICLE SIZE DISTRIBUTION, DISPERSION INDEX (DI), HUMUS; BULK DENSITY, pH, K FACTOR (K_w), SORPTIVITY (s) AND k_s VALUE FOR THE Ap HORIZONS OF THE PLOT SOILS

Plot	% > 2mm	% < 2μm	2-50μm	50-2000μm	DI	humus	BD	pH H_2O	$CaCl_2$	k_w	s cm min$^{-1/2}$	k_s m day^{-1}
1	26.5	27.5	33.9	38.6	2	4.77		7.5	7.1	0.1	0.13	–
2	11.6	48	20.8	31.2	0	1.9	1.22	7.8	7.4	0.1	0.3	2.6
3	32	30	35.2	34.8	1	1.18	1.41	7.7	7.3	0.16	0.3	2.2
5	16	26.5	21.2	52.3	3	1.34	1.31	7.6	7.2	0.18	0.27	0.24
6	6	38.5	24.9	36.6	4	1.73	1.4	7.7	7.4	0.12	0.34	0.38
7	31	28.5	30.1	41.4	2	2.35	1.15	7.7	7.3	0.14	0.21	2.9
8	18.5	23	40.8	36.2	5	0.82	1.3	.7.9	7.4	0.12	0.28	4.09
9	59	24.5	23.5	53.0	4	2.86	1.51	7.5	7.0	0.12	0.41	0.57

Tab. 3: THE AMOUNT OF SOIL LOSS (GRAMS) RECORDED FOLLOWING RAINFALL EVENTS ON THE INDICATED DAY

date 1979	rainfall (mm)	plot 1	2	3	7	8
22 Jan.	12.9	results unreliable				
29 Jan.	7.4	results unreliable				
3 Febr.	4.7	7.6	9.9	4.1	5.8	7.3
13 Febr.	11.2	117	128	84	176	503
15 Febr.	8.9	38	*	385	19	54
20 Febr.	4.6	11	13	8	2.1	7
23 Febr.	8.2	13	24	17	3.6	19
27 Febr.	2.3	4.5	5.3 .	6	3.2	6.5
1 March	5.8	13	47	47	6.8	12
20 March	6.2	13	95	67	4.15	3.9
12 April	?	1.2	15	13	x	x
29 May	?	x	10	7	5.5	2.9
Average rank number		3.3	1.2	2.1	5.0	3.1

x   plot measurements.
Values underlined indicate that overland flow was recorded.

Tab. 4:   AMOUNTS OF SEDIMENT COLLECTED FROM THE TALZDA PLOTS gms.m.$^{-2}$ mm.$^{-1}$ rain

date	1	2	plot 3	(7)	(8)
15.2.1979	2.37	n.r.	18.08	0.9	2.6
20.2.1979	1.32	1.62	0.67	0.21	0.65
23.2.1979	0.9	1.68	0.57	0.2	1.01
27.2.1979	1.08	1.3	1.06	0.64	1.18
1.3.1979	1.25	4.71	3.37	0.55	0.92
20.3.1979	1.2	8.87	4.54	0.31	0.26

Values underlined indicate that overland flow was confirmed.

teristics indicated in Table 1, particularly plot slope and roughness, both of which are related to surface storage. Plot 1, where ponding is frequently indicated by the infiltration measurements, is extremely rough with large deep furrows parallel to the contour. Plot 7 with its relatively gentle slope and high degree of roughness is the least likely plot to produce runoff based on these characteristics. Conversely, very little storage is likely to be possible on plots 2 and 3 where the value of S_y is high (SEGINER 1971).

4.   DISCUSSION AND CONCLUSIONS

The small scale plot measurements indicate that the high potential for erosion reflected in the high erodibility of the soil and low infiltration rates does not necessarily result in high rates of runoff and soil loss. Differences in soil loss could not be explained by differences in soil conditions, although this might not have been the case if more extreme rainfall conditions had been recorded. For the rainfall events that occurred, it would seem that in this semi-arid area, the microtopographic roughness resulting from contour ploughing exerts a greater effect on runoff and soil loss than the infiltration characteristics of the soil. Nevertheless, the infiltration envelopes indicate a varying erosion hazard at the different plot sites. They also go some way in providing an explanation for some of the variability in runoff plot data and enable runoff to be estimated, if surface storage conditions are known, for rainfall events of different recurrence intervals.

Apart from the effects of surface storage and slope on actual runoff and soil loss, two other factors mentioned in the introduction influence the variability of the data. Sediment concentrations during floods in the wadi Beni Boufrah and Wadi Cala Iris (Fig. 1) vary in a way which suggests that clay particles are being dispersed as a result of a combination of a high exchangeable sodium percentage (ESP) and a relatively low electrolyte concentration (IMESON & VERSTRATEN 1981). Dispersion as a result of relatively high ESP values has been demonstrated to produce surface seals with infiltration rates lower than those of crusts formed by rainfall and sedimentation (AGASSI et al. 1981, SHAINBERG 1981). For the plot sites considered here, laboratory measurements of exchangeable cations and water soluble salts indicated that ESP values were too low and electrolyte concentrations too high to cause dispersion. At nearby sites, 2 km to the north, where soluble salts have accumulated in the soil profile, this was not the case (IMESON, KWAAD & VERSTRATEN 1982) and ponding times were much shorter than those described above. Apart from reducing the ponding time, dispersion also results in the runoff containing higher concentrations of suspended sediment. Soil from plot 3 and saline soil from Koubi, for example, were subjected to a number of laboratory experiments with a rainfall simulator and the sediment concentration of the runoff measured under ponded conditions. With a 3 mm waterfilm, maximum concentrations of suspended solids reached almost 4000 mg l^{-1} in the experiments with the saline soil, but only 2300 mg l^{-1} in soil from Talzda. With a waterfilm of 10 mm, corresponding maxima were respectively 320 and 23 mg l^{-1}. These experiments clearly indicate that temporal and spatial variations in sediment concentrations will be considerable as waterfilms develop and thicken as a result of ponding, and furthermore, that the chemistry of the soil solution and runoff are also important factors which need to be considered.

ACKNOWLEDGEMENT

Drs. F.J.P.M. Kwaad, with whom the fieldwork reported was jointly undertaken, is gratefully thanked for his advice and support. This work was carried out within the framework of the REDRA project, supported by the Netherlands Council for Pure Scientific Research (ZWO). Drs. M. Vis is thanked for his help and advice, and J.C. Venema, A. Vlaanderen and H.v.d.Brink for performing some of the fieldwork. Mrs. M.C.G. Keijzer–v.d. Lubbe is thanked for the German Zusammenfassung and for preparing the manuscript.

REFERENCES

AGASSI, M., SHAINBERG, I. & MORIN, J. (1981): Effect of electrolyte concentration and soil sodicity on infiltration rate and crust formation. Soil Sci. Soc. of America Journal **45**, 848-851.
AHUJA, L.R., DANGLER, E.W. & EL–SWAIFY, S.A. (1976): Predicting runoff initiation times under field conditions in tropical (Hawaii) soils. Soil Sci. Soc. of America Journal **40**, 777-779.
BRYAN, R.B. & CAMPBELL, I.A. (1980): Sediment entrainment and transport during local rainstorms in the Steveville badlands, Alberta. CATENA **7**, 51-65.
BRYAN, R.B. & SHIU–HUNG LUK (1981): Laboratory experiments on the variation of soil erosion under simulated rainfall. Geoderma **6**, 245-265.
DUNIN, F.X. (1976): Infiltration: its simulation for field conditions. 199-227. In: RODDA, J.C. (Ed.): Facets of Hydrology. J. Wiley & Sons Ltd., Chichester.
IMESON, A.C. (1977): A simple field-portable rainfall simulator for difficult terrain. Earth Surface Processes **2**, 431-436.
IMESON, A.C. & KWAAD, F.J.P.M. (1980): Field measurements of infiltration in the Rif Mountains of Morocco. Studia Geomorphologica Carpatha Balcanica, Krakow.
IMESON, A.C., KWAAD, F.J.P.M. & VERSTRATEN, J.M. (1982): An examination of the relationship between soil physical and chemical properties and the development of badlands in Morocco. In: BRYAN, R.B. & YAIR, A. (Eds.): Badland Geomorphology and Pipe Erosion. GeoBooks, Norwich.
IMESON, A.C. & VERSTRATEN, J.M. (1981): Suspended solids concentrations and river water chemistry. Earth Surface Processes **6**, 251-263.
JUNGERIUS, P.D. (1982): Soils. In: PASCON, P.H. & VAN DER WUSTEN, H.: En marge de la Société marocaine. Une étude socioécologique de la vallée de Beni Boufrah dans le Rif Central, Rabat.
LI, R.M. (1979): Water and sediment routing from watersheds. 21-84. In: H.W. SHEN: Modelling of Rivers. Fort Collins.
LOVEDAY, J. & PYLE, J. (1973): The Emerson dispersion test and its relationship to hydraulic conductivity. Division of Soils Techn. Paper **15**, 1-7 (CSIRO, Australia).
LOW, A.J. (1954): The study of soil structure in the field and in the laboratory. Journ. of Soil Sci. **5**, 57-74.
MOORE, I.D. & LARSON, C.L. (1979): An infiltration model for soils with disturbed surface. American Soc. of Agric. Engineers, Meeting of ASAE & CSAE Winnipeg 1979, paper 79-2044, 28 p.
PARLANGE, J.Y. & SMITH, R.E. (1976): Ponding time for variable rainfall rates. Can. Journ. of Soil Sci. **56**, 121-123.

RUBIN, J. (1968): Numerical analysis of ponded rainfall infiltration. Internat. Assoc. of Scientific Hydrology, Publication Wageningen Symposium June 1967, 440-451.
SCOGING, H. & J.B. THORNES (1980): Infiltration characteristics in a semi-arid environment. Int. Assoc. Scientific Hydrology, Publ. **128**, 159-168.
SEGINER, J. (1971): A model for surface drainage of cultivated soils. Journ. of Hydrology **13**, 139-151.
SHAINBERG, I., RHOADES, J.D. & PRATHER, R.J. (1981): Effect of low electrolyte concentration on clay dispersion and hydraulic conductivity of a sodic soil. Soil Sci. Soc. of Amer. Journal **45**, 273-277.
SMITH, R.E. (1972): The infiltration envelope: results from a theoretical infiltrometer. Journ. of Hydrology **17**, 1-21.
SMITH, R.E. & PARLANGE, J.Y. (1978): A parameter efficient hydrologic infiltration model. Water Resources Research **14**, 533-538.
THORNES, J.B. (1980): Erosional processes of running water and their spatial and temporal controls: a theoretical viewpoint. 129-182. In: KIRKBY, M.J. & MORGAN, J. (Eds.): Soil erosion. J. Wiley & Sons Ltd., Chichester.
WISCHMEIER, W.H. & SMITH, D.D. (1978): Predicting rainfall erosion losses – a guide to conservation planning. United States Dept. of Agriculture. Agricultural Handbook **537**, 58 pp.

Address of author:
A.C. Imeson, Laboratory of Physical Geography and Soil Science, University of Amsterdam Dapperstraat 115, Amsterdam, The Netherlands

Jan de Ploey (Ed.):
Rainfall Simulation, Runoff and Soil Erosion
CATENA SUPPLEMENT 4, BRAUNSCHWEIG 1983

POTENTIAL AND ACTUAL EROSION AROUND ARCHAEOLOGICAL SITES IN SOUTH EAST SPAIN

J.B. Thornes, London
A. **Gilman**, Northridge

SUMMARY

Attempts are being made to assess the erosion in the site territories around 34 archaeological sites of Argaric age in south east Spain. A model based on the Musgrave formula is driven by two hydrological submodels; one (due to KIRKBY) for high frequency, low magnitude events; the other (due to SCOGING & THORNES) is for extreme events. Each is considered for vegetated and bare slopes. The results indicate relatively low overall rates except on bare gullied marl slopes. These are found to be comparable with estimates based on other rates. The reasons for the overall low rates are discussed. An explanation involving the limit of gully development is preferred.

1. INTRODUCTION

Cooperative archaeological and geomorphological research has a long history (ZEUNER 1946, HADLEY & SCHUMM 1957 for example). Although in early interdisciplinary studies the emphasis was on stratigraphic work, more recently interest has focussed on the environment of archaeological sites (BUTZER 1977, KIRKBY 1977).

In the course of this joint work, approaches have become technically more sophisticated and have exhibited a progressively less speculative understanding of the geomorphological processes at work on the deposits and landscapes to be interpreted.

In the development of both stratigraphic interpretations and ecological appraisals, a knowledge of soil erosion is of very considerable significance. In the first case it is instrumental in determining the nature and distribution of valley floor sediments and in the second it is responsible for the changing potential of the environments near archaeological sites for crop production and livestock rearing. Just as the processes of soil erosion are themselves complicated (THORNES 1980a) so too are the spatial and temporal manifestations of these processes. As the spatial and temporal dimensions over which one's research is carried out increase, it becomes necessary to choose between the level of complexity of the models used to evaluate actual and potential soil erosion on the one hand, and the number and observability of the coefficients and parameters which such models require on the other. In this paper we attempt to reach one particular balance in this trade-off process.

The joint research of which this paper is one contribution seeks to study prehistoric land use in south-eastern Spain during the Neolithic, Copper, and Bronze Ages. The agricultural character of the prehistoric settlements of that period is firmly established and the aridity of much of the region in which they are placed, as well as the nature of the cultural developments involved (notably the emergence of a class society: GILMAN 1976), suggest that irrigation (among other intensive farming practices) may have been developed during the course of the cultural sequence (cf CHAPMAN 1978). Our research encompasses the landscapes in the vicinity of thirty-five of the better-known settlement sites in southeast Spain. In order to evaluate the economic potential of the area near these sites it is necessary to assess both the potential for irrigation and the extent of land (and more particularly, soil) available for both irrigated and non-irrigated crops. At some sites there is evidence that the pattern of drainage and the gross morphology of the hillslopes in their vicinity have changed little in the 3500 to 4000 years since the sites were occupied (WISE, THORNES & GILMAN, in press). In this paper we attempt to establish the relative erodibilities of different areas within and between the site territories. The distribution of the sites with which we are concerned is shown in Figure 1.

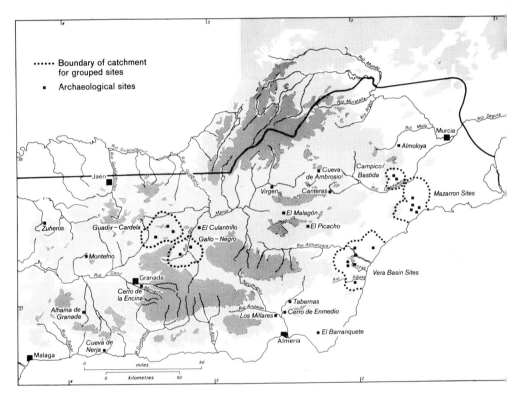

Fig. 1:   Archaeological sites under investigation. 'Catchment' here refers to the limit of exploitation from a single archaeological site.

Southeast Spain is a region of contrasting relief and climate. Strongly folded mountains are interspersed with basins deeply filled with mostly unconsolidated deposits, including marls, limestones, and sands and gravels. These formations give rise to various landforms ranging from glaciated mountains to playa basins (BIROT & SOLE 1959). Climatically the region is characterised by generally low and seasonally contrasted rainfall which is strongly relief dependent. In the east near Alicante the rainfall occurs in two wet seasons (September–October and April–May), while in the west at Malaga there is a single winter wet season from November to March. Rainfall amounts and intensities fall into three groups. The coastal zone between Adra and Alicante receive generally less than 300 mm mean annual rainfall (median values are still lower). The interior basin around Guadix and Baza also has low rainfall. An intermediate zone has rainfalls of 300-600 mm with less evaporation and evapotranspiration, while high mountains such as the Sierra Nevada and Sierra de los Filabres receive more than 600 mm. Further details are given by GEIGER (1970). The natural vegetation only survives in small and remote pockets in this region and large areas are covered with maquis (merging with artemisia steppe and even semi-desert scrub) in the drier areas and with secondary evergreen oak forest and planted conifers in the upland areas. FREITAG (1971) has reconstructed what would have been the natural vegetation (see also RIVAS GODAY & RIVAS MARTINEZ 1971). At higher elevations (about 500 mm), where rainfall is above 450 mm annually, there would have been typical Eu-Mediterranean sclerophyllous forest; at lower elevations, where rainfall is between 250 and 450 mm, the evergreen forest would have constituted a more stunted chaparral; the driest regions would have been sub-desert shrublands of pre-Saharan character. According to FREITAG, the present degree of severe deforestation was produced in Moorish and post-Reconquest times. Although the patchy available evidence suggests that no strong climatic changes have occurred in recent times, there is as yet no clear picture of the detailed fluctuations in climate which may have occurred since Neolithic times.

Our attempt to assess erosion potential necessarily must operate within certain clearly defined limits. The first is that the approach adopted must be able to rely on relatively simple climatic information. Knowledge of recent climatic fluctuations is improving, but for the greater part of the time span which concerns us here the best we can do is to make intelligent guesses as to the rainfall totals per annum and perhaps say something about the relative distribution of extreme events. Secondly, although we know that land use (especially as it affects vegetation cover) is important in controlling erosion, we do not know what the land use or, indeed, the natural vegetation was in prehistoric times. Even if we did, the third constraint – the spatial scale on which we are operating – would inhibit a detailed analysis of vegetation's effect on erosion at anything other than a quite general level. Finally, we have to realise that the art of modelling soil processes is itself still only imperfectly developed, especially for semi-arid environments (see, for example, RENARD 1980). Most approaches are based either on highly area-specific multiple regression curves (whose extrapolation to southeast Spain would be problematical) or on very elaborate dynamical models (which can only be applied to relatively small, intensively studied areas). Other constraints on what can actually be achieved reflect the paucity of precipitation, run-off, and sediment yield data and the desire to obtain results within the lifetime and limits of project funding.

Our goal is not so much to reconstruct **absolutely** the land use potential of each of thirty-five site territories (the area within a two hour's walk of a prehistoric settlement) as to elucidate the **contrast** in such potential between and within the territories. We do not seek here to determine exactly how much soil has been lost over the past several thousand years at particular localities but to assess to what extent the process of erosion has affected various parts of the site territories differentially. The contrasting effects on erosion of different rainfall amounts and vegetation densities between the site territories under study depend largely on gross physiographic factors and can be assessed using available published data. Consequently, we have oriented our fieldwork towards the lithological, topographical, and hillslope-hydrological parameters affecting erosion potential.

2. AVAILABLE APPROACHES

The simplest approach would be to assume that an empirical relationship between erosion and selected climatic variables obtained in another area will hold for southeast Spain. An example is the Langbein-Schumm curve (SCHUMM 1965) which expresses global mean annual sediment yields as a function of mean annual "effective precipitation" (essentially run-off), which itself is determined from rainfall and temperature curves. Another example is FOURNIER's (1960) set of equations relating mean annual sediment yield to seasonality and relief. This type of approach has the benefit of producing an actual figure in tonnes/km/yr. Both incorporate assumptions about the relationship between rainfall and vegetation which are not made specific, however, and both fail to identify the relative significance of storms of different magnitude or intensity. The latter might be especially important in considering climatic fluctuations, since shift in their mean values would, if large enough, produce changes in the sediment yield totals. However, changes of distribution, intensity, or even the incidence of large storms within a given year would show no effect provided that the yearly means for rainfall remained the same. These models would prevent us, moreover, from considering variations in vegetation cover, variations which can be approximated using simple interception-consumption models.

Another approach would be to estimate the total contemporary sediment yield from observation data, as FLAXMAN (1972) has done for the Western United States. For the short term this implies measuring erosion on selected plots on different lithologies under controlled conditions. For the intermediate term it implies utilising such sediment yield data as are available from stream gauging stations or (on a somewhat longer time-scale) estimating amounts from depositional features such as reservoirs, harbors, or deltas (eg. LOPEZ BERMUDEZ 1973, 221, BOVIS 1975). Logistics constitute the main impediment for such an approach. Time is not available for the actual measurement of sediment yield under controlled conditions. The areas we study are large and highly variable and data on sediment yields only refers to a small portion of the territories in which we are interested. Furthermore, these techniques, like those just discussed, represent the integrated effect of sediment yield over an entire catchment, with all that this implies in terms of lagged storage, partial contributing areas, and similar complications. Finally, because these approaches correlate various possible contributing factors (rainfall, vegetation cover, catchment size, etc.) with sediment yield without providing an account of the causes of the observed results, anomalous findings become very difficult to interpret. It is better, then, to use these strategies as a check on our results than to use them as the basis for our findings.

A third approach is to use a dynamic model based on physically realistic assumptions concerning underlying causes, a model in which the processes are driven by a set of inputs to operate on a pre-existing set of conditions to produce variations in the response variable. A great many such models are available in the literature varying widely in their degree of complexity. The essential breakpoint in this spectrum is whether the hillslope flows themselves are to be routed (ie. whether there is concern for the character and timing of flows of water and sediment across individually defined hillslopes) or whether the process is to be generalised to a larger area and time-scale. For the first one would have to consider parameters difficult to measure on a wide scale (eg. ground roughness, individual vegetation elements). We have opted, therefore, for the second, "lumped" approach and operate at a scale of a square kilometer or more.

3.   GENERAL PROCEDURES

In view of our archaeological objectives our specific requirements are:
i)   to be able to identify those areas in which sheet wash and concentrated flows are most important:
(ii)   to be able to assess the relative significance of these processes in different areas **within** the site territories so as to enable us to assess past land use in terms of present ones;
(iii)   to employ basic, readily obtainable climatic data and be able to respond to assumed fluctuations in climatic input.

The first of these points requires further clarification. Two processes other than overland flow are relevant to erosion. The first, mass movement, does not occur widely, but in some areas (particularly the Guadix basin) it forms a major component of landscape change (see WISE, THORNES & GILMAN, 1983). Unfortunately it is at the moment impossible to quantify the nature of land-loss due to these processes. Since the characteristic effects of mass movement do not involve widespread soil loss and since such events occur sporadically, we leave it to one side. The second, rain-splash, is important because it breaks up the surface (FARRES 1978), it breaks down the size of aggregated materials (BRYAN 1976), and it helps start materials moving during overland flow (MOYERSONS 1975). Nonetheless, we do not consider it here directly because simple models in which the rain-splash effect would be controlled by easily obtained information (such as rainfall intensities or slope gradients) seem inadequate; this is all the more true in that the efficacy of rain splash in erosion depends heavily on rill density, a variable difficult to measure on a wide scale. Accordingly, at the expense of some inevitable simplification, we assume that the capacity and competence of flowing water to remove material is the most critical factor in determining overall soil loss.

These considerations have led us to use the well-known "Musgrave type" formula for estimating soil loss:

$$Y = kq^m s^n \tag{1}$$

where Y is the sediment yield, q is the overland flow responsible for the yield and s is the tangent of the slope angle over which the flow takes place. The parameter k is a coefficient which, among other things, depends upon the character of the material entrained in the flow. The exponents m and n are empirically determined; a wide spread of literature, together with theoretical considerations (see the review by MORGAN 1980), lead to values of 2.0 for m and 1.66 for n. Following the work of HORTON (1945), CARSON & KIRKBY (1972) present a reasoned argument for this expression of the Musgrave approach and FOSTER & MEYER (1975) adopt a comparable equation for both detachment and transport by overland flow, the former being the limiting condition for the latter. Further discussion of the suitability of this model for semi-arid environment is contained in THORNES (1976).

The coefficient (k) in the Musgrave equation (equation 1) should incorporate the effects of lithological constraints on the availability of materials for erosion. The ratio of mean particle size to the sorting of sizes in the material to be transported would, in principle, form a logical way to establish the value of k since it expresses the relative availability of different materials for entrainment by overland flow. Other factors which would have to be considered are the roughness of the surface and the mean distance over which transport might take place as well as electrostatic forces and unfortunately, in the past this complex parameter has been determined empirically (e.g. in the USLE; MITCHELL & BUBENZER 1980) so as to fit particular conditions so that no really sound theory is as yet available for its determination. Some of the background to this problem is discussed in THORNES (1980b) and KIRKBY (1980a). For the moment we can do no better than to set k at a constant value of 0.02 (a conservative estimate) and to discuss the characteristics of the regolith and the factors controlling them on a qualitative basis in Section 7. In so far as k is a linear coefficient it could simply be adjusted to coincide with empirical data, but this is not necessary since the results obtained by our model are in fact of a comparable order of magnitude to those actually observed in southeast Spain and elsewhere under similar conditions. Only weak claims concerning the absolute amounts of erosion can be derived from the model, but we can avoid spurious accuracy because our primary concern is with relative erodibilities. By adopting a constant value for k we do not distort the relative magnitudes of our results. Finally, we may note that the role of this parameter is not too critical since the model is much more sensitive to the effects of vegetation cover and the control produced by lithology on excess water generation, as described below.

In following this approach it is essential to distinguish between gullied and ungullied slopes, ie between slopes which have dominantly concentrated flows and slopes which mainly have sheet wash. This distinction is primarily related to drainage density and hence is a property of the scale over which such densities are measured. Most discussion of this distinction (eg. by MEYER, FOSTER & ROMKENS 1975) is based on rilled and unrilled slopes and tends to relate to experimental plots, but logically the principles involved can be extended to consideration of larger scale systems. The significance of the distinction lies in the way in which the area of (and, hence the runoff in) a gully increases with the gully's length or, in other words, as a function of contour convergence. For channeled flows the catchment area tends to increase as the square of the distance downstream, whereas for unchanneled flows (or, in other words, on rectilinear hill slopes with negligible contour curvature) it will increase as a linear function of slope length. This is why the initiation of gullies is so important: they are able to capture a much larger area of overland flow.

Controlled field measurements (MEYER, FOSTER & ROMKENS 1975), theory (KIRKBY 1980a), and qualitative field observations suggest that on unrilled slopes there is a rapid increase (over a few meters) of sediment load carried by overland flow to a capacity which remains relatively constant regardless of slope length. This is partly attributable to the fact that the average distance over which sediment is transported in a flow is a function of the availability of sediment for removal from the slope. However, it is also a function of the propensity for reinfiltration, especially in semi-arid environments, where much moisture can be stored in the soil. Here the travel time of overland flow and the storm length become critically important. For example, if one takes typical overland flow speed to be about 2 cm sec^{-1} in a 20 minute storm flows arising at a distance greater than 24 m from the channel at the base of the slope would not reach the channel because of reinfiltration along the way. In short, on an unrilled slope flows do not cumulate as they progress towards the channel.

For these reasons, we assume that the overland flow component of equation 1 is given, on **ungullied** slopes, by the excess water production (p) per unit area. The Musgrave equation (equation 1) then becomes

$$Y = Kp^2s^{1.66} \tag{2}$$

For **gullied** slopes (which are usually short and steep and where the physical resistance of the lithologies is low) overland flow is made a function of the area over which excess water production is concentrated and that area is, in turn, taken to be a linear function of the distance from the base of the slope to the divide at the summit. We have then taken equation 2 for gullied slopes to be:

$$Y = k(p \cdot L)^2 s^{1.66} \qquad (3)$$

where L is the average slope length.

Two sets of properties influence the above model. The hydrological properties of the lithologies which make up the slopes determine the excess water production (p). The topographic properties of the slopes determine their lengths and gradients (l, s). These are now discussed.

4. HYDROLOGICAL MODELS

We wish to consider both the average rate of soil loss (i.e. on an annual basis) and that due to extreme events. Ideally one would like to construct a curve showing the effective work carried out on slopes by events of all magnitudes and frequencies, but unfortunately the data permitting this to be done is not available. We have chosen, therefore, to use a model developed by KIRKBY (1977) to estimate annual excess water production and a model developed by SCOGING AND THORNES (1980) to estimate excess water production in extreme events.

4.1. K–MODEL

The model to consider annual excess water production (hereafter the K-model) takes overland flow to be a function of the estimated amount of rainfall lost to storage in a rainfall event (r), which is not available for run-off, and the mean rainfall per rainday (r_0). A rainday is one having more than 0.1 mm of precipitation. The distribution of daily rainfall magnitudes is assumed to be exponential so the equation for total annual overland flow becomes:

$$q_{ann} = R \cdot \exp{(-r_c/r_0)} \qquad (4)$$

where R is the mean annual rainfall. As the total storage (r_c) increases the total depth of overland flow decreases. Conversely as the mean rainfall per rainy day (r_0) increases, q_{ann} increases. The assumption of a simple negative exponential distribution of events could be replaced by a direct estimation of the characteristics of the curve, but unfortunately data constraints make this impossible. Empirical estimates from the Ugijar region of southeast Spain (adjacent to our study area) are available and they demonstrate that the exponential assumption is a very reasonable one (THORNES 1976, SCOGING 1976).

For bare slopes r_c is estimated by procedures to be described in section 4.2. below. On vegetated slopes (where rainfall is intercepted before reaching the ground), the amount of precipitation lost to storage has been estimated from the following equation:

$$r_c = 100 \, (E_a/E_p)^{0.5} \qquad (5)$$

where E_a is the actual annual evapotranspiration and E_p the potential annual evapotranspiration. As the actual annual evapotranspiration and the potential become equal (i.e. as vegetation cover becomes more dense), storage approaches 100. The larger the potential evapotranspiration is relative to the actual amount, the sparser the vegetation cover and the

8

lower the storage because of higher erosion and lower weathering rates, producing thinner soils. Both equations (4) and (5) assume that rainfall events are independent of one another, a very likely proposition in arid and semi-arid environments. Individual storms are statistically independent in terms of volumes and durations and the amount of moisture stored from one event to the next is certainly very small on hill-slopes. In stream beds, however, the changing character of their hydrographic properties over the course of the year means that in southeast Spain at least for winter events, there is not strict independence.

4.2. ST–MODEL

The hydrological model for extreme storm events derives from the work of SCOGING & THORNES (1980) who showed from sprinkler experiments that the simplified version of the Green-Ampt equation consistently gave the best prediction of infiltration for soils in this region. That equation is:

$$F_t = A + B/t \qquad (6)$$

where F_t is the infiltration rate at time t (after the start of infiltration) and A and B are parameters. The A parameter is the final infiltrability of the standard ring infiltrometer test, while the B parameter represents the gradient of the infiltration curve through time. In the model adopted here (figure 2) we assume that the soil can be represented by a box with a leaky bottom and a perforated top. If the rainfall intensity exceeds the infiltration capabilities of the soil, excess (Hortonian) overland flow will occur at once, although some water will also infiltrate into storage. As the storage fills and the soil becomes saturated, overland flow will again occur, even with low intensity rainfall on soils with high infiltration properties. The digital simulation used to model this process follows the path defined by the flow diagram shown in figure 3.

In order to operate this model one must define the storage capacity of the soil at the beginning of a storm. For a moist soil this is a function of the potential less the antecedent storage. For a dry soil the full potential storage is realised and it is defined here by use of standard ring infiltrometer techniques. The ring infiltrometer usually overestimates infiltration rates, especially for small infiltration rates (SCOGING & THORNES, 1980) but provides reliable estimates of the storage volumes. As shown in figure 4, the storage is calculated as the area beneath the infiltration curve bounded by t = 1 minute (to avoid infinitely large infil-

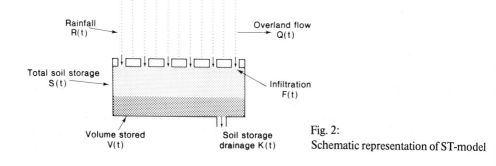

Fig. 2:

Schematic representation of ST-model

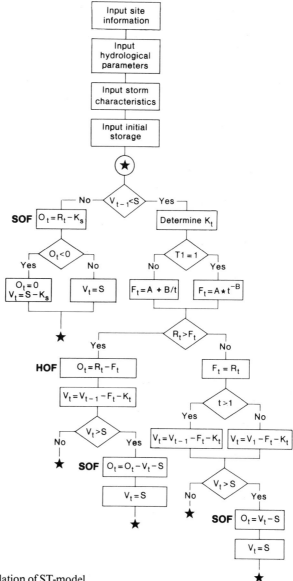

Fig. 3:   Flow diagram of digital simulation of ST-model

tration rates) and K_s = A, the final infiltrability. In practise, the lower bounding curve should rise from t = 1 to K_s (instead of being the horizontal line depicted in figure 4) since the value of K(the soil's conductivity) is virtually zero in the initial stages of storage in a dry soil. Over a one hour storm, however, the difference in total storage is probably very small, as is indicated by the pentration depth of the wetting front under usual conditions. We have also used this storage model to operate the K model (section 4.1.) for bare slopes (i.e. r_c is the storage volume of the soil in the absence of vegetation). As we will discuss further below in

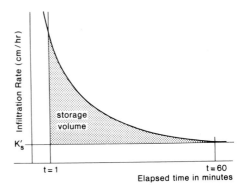

Fig. 4:   Infiltration curve defining
storage volume

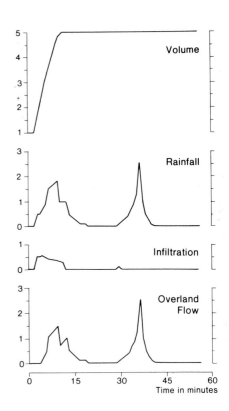

Fig. 5:   Simulated storm sequence

arid areas (where vegetation is sparser) on certain lithologies the r_c value obtained from
equation (5) is greater than that for vegetated slopes. In this case it is logical to use the higher
of the two values to estimate storage capacity on both vegetated and bare slopes.

   The operation of this storm event storage model is shown for a hypothetical case in figure
5. Here the rainfall comes in two well defined storms. In the first storm rapid infiltration leads

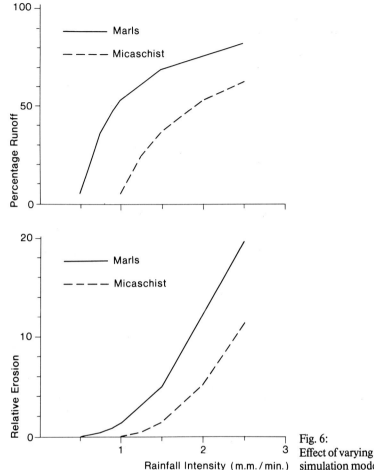

Fig. 6:
Effect of varying rainfall intensity in
simulation model on two lithologies

to an increase in the storage volume until the storage capacity is reached after which infiltration ceases and overland flow shows a slight increase. In the second storm the storage
volume is already almost full and the saturated excess production mirrors the rainfall.

In figure 6 we show the model in operation on two lithologies with contrasting storage
properties. Marls have low storage and mica-schists a relatively high storage. Run-off for a
storm of one-hour duration is shown as a function of the intensity of rainfall during the
storm, the runoff being expressed as a percentage of the rainfall. Runoff occurs at lower
intensities for marls than for mica-schists and on marls the rate of increase of percentage
runoff with intensity is much steeper at low and intermediate intensities. At very high intensities there is a linear increase in percentage runoff with intensity on both lithologies. The
combination of this hydrological model with equation (3) is shown in the lower graph. The
increase of sediment yield with an increase in intensity is higher on the marls than on mica-
schists.

5. DATA COLLECTION

Given that vegetation cover in southeast Spain is often sparse and that most soils are poorly developed (when they do not simply consist of a C-horizon), lithology and relief are particularly significant determinants of the amount of soil erosion. Accordingly, a set of 1:50000 scale maps were prepared for each site territory or intersecting set of territories. These describe the distribution of lithological and topographic types as determined by field survey and from air photographs and published maps. These maps were used to stratify the sampling schemes by which other data were collected. The lithologies were grouped under eight major headings. **Limestones** range from crystalline metamorphic dolomites to massive fossil-rich marine beds and are sometimes interspersed with two other major 'hardrock' groups: **mica-schists** and **mixed metamorphics** (quartzites, slates, granulites). These, the main constituents of the mountainous areas, have been broken up and redeposited as beds of **conglomerates**. Sometimes the conglomerates have been weathered, redeposited (mainly in the Quaternary), and cemented into a thick calcareous crust which is then termed a **calichified conglomerate**. Marine **marls** (occasionally with a significant sodium content) are mainly Tertiary deposits postdating the main orogeny and occupying substantial areas in the basins between the mountain chains. **Chalk**, a soft limestone with shear strengths higher than marls but lower than metamorphosed and crystalline limestones, occurs mainly in the area north and west of Sierra Nevada and is strongly folded, but little altered. Finally, in the area along the Mediterranean coast a variety of **volcanics** (lavas and ashes)also occur. Further, more detailed descriptions of these lithologies and their associated regoliths are given in THORNES (1976) and GILMAN & THORNES (in press).

Within this stratification and consistent with a broad spatial coverage of our study area, some forty locations were chosen at random in order to obtain infiltration measurements and bulk density samples. At each site four infiltration tests were carried out and bulk density samples extracted from unvegetated, level tracts. After the initial series of 160 tests were completed, a further sixty were made in order to reduce the variance within certain lithological groups, the fifteen locations again being chosen at random. The infiltration tests were carried out using a single standard gauge infiltrometer supplied by a burette or simply topped up at regular intervals. Each infiltrometer test was run for one hour and the storage volumes were computed from the consequent infiltration curves. The soil moistures were determined gravimetrically. Seventy of the soil samples have been measured in the laboratory to obtain mean particle size and water stable aggregate size. For the latter, following the work of BRYAN (1976), we have taken the percentage of water stable aggregates greater than 3.35 mm in (sieve) size to be a critical feature in determining the erodibility of the soil (see further discussion below).

Topographic information was obtained by field measurements, from maps, and from air photographs. Mean slope was measured from 1:50000 sheets of the Mapa Militar de Espana using the contour intersection method at each of 25 cells within each lithology in each of the site territories and slope lengths were measured from air photographs using the same sample of locations. Both measurements have been compared with field observations based on sampled profiles within randomly selected kilometer squares. These observations also yielded information on slope shape. Comparison of field-derived and map-derived data on mean slopes indicates that the latter tend to underestimate gradients slightly.

Mean annual rainfall totals and monthly rainfall totals are available from many stations throughout southeast Spain, but information on the number of days with more than 0.1 mm rainfall, like data for potential evapotranspiration (E_p in equation 5), are only available for the provincial capitals. Penman estimates of E_p for particular site territories were taken for the nearest appropriate provincial capital or estimated from isolines (ELIAS CASTILLO & GIMINEZ ORTIZ 1965). Values for actual evapotranspiration (E_a in equation 5) are not published and were estimated from the difference between rainfall and runoff in the river basins containing or contained within site territories. (Data on runoff was obtained from selected guaging stations published by the regional river authorities). This may be a significant source of error because the rainfall-runoff difference includes not only losses by evapotranspiration but losses to storage and various effects of abstraction. Storage losses may well level out on an annual basis, but because of the reapplication of the same water in irrigation, abstraction can only tend to heighten the apparent evapotranspiration and thereby inflate the values of r_c (in equation 5) and cause soil storage to be overestimated. Since we are using our estimate of E_a to assess the effect on erosion of slopes being vegetated instead of bare, the net effect will be that the amount of vegetation expectable from the E_a/E_p ratio will be overestimated. This in fact may bring our estimates for erosion under vegetated conditions closer to the situation which would be obtained if the natural vegetation of southeast Spain had not been degraded. Since our error is in the right direction, we have not attempted to adjust the E_a figures we have obtained.

6. RESULTS

6.1. Consider first the characteristics of the hydrological properties of the different regolith types developed on different lithologies. These are shown in table 1. There are two well defined groups, the chalks and marls on the one hand, and the mica-schists, limestones, conglomerates, calichified conglomerates and volcanics on the other. The mixed metamorphics occupy an intermediate position between the two. The first group have low storage volumes, reflecting the dominantly finer grain sizes and lower overall porosities. This is in agreement with the results of BORK & ROHDENBURG (1981) who carried out a detailed analysis of similar lithological groups near Zurgena in the Province of Almeria. All the lithologies have very high coefficients of variation indicating that within any one lithology we are dealing with a very wide range of storage conditions. It is impossible to make any statements about the statistical distributions since the sample sizes are, generally speaking, too small. The 'final infiltrabilities' represented by the A-parameters (in cms/hr) are too large to represent the natural hydraulic conductivites and simply reflect the shortcomings of the infiltrometer technique which tends to grossly overestimate conductivities. In the model we have assumed the conductivities to be negligibly small which is consistent with the fact that in these soils we are normally at the extreme limits of the soil moisture range. The final infiltrabilities are not involved in the estimation of the storage volumes.

Tab. 1: HYDROLOGICAL PARAMETERS FOR REGOLITHS ON DIFFERENT LITHOLOGIES

Lithology	CH	M	MS	MM	L	C	CC	V
Mean storage (mm)	24.7	28.5	56.5	38.6	47.3	56.4	59.9	57.2
Deviation storage	16.0	29.8	66.8	22.7	33.5	76.2	54.2	26.7
Parameter A	0.192	0.203	0.433	0.467	0.417	0.273	0.535	0.381
Parameter B	0.458	0.639	0.984	0.809	0.915	0.928	1.133	1.120
Number of observations	38	59	41	18	28	30	8	7

Tab. 2A: RAINFALL DATA FOR THE FOUR PROVINCIAL CAPITALS

City	Annual Average (mm)	Days > 0.1 mm	Average rainfall per rainy day
Almeria	233	42	5.547
Granada	473	77	6.142
Malaga	474	56	8.464
Murcia	304	47	6.46

Tab. 2B: TYPICAL OVERLAND FLOWS (in litres/yr) AND RELATIVE SEDIMENT YIELDS (in b₁
FOR A 20 M LONG, 10°RILLED BARE SLOPE ON DIFFERENT LITHOLOGIES.
Erosion coefficient (k in equation 4) is set at 0.02.Annual figures based on KIRKBY (1974). NA = no case₁

	L	MS	MM	C	CC	M	CH	V
Almeria	0.92	0.18	4.0	0.18	0.095	27.0	NA	0.16
	(0.00095)	(0.000035)	(0.02)	(0.000035)	(0.000010)	(0.84)		(0.00
Granada	4.3	0.907	18	0.97	55	91	170	NA
	(0.021)	(0.0011)	(0.34)	(0.0011)	(0.00034)	(9.3)	(32.2)	
Malaga	35.0	12.0	NA	12	8.0	NA	NA	NA
	(1.4)	(0.2)		(0.2)	(0.08)			
Murcia	4.0	1	15	1	0.6	74	NA	1.0
	(0.018)	(0.0011)	(0.27)	(0.0011)	(0.00037)	(6.17)		(0.00

NA = Not Applicable

Tab. 3:   ANNUAL OVERLAND FLOW AND RELATIVE SEDIMENT YIELDS DELIVERED
FROM RILLED AND UNRILLED 20 m LONG, 10° VEGETATED SLOPES WITHIN SITE
TERRITORIES. r_c = 100 $(Ea/Ep)^{0.5}$ USING RAINFALL DATA FROM THE MOST
APPROPRIATE PROVINCIAL CAPITALS AND EVAPOTRANSPIRATION DATA DERIVED
FROM RAINFALL AND FROM DISCHARGE MEASURED AT LOCAL STREAM GAUGING
STATIONS.

Site territories	Capitals	r_c	Overland flow $(1 \cdot yr^{-1})$	Rilled slopes $(x10^{-4})$	Unrilled slopes $(x10^{-6})$
Vera Basin sites, Gatas, El Oficio, Los Millares, Enmedio, El Barranquete	Almeria	46	1.16	15	3.8
Tabernas	Almeria	47	0.97	10	2.6
Almoloya	Murcia	51	2.28	58	14
Virgen	Granada	51	2.34	63	14
Mazarron sites	Murcia	53	1.43	23	5.8
Campico/Bastida	Murcia	54	1.67	31	7.9
Ambrosio, Canteras Culantrillo,	Granada	62	0.39	2	0.42
Gaudix sites	Almeria	63	0.054	33	0.0083
Nerja	Malaga	64	0.49	270	4.0
Alhama El Picacho	Granada	64	0.28	8.9	0.22
Malagon, Zuheros	Granada	65	0.24	0.61	1.4
Laborcillas Montefrio	Granada	69	0.13	0.18	0.043
Encina	Granada	77	0.034	0.013	0.0033

6.2.   Table 2A gives the rainfall data for the four provincial capitals and table 2B indicates typical overland flows and relative sediment yields computed using the K-model, using the storage values from table 1, and assuming that there is complete lack of vegetation cover. The greatest excesses are produced on the chalks and marls of the Granada area reflecting a combination of high rainfall, moderate intensities (by number of days of rain) and low storage. By contrast, the figures for Almeria are relatively small; conglomerates and calichified conglomerates, volcanics and mica-schists all have low relative erosion rates. This table essentially reflects the combination of climate and storage parameters at work in the model on a 'regular' event basis, the lengths and angles having been kept constant.

In table 3 we illustrate the relative magnitudes of erosion for the K-model under 'vegetated' conditions by using equation 5 to determine the r_c values. These reflect existing vegetation, though there is some overestimation for the reasons noted in the last section. The values of r_c range from 46 to 77 mm covering more than one quarter of the entire range. Although they are fairly evenly graded the extremes represent the contrast between the extremely dry sites on the east coast, such as the Vera basin sites and the cooler moister interior uplands of the areas around Granada. Two distinctive features are to be observed. The first is the sharp reduction in overland flow volumes and erosion amounts when compared with the bare slope figures given in table 2A for comparative conditions, notably for sites in which the r_c calculated from lithology is appreciable lower than the r_c calculated from equation five. The second contrast, to be expected from the model, is the strong difference between rilled and non-rilled slopes in sediment production. One apparent anomaly in this set is the relatively low position of the Guadix sites. The Guadix basin has precipitation generally below 350 mm, however it also has extremely cold winters which tend to supress the potential evaporation amounts in winter and introduce a much stronger seasonal bias than is intended by the estimating equation.

Tab. 4:   ESTIMATED EXCESS WATER PRODUCTION (mm) WITH K_s = 0 AND NO INITIAL STORAGE ON BARE SOIL

	Storm intensity	
	60 mm/hr	120 mm/hr
Limestone (L)	12.7	72.7
Mica-schists (MS)	3.5	63.5
Mixed metamorphics (MM)	21.4	81.4
Conglomerates (C)	3.6	63.6
Calichified conglomerates (CC)	0.09	60.1
Marls (M)	31.65	91.5
Chalk (CH)	35.3	95.3
Volcanics (V)	2.8	62.8

In table 4, the excess water produced from a 1 hour storm of 60 and 120 mm are given. A 60 mm storm occurs about once every 30 years in Alicante, every 100 years in Almeria and every 150 years in Murcia (ELIAS CASTILLO & RUIZ BELTRAM 1979). On the other hand there have been some quite exceptional storms in recent years, such as the devastating storm of 1973. In this storm rainfalls in excess of 250 mm were consistently reported over a belt from Motril to Puerto Lumbreras in a few hours (usually about 3) and at some locations up to 600 mm are said to have fallen (THORNES 1974). Thus, even storms of 120 mm/hr may reasonably be expected to have occurred several times in the last 4000 years. As the table shows, there is a sharp contrast between the lithologies, simply reflecting the storage estimated from the field. It also reveals the different response according to rainfall intensity. For the lower intensity the ratio of the highest to the lowest values is 392 whereas for the highest intensity it is only 1.6. This is a typical feature of storage models of this type.

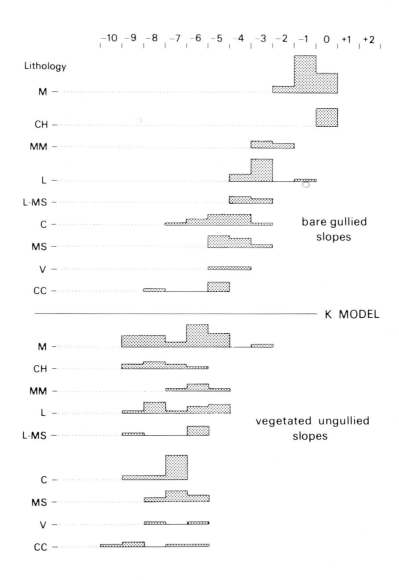

Fig. 7: Distribution of erosion values on different lithologies according to K-model. Heights of columns are proportional to the percentage of cases in each erosion class.

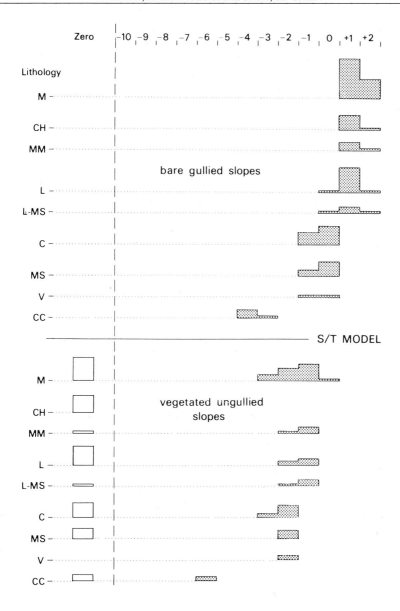

Fig. 8: Distribution of erosion values on different lithologies according to ST-model. Heights of columns are proportional to the percentage of cases in each erosion cases.

6.3. It is impossible in the space available to illustrate all the simulations possible for all the archaeological sites with the different lithologies and the different ground conditions for both models. Instead, for the purposes of this paper, we have chosen to illustrate the extreme cases for both models in figures 7 and 8. In these diagrams we have divided the sediment yield values determined by equations (3) and (4) by the slope length (gullied slopes) and the square of slope length (ungullied slopes) to obtain some idea of relative groundloss. These diagrams reveal the combination of the model effects and the field parameters applied to the model. The abcissa in these diagrams is in **logged** form, the values being the exponents of the natural logarithms. Each block is a histogram with the height representing the absolute number of values in that ground loss class from all the sites. With vegetated, ungullied slopes low slopes and dry areas are generating no overland flow and hence no erosion. This is because the r_c value for vegetated slopes are in some areas greater than the rainfall being supplied. These are shown as clear blocks on figure 8.

In examining the details of figures 7 and 8 one needs to emphasis that they represent the joint constraints provided by the assumptions of the model and by the parameter values recorded in the site territories studied. To some extent, then, they will inevitably reflect our preconceived notions of the way the system operates. Our comments fall into two parts: the first set relate to contrasts within the K-model and ST-model subsets, the second to the contrasts between them.

For high and intermediate frequency low magnitude events (figure 7) the bare gullied slopes exhibit most clearly the effects of lithologically controlled storage values. There are roughly two orders of magnitude difference between the low and high storage values. Superimposed on this broad differentiation are the effects of high slopes (eg. on limestones and mixed metamorphics). By contrast, and as expected, the 'vegetated' slopes are much less differentiated by lithology and the generally much lower rates (of the order of 1×10^{-6} mm yr^{-1}) tend to be more widely distributed and have a tendency to bimodality. This reflects the operation of the 'vegetational' storage components between mountain and upland sites, on the one hand, and the dry lowland sites, on the other. Slope plays a more dominant role here, though to the extent that these are still lithologically controlled through drainage density, the marls persist in having the highest overall rates. The main contrast between the upper and lower parts of figure 7 is therefore due to lithological effects.

For the extreme events of high magnitude and low frequency lithology plays a much less significant role and the contrasts among bare, gullied slopes arises mainly from mean slope angle. This reflects the fact that at high intensities the role of storage is significantly subordinated. In a 60 mm event typical amounts of soil loss on bare gullied slopes are of the order of 0-100 mm and for vegetated, ungullied slopes 0.001-0.01 mm. For the latter, the slopes again play an important role, separating out the marls, chalks, mixed metamorphics and limestones from the conglomerates, mica-schists, volcanics and calichified conglomerates. The latter are essentially pediment and hill-country terrains while the former combine upland and mountain sites (with long slopes and steep gradients) and erodible deposits formed in more or less recent basins (marls and chalks). On the basis of the model the contrast between gullied and ungullied slopes should be greater the longer the mean slope and, in fact, the data for extreme events allow this contrast to appear.

7. DISCUSSION

Tables 2B and 3 are in effect measures of the sensitivity of the model. Given a fixed slope angle and length, the question posed was how does the model react to variations in lithology and climate controls (through vegetation). In the last section, in figures 7 and 8, some of the general properties of the model were illustrated with respect to the actual parameters and variable values as they occur within the site teritories. In this final section we address the question – Are the results meaningful and what implications have they for statements about erosion in south-east Spain and for erosion processes in general?

7.1.   The first question can at this stage be addresses only qualitatively or semi-quantitatively. Qualitatively it can be said that the apparent pattern of erosion in south-east Spain agrees fairly well with the pattern simulated by the models.

For example the marls are intensively dissected in some areas and little dissected in others according to the slope. On moist limestone uplands, especially on well-vegetated slopes there are extensive soils some of which are probably of considerable antiquity. In many areas away from gullies there are hillslopes which have not changed their surface form for several thousands of years. There are however several anomalies to the patterns suggested by the model. One of these is that some sites even in gullied areas give the impression of having changed little in the past 4000 yr (WISE, THORNES & GILMAN, in press). The other main anomaly is that the chalk areas are described by the model as having extremely high erosion rates and yet, by comparison with marls of comparable gradient, they exhibit smooth, well rounded convex hillslopes leading to broad gently valleys. This phenomenon might be explained by greater lithological resistance to erosion through the shear properties of the bedrock. Alternatively, it might be that these slopes are very stable with respect to gully development. A third possible explanation is that the soils on the chalk slopes have only recently been cleared. The Catastro de la Ensenada tax survey of 1752-1753 gives detailed summaries of land uses for all municipalities in south east Spain. In many of those localities whose jurisdictions overlap with our site territories and in which chalk is an important lithology (the Alhama, Montefrio, Zuheros and Laborcillas site territories), much less land was cleared for cultivation in the 18th century than now. That clearance must have taken place mainly on chalk hills. Since clearance, the land has been regularly ploughed and rill formation has been inhibited.

A major inadequacy of the model is the failure to accommodate variations in resistance to erosion, at last in the present form. Erosion control is expressed only through hydrological properties. In practise, the availability of material for transport (both in terms of amount and ease of detatchment) is an important factor. In the model this has been assumed uniform over the lithologies. In a very real sense the erosion estimates are potential rather than actual on steep hard-rock slopes such as limestones, mica-schists, calichified conglomerates and so on. Once the weathered material has disappeared the rate of weathering is so slow that it is the principal constraint on removal and given the high potential erosion rates such slopes are usually bare of soil. On the unconsolidated marls and Quaternary alluvia and on those hard rocks with well developed regoliths, the main constraint is the detachment and transporting capacity of overland flow. It might be expected that the differences between the chalks and marls would be accounted for by a difference in detachability. So far only a preliminary evaluation of regolith properties have been carried out on a small sample. Following BRYAN (1976) we calculated the percentage of water stable aggregates greater than 3.35 mm diameter. This is a tolerable indicator of propensity for entrainment. The percentages in the marl and chalk samples do not differ significantly but these two lithologies contrast with all others. This suggests that the distinction between chalk and marls is related more to regional denudational history than to the propensity for erosion. This belief derives from the fact that around the edge of the Gaudix Basin, where marls and chalk are juxtaposed, the extensive areas of gullying are contiguous and appear to be related to the high density drainage patterns about the Fardes and Gor rivers. For this reason, or some other, the convex chalk slopes appear highly stable. Further work on this contrast would be illuminating.

7.2.   It is also possible to make some crude semi-quantitative evaluation of the model. The model is roughly calibrated to give ground loss in millimetres. Converting these to tonnes/km^2 for a year or for the 60 mm event and assuming a bulk density of 2.0 (the average of our samples) the following results are suggested.

(i)   K-model, bare gullied slopes: group 1 (low storage) 50-5000 t/km^2/yr; group 2 (high storage) 0.005-5 tonnes/km^2/yr.

(ii) K-model, vegetated, ungullied 0.05-0 tonnes/km^2/yrs.

(iii) ST model, 60 mm storm, bare, gullied slopes: group 1 5000-500,000 tonnes/km^2 group 2 50-5000 tonnes/km^2.

(iv) ST-model, 60 mm storm, vegetated gullied slopes: group 1 5-500 tonnes/km^2 group 2 0.5-50 tonnes/km^2.

Apart from the 60 mm bare gullied slopes upper limit, which seems far too high, the results seem within the ranges reported in the literature. For example the figure given by HOLEMAN (1968) of 380 tonnes/km^2/yr for the Colorado river is comparable with the figures for the K-model on unvegetated slopes. The rates quoted by YOUNG (1974) for surface wash are 1000 tonnes/km^2/yr from SCHUMM (1964) and 450 tonnes/km^2/yr from CAMPBELL (1970) in comparable environments. The expected sediment yield for the LANGBEIN & SCHUMM (1958) curve for comparable conditions range from 200-400 tonnes/km^2/yr. Estimates using the models of FOURNIER (1960), CARSON & KIRKBY (1972), LANGBEIN & SCHUMM (1958) and JENSEN & PAINTER (1974) for the Guadix basin group around 25 tonnes/km^2/yr. The K-model for bare gullied slopes for this area suggest rates of about 1000 tonnes/km^2/yr whereas the K-model for bare, ungullied slopes yields values of between about 0.0002 tonnes/km^2/yr (i.e. very low). Both types of slope occur side by side in the Guadix basin. Measured rates, based on the very limited data on suspended sediment yield from the region, indicate values of about 16 tonnes/km^2/yr (with upper and lower quantiles of 72 and 7 tonnes/km^2/yr.

In virtually all cases the rates calculated by the various empirical indices, from the limited available observations and from the 'vegetated' models outlined above indicate quite **low** rates of erosion rates for low magnitude, high frequency events in the south-east of Spain. This is consistent with the recently held general belief that in semi-arid environments virtually all the work is done in extreme events. Only in highly localised, heavily gullied landscapes or under extreme events do the rates reach significant proportions.

Finally we may note, that in the extreme event of 1973, referred to above, TORRE (1973) estimated ground losses of between 56 and 420 mm on Mica-schists in the Alpujarras; the mean value of 14 locations was 151 mm. The value for mica-schists in the Nerja area for the 60 mm modelled storm is about 460 mm. Although the model appears to be overestimating, the slopes in the Nerja site catchment are appreciably steeper than in the Alpujarran mica-schists. Our intention is not to carry out a detailed comparison: on the one hand the errors in the model are admittedly large; on the other, there are virtually no data on which such a comparison could be reliably made. The most we can say is thet the model is producing values of the right order of magnitude in absolute terms and is probably representing the **relative** differences between sites reasonably faithfully. As yet the knowledge of Holocene climatic changes is too inadequate to enable us to investigate their effects on between site erosional differences.

7.3.   Returning to the question of the archaeological sites it is apparent that the main question at issue is the relative stability and growth rates of the gully systems. In an earlier paper (WISE, THORNES & GILMAN, 1983) we noted that at many sites **in situ** deposits and materials have been able to survive even on the relatively unresistant lithologies. At two sites in the Guadix basin they occur on relatively steep slopes (up to 25°) and at one site (Cerro del Gallo) ceramics, apparently **in situ**, were found at relatively low levels in the gully walls. In this paper we have indicated that the simulations based on physically reasonable suppositions and field-determined parameters lead to low erosion rates in all areas except for gullied marls for low magnitude, high frequency events. Even for extreme events the rates of ground-loss are relatively low for slopes which are 'vegetated' in terms of today's climate. The summed effective work done by forty 100-yr events is, incidentally, appreciably greater than that of 4000 years at the annual frequency.

If the rates of erosion **are** relatively low, in terms of this model, in terms of the crudely estimated yields, in terms of models based on empirical estimates elsewhere and in terms of our knowledge of th archaeological sites, why is the landscape so deeply dissected and the drainage density so high? There appear to be three possible explanations:

a) the magnitude and frequency pattern of work producing events has changed between the late Tertiary when tectonic stability first appeared and the late prehistoric period by which time much of the existing drainage system had evolved.

b) the network is now so extended that in large areas, given the magnitude and frequency of overland flow production, the drainage density is well adjusted to the prevailing conditions so that slopes have become relatively stable, or

c) the system only operates at even more extreme events than these considered here and responds non-linearly (as implied above) so that only a few events per thousand years are of relevance in determining the overall density.

The work done so far does not lead to a logical choice between these three. The whole problem of the inconsistency in chalk terrains between expected high erosion rates and low drainage densities and smooth, concave, regolith-covered slopes does suggest that, unlike glaciated temperate areas, the dynamics of drainage extension and hydrological production are in an extremely well adjusted and stable state. In short, we favour the second of these explanations.

8.   SUMMARY AND CONCLUSIONS

A simple set of previously published soil erosion models, which are variants on the Musgrave equations based on HORTON (1945) have been operated through field parameters using topographic and hydrological inputs. The results, which appear to be of the right order of magnitude, indicate contrasts between gullied marls and other lithologies, suggest the magnitude of the effects of vegetation cover and generally show low amounts of erosion, particularly on vegetated slopes. The highly dissected appearance of the landscape in many areas of south-east Spain is partly due to the sparse vegetation cover but probably mainly reflects a limiting degree of network and hillslope stability as a result of extensive and rapid growth between the late Tertiary and the early Holocene.

ACKNOWLEDGEMENTS

We wish especially to thank Stephen Wise and Donald Thompson for the fieldwork assistance they gave in preparation for this paper. The "Prehistoric Land Use in Southeast Spain" project, of which this paper is a contribution, has been funded by the Tinker Foundation, the National Endowment for the

Humanities, the Fundacion Juan March, the Sociedad de Estudios y Publicaciones, the Fundacion Universitaria Espanola, Northridge Archaeological Research Center, the Institute for Social and Behavioral Sciences (California State University – Northridge), and the California State University Foundation, Northridge.

BIBLIOGRAPHY

BIROT, P. & SOLE SABARIS, L. (1959): La morphologie du sud-est de l'Espagne. Revue de Geographie des Pyrenees et du Sud Ouest XXX, 119-84.

BORK, H.R. & ROHDENBURG, H. (1981): Rainfall simulation in southeast Spain: Analysis of overland flow and infiltration. In: MORGAN, R.P.C. (ed.), Soil Conservation: Problems and Prospects. Wiley, 293-302.

BRYAN, R.B. (1976): Considerations on soil erodibility indices and sheetwash. CATENA 3, 99-111.

BUTZER, K.W. (1977): Geomorphology of the Lower Illinois Valley as a spatiotemporal context for the Koster Archaic site. Illinois State Museum Report of Investigations 34, 1-60.

CAMPBELL, I.A. (1970): Erosion rates in the Steveville Badlands, Alberta. Canadian Geographer 14, 202-16.

CARSON, M.A. & KIRKBY, M.J. (1972): Hillslope Form and Process. Cambridge University Press, 475 pp.

CHAPMAN, R.W. (1978): The evidence of prehistoric water control in southeast Spain. Journal of Arid Environments 1, 261-277.

ELIAS CASTILLO, F. & GIMINEZ ORTIZ, R. (1965): Evapotranspiraciones potenciales y balances de agua en Espana. Spain, Direccion General de Agricultura, Madrid.

ELIAS CASTILLO, F. & RUIZ BELTRAN, L. (1979): Precipitaciones Maximas en Espana. Ministerio de Agricultura, Institute Nacional para la Conservacion de la Naturaleza, Monografia 21.

FARRES, P. (1978): The role of time and aggregate size in the crusting process. Earth Surface Processes 3, 279-283.

FERRE BUENO, E. (1974): Iznalloz. Un municipio de los montes orientales granadinos. Estudios Geograficos 35, 53-106.

FLAXMAN, E.M. (1972): Predicting sediment yield in Western United States. Journal Hydraulics Division, American Society Civil engineers 98, (12), 2073-2085.

FOSTER, G.R. & MEYER, L.D. (1975): Mathematical simulation of upland erosion mechanics. United States, Department of Agriculture, Agricultural Research Service, ARS-S-40, 190-207.

FOURNIER, F. (1960): Debit solide des cours d'eau. Essai d'estimation de la perte en terre subie par l'ensemble de globe terrestre. International Association for Scientific Hydrology, Helsinki.

FREITAG, H. (1971): Die natürliche Vegetation des Südostspanischen Trockengebietes. Botanisches Jahrbuch 91, 147-308.

GEIGER, F. (1970): Die Aridität in Südostspanien. Stuttgarter Geographische Studien 77, 1-173.

GILMAN, A. (1976): Bronze Age dynamics in south east Spain, Dialectical Anthropology 1, 307-319.

GILMAN, A. & THORNES, J.B. (in press): Land use and prehistory in south-east Spain. University of London Monograph Series, Allen and Unwin.

HOLEMAN, J.N. (1968): The sediment yield of major rivers of the world. Water Resources Research 4, 737-47.

HORTON, R.E. (1945): Erosional development of streams and their drainage basins. Geological Society of America Bulletin 56, 275-370.

JENSEN, J.M.L. & PAINTER, R.B. (1974): Predicting sediment yield from climate and topography. Journal of Hydrology 21, 371-380.

KIRKBY, M.J. (1974): Hydrological slope models. The influence of climate. University of Leeds, Department of Geography, Working Paper 89.

KIRKBY, M.J. (1980a): Modelling water erosion processes. In: KIRKBY, M.J. & MORGAN, R.P.C. (Eds.), Soil Erosion. Wiley, 183-216.

KIRKBY, M.J. (1980b): The stream head as a significant geomorphic threshold. In: COATES, D.R. & VITEK, J.D. (Eds.), Thresholds in Geomorphology. George Allen and Unwin, 53-74.

LANGBEIN, W.B. & SCHUMM, S.A. (1958): Yield of sediment in relation to mean annual precipitation. Transactions of the American Geophysical Union 39, 1076-84.

LOPEZ BERMUDEZ, F. (1973): La Vega Alta del Segura. Universidad Murcia, 228 pp.

MEYER, L.D., FOSTER, G.R. & ROMKENS, M.J.M. (1975): Source of soil eroded by water from upland slopes. United States Department of Agriculture, Agricultural Research Service ARS-s-40, 177-89.

MORGAN, R.P. (1980): Modelling water erosion processes. In: KIRKBY, M.J. & MORGAN, R.P.C. (Eds.), Soil Erosion. Wiley, 183-216.

MOEYERSONS, J. (1975): An expermental study of pluvial processes on granite. CATENA 2, 289-308.

MUSGRAVE, G.W. (1947): The quantitative evaluation of factors in water erosion: A first approximation. Journal of Soil and Water Conservation 2, 133-138.

RENARD, K.G. (1980): Estimating erosion and sediment yield from rangeland. Watershed Management '80, American Society of Civil engineers, 164-175.

RIVAS GODOY, S. & RIVAS MARTINEZ, S. (1971): Vegetacion potencial de la provincia de Granada. Trabajos del Departmento de Botanica y Fisiologia Vegetal 4, 3-85.

SCHUMM, S.A. (1964): Seasonal variations of erosion rates and processes on hillslopes in Western Colorado. Zeitschrift für Geomorphologie, Supplement Band 5, 215-238.

SCHUMM, S.A. (1965): Quaternary palaeohydrology. In: WRIGHT, H.E. & FREY, D.G. (Eds.), The Quaternary of the United States, Princeton, 783-794.

SCHUMM, S.A. & HADLEY, R.F. (1957): Arroyos and the semi-arid cycle of erosion. American Journal of Science 255, 161-174.

SCOGING, H.M. (1976): A stochastic model of daily rainfall simulation in a semi-arid environment. Graduate School of Geography Discussion Paper. London School of Economics 59, 31 pp.

SCOGING, H.M. & THORNES, J.B. (1980): Infiltration characteristics in a semi-arid environment. International Association Scientific Hydrology, Publication 128, 159-168.

THORNES, J.B. (1974): The rain in Spain. Geographical Magazine April 1973.

THORNES, J.B. (1976): Semi-arid Erosional Systems: Case Studies from Spain. London School of Economics, Geographical Papers 7, 79 pp.

THORNES, J.B. (1980a): Erosional processes of running water and their spatial and temporal controls: a theoretical viewpoint. In: KIRKBY, M.J. & MORGAN, R.P.C. (Eds.), Soil Erosion. Wiley, 129 -182.

THORNES, J.B. (1980b): Structural instability and ephemeral channel behaviour. Zeitschrift für Geomorphologie, Supplement Band 36, 233-244.

TORRE, J. (1973): Informe sobre los effectos de las lluvias de los dias 18 y 19 Octubre, 1973, en el sureste de Espana. Spain, Centro de Estudios Hidrograficos, Madrid.

WISE, S., THORNES, J.B. & GILMAN, A. (1983): How old are the badlands? A case study from south-east Spain. In: BRYAN, R.B. & YAIR, A., Piping and Badland Erosion. Geobooks.

YOUNG, A. (1974): The rate of slope retreat. In: BROWN, E.H. & WATERS, R.S. (Eds.), Progress in Geomorphology, Papers in Honour of David L. Linton. Institute of British Geographers, Special Publication 7.

ZEUNER, F.E. (1946): Dating the Past. Methuen and Co., 516 pp.

Addresses of authors:
J.B. Thornes, Department of Geography, Bedford College, Regent's Park
London NW1 4NS, UK
A. Gilman, Department of Anthropology, California State University
Northridge CA 91330, USA

Jan de Ploey (Ed.):
Rainfall Simulation, Runoff and Soil Erosion
CATENA SUPPLEMENT 4, Braunschweig 1983

SOIL EROSION ON VINEYARDS IN THE TERTIARY PIEDMONTESE BASIN (NORTHWESTERN ITALY) STUDIES ON EXPERIMENTAL AREAS

D. Tropeano, Torino

SUMMARY

The rate of soil erosion in the Piedmontese vineyards is reported, based on field measurements of rainfall and soil loss in three experimental areas during 1981. The first site is located on a slope recently prepared for vine cultivation, where work is fully mechanized; the second is a traditionally cultivated vineyard, at intervals machine-tilled, and the last one is an old vineyard, cultivated with manual tools only.

The soil loss was over 7000 g/m^2 in the first case, about one half in the second and practically negligible in the third. From this it is apparent that the rate of soil erosion was strongly affected by the manner of cultivation, being on the whole much higher than in other experimental areas in European vineyards.

1. INTRODUCTION

For some years in Europe the need for research into the dynamics and rate of soil erosion on slopes devoted to vine cultivation has been felt, and both cartographical approaches (SCHWING 1979, SCHWING & VOGT 1980, VOGT 1979) and surveys on experimental plots are currently being made. In Hungary such studies have been going on for over 20 years (PINCZÉS 1979); in Germany since 1974 (RICHTER 1980); and in France since 1976 (MESSER 1980).

In Italy, more than 18119 km^2 of hillslopes are employed in vine production (ISTITUTO CENTRALE DI STATISTICA 1980). However, as already noted by CHISCI (1973), "in our Country ... quantitative evaluations on runoff ... for various rainfall events and different seasonal periods and on the rate of soil erosion ... are totally lacking", and therefore "there is a great need to increase and emphasize studies on this problem". Again according to data from the above mentioned Institute, vineyards in Piedmont occupy over 863 km^2 of hilly slopes mostly in the Monferrato and Langhe area, i.e. the "Tertiary Piedmontese Basin". Such landforms cover more than 3820 km^2 (pers. com. Dr. G. MORTARA) so that vineyards occupy about 22.6% of the region.

That soil erosion processes occur on slopes devoted to vine cultivation was dramatically emphasized when the downpours of November 1968 (GRASSO 1970), April 1969 (FRANCESCHETTI & MERLO 1970) and October 1977 (Photo 1) affected large areas of the region and most vineyards were severely damaged by erosion and mass movement phenomena.

For the purpose of collecting quantitative data on runoff and soil loss in a vineyard system, three localities in Central Piedmont were equipped with measuring devices in the Winter 1980-1981. These sites may be considered typical, with respect to lithology, geomorphology and climate, of a large part of the "Tertiary Basin".

Photo 1:   Vineyards damaged by heavy erosion and mass movement processes on 6-7 October 1977 near Gavi (Southern Piedmont).

2.   THE EXPERIMENTAL SITES

One or more sample areas were selected in each site on reaches of slope morphologically homogeneous, plane and evenly inclined. It was thought inadvisable to place lateral boundaries around the plots, because (MORGAN 1977) this could influence runoff, and moreover would interfere with cropping practices. On the other hand, it is reasonable to assume, at least in theory, that drainage into and out of the catchment area of the plot counterbalance one another. Obviously, for this condition to be valid, special care was needed in choosing the measuring points along the slopes, keeping in mind that surface hydrology in a vineyard system may strictly be affected by even the occasional contribution of drainage ditches, trails and particularly by the presence of contour benches. These are frequently built not only for convenience of crop management, but also to break the slope and consequently the flow of water. The surface waters in some cases tend therefore to flow obliquely to the contour lines. A preliminary survey of the soil microtopography made it possible to minimize this problem, so that both the reliability and the repetition in time of the data collected are ensured. Only if the above conditions are respected may we assume that the data so obtained at the measuring point refer to a given area, the two dimensions of which are the length of the reach of slope above the trap and the length of the trap itself.

Runoff and soil losses were measured in trays, placed at right angles to the lines of maximum slope. These are constructed from galvanized sheet-iron and differ from the throughs proposed by GERLACH (1967) only in their increased capacity (m 1 × 0.3 × 0.1) allowing even large amounts of sediments to be stored, and in having a totally removable lid for ease of sediment collection; each trap is equipped with a 120-litre drum.

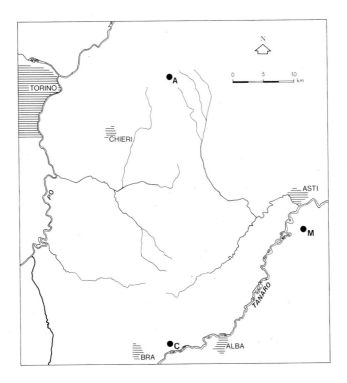

Fig. 1:   Location of the experimental sites (A = Albugnano, M = Mongardino, C = Cinzano, near S. Vittoria d'Alba).

The measurement sites are the following (Fig. 1):

1) **Albugnano**, just Northwest of the Vezzolano Abbey. It is located in a larger experimental area where the C.N.R. Istituto per la Meccanizzazione Agricola has for a few years tested experimentally the control of rainwater flow, taking at the same time into account the needs of a full agricultural mechanization (LISA 1976). The present research is carried out in co-operation with this Institute.

Elevation: 450 m a.s.l.

Mean annual rainfall: 862 mm (recorded at the raingauge of the C.N.R. Institute, period 1962-1980).

Geolithology: Baldissero Formation, middle Miocene. Marls wit sporadic thin arenaceous beds, steep dipping downslope.

Soil particle size: clay loam (30% sand, 48% silt, 22% clay).

Areas A 1–2–3, with identical topographic features (length 30 m, slope 20°, aspect S).

Remarks: on September 1980 the field was prepared to plant a vineyard for the first time, with deep ploughing (from few dm up to 1 m) by up- and downhill operation by a bulldozer, followed by rotovation. The vegetal cover re-established after some 6 months, with the occurrence of weeds, subsequently uprooted. The soil was then repeatedly reworked mechanically (borings for lodging the young vine trees, tillage, mulching, etc.) until October 1981 (Photo 2).

2) **Mongardino** (la Varìa): is a privately owned vineyard, made available for field surveys by the courtesy of Dr. V. BOSCO.

Elevation: 175 m a.s.l.

Mean annual rainfall: 639 mm (at the raingauge of Asti, period 1921-1970).

Geolithology: silt and fine sands, lying between "Argille di Lugagnano" and "Sabbie di Asti" Formations (middle Pliocene), in nearly horizontal strata.

Soil particle size: silt loam (9% sand, 73% silt, 18% clay).

Area M 1 (length 31 m, slope 17°, aspect W).

Remarks: the vineyard was established some 30 years ago, using only manual tools. The rows are horizontal, equally spaced at 1.4 m, with very small benches inbetween. Every other year the crop is treated with herbicides or machine tilled to a depth of 25-30 cm. Weed cover practically lacking (Photo 3).

3) **S. Vittoria d'Alba**: is a vineyard of the wine-producing factory "CINZANO S.p.A.", almost at the foot of the River Tanaro Valley left slope.

Elevation: 210 m a.s.l.

Mean annual rainfall: 668 mm (at the raingauge of Bra, period 1860-1980) – 800 mm (raingauge of Alba, period 1921-1976).

Geolithology: silty-clayey marls, lying between "Formazione Gessoso–Solfifera" (late Miocene) and "Argille di Lugagnano" (early Pliocene). Strata gently inclined upslope.

Soil particle size: silty clay loam (13% sand, 59% silt, 28% clay).

Areas: C 1 (length 29 m, slope 23°), C 2 (length 44 m, slope 26°), C 3 (length 58 m, slope 22°); the aspect is S for the three of them.

Remarks: the vineyard was established over 60 years ago and replaced in 1967 only by manual means. Rows are aligned along contour lines, equally spaced at 1.6 m. Small benches are present in the Area C 2. Herbicides are employed twice a year with occasional manual digging to a maximum depth of 20 cm. The soil is covered by tufts of grass and weeds.

3. DATA PROCESSING AND COMMENTARY ON THE RESULTS

Surveys made between February and December 1981 revealed 22 different rainfall events. At the end of each rainfall event the total volume of water and sediment stored in the collecting trays and drums was measured and sampled. Soil moisture conditions preceding the rainfall event were not monitored for two main reasons: 1) the scarce reliability of soil hygrometers (point measurements may be affected by local conditions and cannot easily be extrapolated to wider areas); 2) practical difficulties in sampling the soil before every rainfall event (no member of our staff works full time in the neighbourhood of the test sites).

An important aim of the present research program is to stress the quantitative

Photo 2: The experimental slope at Albugnano, in March 1981. Arrows mark the traps.

Photo 3: The Mongardino vineyard, traditionally cultivated in horizontal rows. The sediment trap is marked by an arrow. (Photo G,M. Caiazzo)

relationships between rainfalls of various intensities and durations and amounts of runoff and soil loss. To this end, results have already been obtained on small plots East of Biella (CARONI & TROPEANO 1981) from which empirical formulae for predicting the rate of soil erosion have been established. In the present study a good correlation between rainfall and soil losses is hindered by the following main factors:

– variations in the rate of runoff under intense rainstorms, controlled by pre-existing or newly induced rills;
– changes in the angle of raindrop impact from one event to another or during the same event, which cannot be evaluated by an ordinary rainfall recorder;
– progressive increase of the foliage during the year and consequently increased selective screening effects produced by the rows in respect to the directions of raindrops, when rainfalls with a high degree of inclination occur;
– variations of the microrelief, induced by human effects (deambulation, farm operations), biological activity, etc.;
– changes in runoff for random changes in the rate and the directions of incoming liquid fillets, also as a consequence of the preceding point.

From the foregoing it can be explained why, all other physical conditions being equal, a maximum cumulative spread of 39% is to be found in areas A 1-2-3; only average values from the three areas have therefore been taken into account in processing the data.

It was repeatedly observed that soil loss in appraisable quantity (i.e. approximately 100 g) occurred indifferently in all the areas considered for rain intensities of 0.08 to 0.16 mm/min. For ease of computing, in analysing raingauge data, an average of 0.12 mm/min was assumed as a threshold value, all rainfall intensities equal to or exceeding this value being considered "erosive". Rainfall intensity was measured over time intervals not shorter than 5 minutes.

The amount of oven-dried sediment stored in each collecting tray, was used as a dependent variable in a multiple regression analysis, with the following hydrological parameters as independent variables:

– cumulative rainfall (mm);
– maximum peak intensity (mm/min);
– total "erosive" rain (mm);
– duration of cumulative rainfall (min);
– mean rainfall intensity (mm/min);
– cumulative runoff (l).

For each area analytic comparisons between the various amounts of soil loss and runoff and all the possible combinations of the above mentioned parameters were made, to detect

Tab. 1:   CORRELATION COEFFICIENTS BETWEEN RAINFALL AND SOIL LOSS, RAINFALL AND RUNOFF (VALUES IN BRACKETS), AND RUNOFF AND SOIL LOSS (UNDERLINED). The parameters used are listed in each subdivision (Rc = cumulative rainfall, Re = "erosive" rainfall, Imax = maximum peak intensity, T = duration of the rainfalls, Im = mean intensity).

A 1-2-3	M 1	C 1	C 2	C 3
0.71	0.88	0.87	0.88	0.86
Imax, Im, T	Rc, Imax	Rc, Imax, Re	Rc, Re, T	Rc, Imax, Re
(0.72)	(0.87)	(0.88)	(0.89)	(0.87)
Rc, Imax, Re, T	Rc, Imax	Rc, Imax	Rc, Imax	Rc, Imax
0.92	0.99	0.93	0.99	0.94

the best fit. Though these data are to be considered as preliminary only, for the relatively low number of events considered, the following conclusions can be made (Tab. 1):

–   the best correlations result from the combination of no more than 2-3 significant parameters;

–   runoff and soil loss appear very highly correlated (from $r = 0.92$ to $r = 0.997$) in all the experimental areas; this depends undoubtedly upon the dynamics of erosion processes in relation to soil characteristics. While detachment of soil particles is caused by splash energy, it was also observed that the soil, mainly composed of small loose materials (D_{50} ranging from 0.02 to 0.006 mm) is subsequently transported by running water, which itself causes erosion. This is a process completely different from the one we observed on regolithes East of Biella, where "splash" erosion results in both detachment and transport of soil particles having a $D_{50} = 2$ mm (CARONI & TROPEANO 1981);

–   except on one occasion (area C 3) the parameter "maximum peak intensity" is always present in the rainfall/runoff and rainfall/soil loss correlations. This parameter was also recognized as a main factor in soil erosion in Alsace vineyards (MESSER 1980). Also the parameter cumulative rainfall is nearly always highly correlated with runoff and soil loss;

–   it should be noted that the values of the correlation coefficients in the area of Albugnano are rather low, though runoff and soil loss values are mean values of the three measuring points. This is clearly due to the strong influence of human activity during the survey period.

An attempt to find simple correlations between the amounts of soil loss and the products of total rainfall values by maximum peak intensities has been made in the form of the A Im index (LAL 1976); the correlation coefficients obtained here were lower than the corresponding values shown in Tab. 1; in some instances even by two decimal units.

The data collected up to now allow, within the limits of the three test sites, a first approximate range of threshold values of the severity of erosion to be identified. These values, obviously, are to be considered indicative only, in consideration of the short period of survey.

Ordinary erosion took place for rain intensities ranging from 0.08 to 0.33 mm/min, lasting 20 to 30 min, with prevailing processes of sheet erosion; sediment concentrations were usually lower than 50 g/l. Maximum soil loss was below 30 g/m^2.

Intense erosion appeared for peak intensities of between 0.33 and 0.5 mm/min, lasting at least 15 min, with occasional rills and maximum turbidity values in the region of 100 to 150 g/l. Soil losses were observed of up to 150 g/m^2.

Heavy erosion occurred starting from rain intensities of 0.5 up to 1.2 mm/min, lasting at least 15 min. Rills were always observed, either newly induced or by enlargement of pre-existent rills. Suspended sediment in some cases exceeded the said upper limit, to attain more than 300 g/l (in the area of Albugnano). Soil losses were even greater than 1800 g/m^2.

In Tab. 2 the total rainfall amounts between the end of March and the end of October 1981 are compared with the corresponding runoff and soil loss; the month of December was characterized only by snow cover and negligible erosion. The rainfall at the three test sites had revealed different features, owing to their prevailing storm character during the warm months and probably also for the different location of the areas.

The highest rainfall depths occurred at Albugnano, but the heaviest rainstorms were at Mongardino, where nearly one half of the rains appeared to be "erosive". At S. Vittoria

Tab. 2:   RAINFALL, RUNOFF AND SOIL LOSS IN THE EXPERIMENTAL AREAS IN THE
PERIOD APRIL–OCTOBER 1981. The asterisk indicates an unknown value of total runoff; in such
cases runoff coefficients refer to actual values of rainfall.

Area	Cumulative rainfalls (mm)	"Erosive" rainfalls (%)	Runoff (l)	Runoff coefficient	Soil loss per unit area (g/m²)
A 1–2–3	706	28	*	0.034	$\geqslant$ 7018
M 1	566	47	*	0.029	3255
C 1	404	29	48	0.0004	32
C 2	404	29	119	0.001	78
C 3	404	29	295	0.001	273

Tab. 3:   RAINFALL CHARACTERISTICS DURING THE SURVEY PERIOD.

Area	Number of rainfall events	Rainfall depths (mm)	Rainfall depths as % of total	Number of showers	Mean intensity of the showers (mm/min)	"Intense" rainfalls (mm)	Soil loss as % of total
A 1–2–3	9	372	52.7	19	0.43	180	96.1
M 1	11	340	60	15	0.50	191	99.2
C 1	9	257	63.6	13	0.37	100	97.5
C 2	9	257	63.6	13	0.37	100	89.7
C 3	9	257	63.6	13	0.37	100	98.1

d'Alba the lowest rainfall values were recorded. It should be noted that when comparing the areas V 1–2–3 and C 1–2–3 a decrease in runoff coefficients of up to one order of magnitude is observed. Runoff coefficients in single rainfall events did not exceed maximum values of 0.05 to 0.1 in any area.

Soil losses per surface unit appeared to be of over 7 kg/m² at Albugnano, practically were reduced to one half at Mongardino and were relatively negligible at S. Vittoria. If we now divide such values by the relevant cumulative rainfall values, we get a ratio that we will call Su L. A more direct comparison between the three sites can be made by further elaborating the rainfall data: at all sites several events can be identified where high-intensity showers can be singled out (meaning by "high-intensity" showers those having minimum values of 0.18 mm/min); these showers proved to have a strong influence on erosion: in fact it can be observed in Tab. 3 that the soil lost as a result of the cumulative action of a relatively small number of events (expressed as per cent of the total) represents nearly the whole of the soil removed in each area by a much higher amount of cumulative rainfall. Amounts of "intense" rainfall (which are not to be confused with "erosive" rainfall) are so identifiable, as well the values of mean intensity of the corresponding showers. Then we can write

$$\text{Ss L} = \frac{\text{S'u L}}{\text{Hi} \times \text{Im}}$$

where Ss L could be called the specific soil loss, S'u L is the soil loss per unit area (g/m²), Hi is the total depth of the "intense" rainfalls (mm) and Im is the mean intensity of the showers in which such intense rainfalls occurred (mm/min).

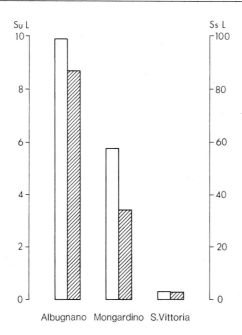

Fig. 2:   Rate of erosion at the three sites, expressed both as soil loss per unit area and per mm of cumulative rainfall (blank column, referring to left scale), and as specific soil loss. For explanation of symbols see text.

The graph of Fig. 2 compares soil loss per unit area/cumulative rainfall ratio to the specific soil loss, as expressed above, at each test site. The two computing procedures show differences for Albugnano and Mongardino, while they give similar results for S. Vittoria. In any case there is a very strong difference between the two extreme conditions of slope management: the disturbance of the soil by repeated mechanical cultivation at Albugnano, and the traditional manual agricultural practices at S. Vittoria. As already said, as the physical characteristics of the three sites do not differ much from one another, it appears that the soil is more or less prone to erosion depending on the way it is tilled.

Of course, differences in sediment yield from one site to another may correspond also to a progressive decrease of cumulative rainfall (see Tab. 2), but there is no proportion between such decrease and the corresponding soil loss values. One can observe that also other parameters, such as slope degree and length, may affect soil erosion in different ways. In reality, while areas C 1–2–3, quite similar in slope, show a likely increase of soil loss as their length increases, they reveal soil loss amounts much lower than areas A 1–2–3 and M1, yet having higher slope and length values.

4. CONCLUSIONS

On the graphs of Fig. 3 the data referring to the survey period are presented with the mean monthly rainfalls, the recorded rain values of Albugnano (20 years), Asti (50 years), where is the nearest raingauge to Mongardino, and s. Vittoria being available. This latter

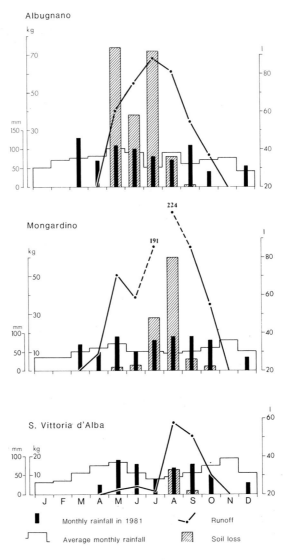

Fig. 3: Monthly values of rainfall, during 1981 and as mean of several years of records (mm), runoff (l) and soil losses (kg). The data from both Albugnano and S. Vittoria refer to average values of soil loss.

village is located between the towns of Bra and Alba (120 and 56 years of rain data, respectively); the average values are so reported on the graph.

Runoff values in Albugnano, relatively low when compared with those in Mongardino, depend upon the high seepage capacity that the newly, deeply ploughed soil proved to have obtained. The deep ploughing may also explain why the loose soil material was easily eroded and carried away, as shown by the peaks of the months from May to July. If we consider the period May–September, when soil losses occurred in all the areas considered, the cumu-

Tab. 4:   MAXIMUM SOIL LOSS RECORDED IN EXPERIMENTAL PLOTS ON VINEYARDS IN EUROPE DURING VARIOUS RAINFALL EVENTS. Soil loss datum supplied by PINCZÉS (1980) for accordance with the others is expressed as weight, assuming 1 cm^3 = 1 g.

ɔcality	Lithology	Dimensions of the plot (m)	Degree of slope	Cumulative rainfalls (mm)	Max. intensity	Soil loss (g/m^2)	Authors
·rgheim, ɔsace	Silty clay on Lias marls	3.4×20	12°	68	30 mm/h	5.7	MESSER (1978)
ɪntzenheim, ɔsace	Loamy sand on granite	3.4×20	12°	35	47 mm/h	6.2	MESSER (1978)
ɛrtesdorf, ɔselle Valley	Coarse regolith on Devonian slates	2.6×8	26°	19.8	7.4 mm in 10 min	72.8	RICHTER & NEGENDANK (1977)
ɔkay, ɪngary	Loess	5×70	18°	22.8	20 mm in 1 h	1480	PINCZES (1980)

Tab. 5:   MAXIMUM SOIL LOSS RECORDED IN THE EXPERIMENTAL AREAS DURING SINGLE RAINFALL EVENTS.

Locality	Lithology	Slope length (m)	Degree of slope	Date	Rainfall (mm)	Max. intensity (mm/min)	Soil loss (g/m^2)
Albugnano	Sandy-clayey silt on marls	30	20°	16 May	24	0.93	1492
				18 July	46	0.75	⩾ 1800
Mongardino	Clayey silt on silt and fine sands	31	17°	17 July	21	1.2	692
				9 Aug.	42.6	1.17	⩾ 1613
				17 Aug.	26.2	1	322
S. Vittoria d'Alba	Clayey silt on marls	58	22°	11 Aug.	27.6	0.45	151

lative rains of each month appear higher than the average monthly values and therefore we can assume that, during 1981, erosion was on the whole heavier than usual.

To obtain an idea of the erosion rate recorded in our areas as compared to what experimentally observed in vineyards in other Countries, let us consider, face to face, Tab. 4, showing rainfall events in which some authors found the highest soil erosion values in their respective plots, and Tab. 5, where the most important single events occurred in our test sites are given. Here the amounts of soil loss per unit area are much greater in general than any value shown in Tab. 4. Perhaps a more suitable comparison, from the point of view of lithology, should be made between our soils and the ones of Bergheim and Tokay. It is to be emphasized that in all the four localities of Tab. 4, as reported by authors, the rows are aligned downslope, while in our test sites, as well as in most of the Piedmontese vineyards, rows are along the contour lines; it is current opinion that this should reduce the rush of waters and thus soil erosion. Furthermore, it should be observed that two soil-loss data (see

Tab. 5) are surely short of reality, because a too high sediment yield in a very short lapse of time even exceeded the storage capacity of both the throughs and drums, which were filled totally with water and sediments.

ACKNOWLEDGEMENTS

This research was carried out with the cooperation of Mr. G.M. Caiazzo and Mr. E. Viola, who contributed to periodic field works. Topographic surveys were made by Mr. F. Godone. Data processing were performed by Mr. E. Caroni.

Helpful informations were given by Dr. L. Lisa, Director of the C.N.R. Istituto per la Meccanizzazione Agricola, as well by the staff of such Institute operating in the area of Albugnano, particularly by Mr. S. Parena. The author is also indebted to Mr. Bosco, of Mongardino, and to Mr. Paganelli, of the Technical Office of "Cinzano S.p.A.", who allowed free admittance to their vineyards. Up-to-date rainfall values recorded at Bra were kindly supplied by Prof. E. Molinaro.

REFERENCES

CARONI, E. & TROPEANO, D. (1981): Rate of erosion processes on experimental areas in the Marchiazza basin (Northwestern Italy). Proceeds. of the Symposium "Erosion and Sediment Transport Measurement", Firenze, June 1981, IAHS Publ. No. 133, 457-466.

CHISCI, G. (1973): Sistemazione del vigneto per la regimazione delle acque e la conservazione del suolo. Annali Istituto Sperimentale Studio e Difesa Suolo 4, 129-142.

FRANCESCHETTI, B. & MERLO, C. (1970): Analisi del paesaggio fisico dell' Astigiano meridionale con particolare riguardo ai suoi riflessi sull' attuale paesaggio agrario. C.R.P.E. Piemonte, 183-234.

GERLACH, T. (1967): Hillslope troughs for measuring sediment movement. Révue de Géomorpholigie dynamique 4, 173.

GRASSO, F. (1970): Studi per la sistemazione idrogeologica della Valle Belbo. C.R.P.E. Piemonte, 235-278.

ISTITUTO CENTRALE DI STATISTICA (1980): Annuario di statistica agraria 26, 323 p.

LAL, R. (1976): Soil erosion on alfisols in Western Nigeria, III. Effects of rainfall characteristics. Geoderma 16, 389-401.

LISA, L. (1976): The contouring of hill land into linked narrow terraces for tree cultivation. Hill Lands, Proceeds. of International Symposium, West Virginia University, Morgantown, W V, U.S.A., Oct. 1976.

MESSER, T. (1978): L'érosion du sol dans le vignoble alsacien. Etude de facteur climatique et étude expérimentale. Thèse 3ème cycle, Strasbourg.

MESSER, T. (1980): Soil erosion measurements on experimental plots in Alsace vineyards (France). In: DE BOODT & GABRIELS (Ed.): Assessment of Erosion, 455-462, J. Wiley & Sons, Chichester.

MORGAN, R.P.C. (1977): Soil Erosion in the United Kingdom: Field Studies in the Silsoe Area, 1973-75. National College of Agricultural Engineering, Cranfield Institute of Technology, Occasional Paper No. 4, 41 p.

PINCZÉS, Z. (1979): The effect of groundfrost on soil erosion. Comptes-rendus du Colloque sur l'érosion agricole des sols en milieu tempéré non mediterranéen, Strasbourg–Colmar, Sept. 1978, 107-112.

PINCZÉS, Z. (1980): The effect of crop production branches and training systems on soil erosion. Communications from the Geographical Institute of the Kossuth University of Debrecen, No. 135, 357-379.

RICHTER, G. (1980): Three years of plot measurements in vineyards of the Moselle Region – some preliminary results. Zeitschrift für Geomorphologie, V.F., Suppl.-Bd. 35, 81-91.

RICHTER, G. & NEGENDANK, J.F.W. (1977): Soil erosion processes and their measurement in the German area of the Moselle River. Earth Surface processes 2, 261-278.

REGIONE PIEMONTE, ASSESSORATO ALLA TUTELA DELL'AMBIENTE (1981): Progetto per la pianificazione delle risorse idriche del territorio piemontese 2, 913-1824.

SCHWING, J.F. (1979): Cartographie de l'érosion en milieu agricole: méthodes et principaux résultats en fonction des différents substrats et pentes. Exemple du vignoble alsacien. Zeitschrift für Geomorphologie, N.F. **23**, 199-214.

SCHWING, J.F. & VOGT, H. (1980): An attempt at a large-scale non-experimental, cartographic approach to the variability of erosion features and land sensitivity to erosion in the Alsace (France) vineyards. In: DE BOODT & GABRIELS (Edit.): Assessment of Erosion, 207-214, J. Wiley & Sons, Chichester.

VOGT, H. (1979): Méthode d'étude complexe de l'érosion agricole des sols, à l'exemple du vignoble alsacien. Comptes-rendus du Colloque sur l'érosion agricole des sols en milieu tempéré non mediterranéen, Strasbourg-Colmar, Sept. 1978, 199-201.

Address of author:
D. Tropeano, C.N.R. Istituto di Ricerca per la Protezione Idrogeologica nel Bacino Padano, Via Vassalli Eandi 18, 10138 Torino, Italy

Jan de Ploey (Ed.):
Rainfall Simulation, Runoff and Soil Erosion
CATENA SUPPLEMENT 4, Braunschweig 1983

WATER EROSION ON SLOPES IN SOME LAND UNITS IN A MEDITERRANEAN AREA

Th.W.J. **van Asch**, Utrecht

SUMMARY

Sediment transport by water erosion has been studied in different land units in a Mediterranean area. Sediment transport by splash and by overland flow was measured separately at different sites. It is shown that in some representative, more or less natural land units the mean sediment transport by splash and by overland flow measured over a period of three months, is of about the same order of magnitude.

It was also possible by means of the measurement results to make a distinction between transport-limited and detachment-limited conditions for overland flow transport. On the agricultural plots with freshly ploughed highly erodible soils, the conditions for overland flow erosion were transport-limited, whereas on more or less natural plots, with compact soils and less run-off, detachment-limited conditions prevailed.

1. INTRODUCTION

In this paper two aspects relating to the process of soil erosion will be discussed:

a. the importance of splash erosion in different land units of a Mediterranean landscape

b. two types of the process of overland flow erosion which can occur in these land units.

The total sediment transport by water erosion on hill slopes is made up of the sum of splash transport and overland flow transport. Splash transport must be considered as a distinctive process with its own transport model which contributes in its own way to the total transport rate. Splashed particles, however, also contribute to the flow and can be further transported in the form of overland flow erosion (splash pick-up process) (see fig. 1).

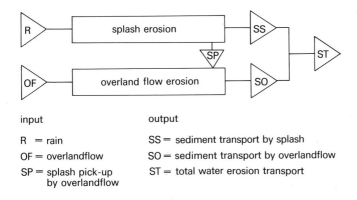

input

R = rain
OF = overlandflow
SP = splash pick-up
 by overlandflow

output

SS = sediment transport by splash
SO = sediment transport by overlandflow
ST = total water erosion transport

Fig. 1:   The water erosion system

It is important to note that in many empirical studies no distinction is made between transport by splash erosion and transport by overland flow erosion. In other words: the results of many measurements do not give any indication about the amount of material which passes a unit width of slope in a unit of time by splashing through the air, or about the amount of material which passes a unit width of slope in the flowing water on the surface (overland flow transport). The first aim of this paper is to show that in different Mediterranean land units the splash transport rate may be as important as the overland flow transport rate. This shows how essential it is for the formulae describing splash transport to be evaluated separately as has been done by for instance DE PLOEY & SAVAT (1968), DE PLOEY & MOEYERSONS (1976), SAVAT (1981), PARK et al. (1982). The second aim of this paper is to study the conditions of sediment transport on the slope. MEYER & WISCHMEIER (1969) and later DAVID & BEER (1975) distinguished two forms of transport viz. under transport-limited and detachment-limited conditions.

Under transport-limited conditions the sediment supply to the flow exceeds the transport capacity of the flow. In that case the formulae describing the sediment transport by overland flow have to be based on the transport capacity of the flow. Under detachment-limited conditions the amount of sediment which is delivered to the water flow by splash detachment and by overland flow shear does not exceed the transport capacity of the flow. In other words the flow is not fully loaded. Under these conditions the transport formulae for overland flow erosion must be based on the rate at which sediment detached by splash and overland flow shear is supplied to the flow.

Tab. 1: THE EXPONENTIAL VALUES OF Q IN DIFFERENT SEDIMENT TRANSPORT EQUATIONS (after MORGAN 1980)

Authors	Exponent of Q in sediment transport formula
MEYER & MONKE (1965)	1.5
CARSON & KIRKBY (1972)	1.75
KOMURA (1976)	1.87
MORGAN (1980)	1.8

In order to obtain evidence for the existence of these two forms of overland flow erosion, curve fitting was carried out for the amount of sediment transport (S) and the amount of runoff (O^{exp}). It is the value of the exponent of Q which may give an indication of the conditions of sediment transport by overland flow. Table 1 gives a survey of exponential values of Q derived from sediment transport formulae, which have been assembled and developed by MORGAN (1980). These transport formulae are based on transport-limited conditions and it can be inferred from the table that the exponential values of Q, according to several authors, vary from about 1.5 to 1.8.

The exponent of Q for detachment-limited conditions must have lower values than the values for transport-limited conditions indicated in table 1:

If under detachment-limited conditions, the sediment supply to the flow only takes place by the process of splash detachment (DAVID & BEER 1975, MORGAN 1979), the sediment transport must be linearly correlated with the rate at which the sediment is supplied to the flow by splash detachment. The rate of splash detachment is correlated to flow depth with an exponent inferior to 1 (PALMER 1965, MUTCHLER 1971, PARK et al. 1982). Flow depth is

Photo 1:
A site (no. 11) chosen in a land unit with soils on metamorphic rocks and olive trees. The soil is ploughed twice a year. a: Gerlach troughs, b: splash troughs, c: portable rainfall simulator.

Photo 2:
The right part of the photo shows the more or less natural slope of measuring site no. 2 in a land unit with soils on metamorphic rocks and a scattered herb and shrub vegetation.

correlated according to the equations of Chezy and Manning with overland flow discharge (Q) with an exponential value inferior to 1 (see also SAVAT 1977). Therefore we may assume that for detachment-limited conditions in which detachment takes place mainly by splash impact, the exponential values of Q can reach a value inferior to 1. If under detachment-limited conditions detachment also occurs through the runoff, we can assume that the exponential value of Q will rise depending on the importance of runoff shear, but it will stay below the exponential values of Q, given above for transport-limited conditions (see also MEYER & WISCHMEYER 1969).

Tab. 2: WATER EROSION AND RUNOFF VALUES OF LAND UNITS IN A MEDITERRANEAN LANDSCAPE

Degree of agricultural activity	Vegetation structure	Parent material	Soil type*	Plot number	Mean splash** gr 100 mm^{-1} rain	Mean total** water erosion gr 100 mm^{-1} rain	Runoff* litre 100 mm rain
freshly ploughed agricultural soil	bare	claystone	"sol brun calcaire vertique"	12	58.6	77.9	2.22
		metamorphic rocks	"sol peu évolué d'apport colluvial modal"	11	30.2	1221.6	41.85
		sandstone	idem	10	54.8	297.9	5.82
no tillage; more or less natural	scattered herbs	claystone	"sol brun calcaire vertique"	1	2.5	2.8	1.65
		metamorphic rocks	sol brun modal	3	6.1	14.7	1.75
			idem	4	6.9	14.9	1.66
		sandstone	"sol peu évolué d'apport colluvial modal"	5	6.8	24.1	5.60
				6	17.7	18.1	0.40
	dense forest	metamorphic rocks	"sol brun faiblement lessive"	2	43.2	57.1	0.84
		sandstone	"sol peu évolué d'aport colluvial modal"	8	19.9	21.0	0.65

Note: *) soils classified according to the French C.P.C.S.–system
      **) measured over a period of three months. Discharges are measured over 0,5 m slope width

2. THE STUDY AREA

The measuring sites were chosen in the drainage basin of the River Savuto and the River Oliva on the West Coast of Calabria (South Italy). The climate has a Mediterranean character with a hot dry summer period of about 3 months and a relatively mild humid winter. The total annual precipitation in this area amounts to 1160 mm. The soils are poorly developed on the dominantly steep slopes and belong mainly to the great groupes of the Orthents, Psamments and Fluvents.

In the study area the percentage of land which is and was used for agriculture is fairly high. The narrow coastal plains and the lowest river terraces are generally used for horticulture. On the steeper terrased slopes, mainly grains and fodder crops are grown in combination with olive trees.

On the steeper slopes in metamorphic rocks and in claystones, there exist also olive plantations without crops (see photo 1). The most gentle slopes which occur in the claystone (ma) area are used exclusively for grains, fodder crops and vineyards. The areas under recent cultivation show the severest erosion.

The live-stock consists mainly of sheep and goats and overgrazing is still common in certain areas. The land units covered with scattered grasses and shrubs serve as natural pastures (see photo 2). On the steepest slopes of the well cemented Mar-sandstone and metamorphic rocks a denser vegetation of herbs and shrubs is found.

Since World War II the agricultural activity of the population has strongly decreased. Abandoned farm land is recognized in the field by the rocky grounds with stone pavements resulting from severe erosion in the past, the presence of cultivation terraces and neglected fruit trees. Herbs and shrubs grow abundantly on these abandoned lands and erosion has strongly decreased (VAN ASCH 1980).

There are not many forests in the study area. They consist mostly of oaks and have deteriorated. At higher altitudes (up to 1000 metre) oak- and chestnut forests are found.

In the study area land units were distinguished on the basis of the variety in landuse, vegetation and parent material of the soil. Seven slopes were selected in land units with scattered herbs and shrubs and dense forest and three sites were selected in land units under active cultivation (see Table 2).

Table 3 gives a survey of the physical and chemical characteristics of the topsoil at the sites.

3. METHODS OF INVESTIGATION

The aims of this investigation as formulated above require instrumentation for the measurement of:

a. sediment transport by overland flow in combination with the amount of run-off water

b. sediment transport by splash erosion.

Two types of instruments were used: the "Gerlach troughs" after GERLACH (1966) and the splash boards which are based on the design of ELLISON (1944) (see photo 1). The Gerlach troughs which are 50 cm in length, were inserted in holes in the soil with a lip on the upslope side, projecting about 1 cm into the soil and $\pm$ 1 cm below the soil surface. The troughs were covered with a plate, which prevented the direct input of rain. Provision was made for the overland flow water to run from the trough into a 10 litre plastic reservoir. With this equipment it was possible to measure sediment transport by overland flow and the amount of runoff water.

In order to catch the material which is transported by splash alone, a splash board 50 cm wide was used with troughs on either sides. This allowed material coming from the upslope direction to be distinguished from that coming from the downslope direction. The net downslope transport rate by splash erosion was calculated by subtracting the amount of sediment splashing upslope from the amount of sediment splashing downslope. A small

Tab. 3:   THE PHYSICAL AND CHEMICAL CHARACTERISTICS OF THE TOPSOIL AT THE MEASURING SITES

site	slope angle	parent material	% surface stones	gravel > 2000 μ	sand 2000-50μ	silt 50-2μ	clay > 2μ	pH(H$_2$O)	pH(KCl)
1	25°	Ma–claystone	5	–	29.40	55.61	15.07	7.78	7.09
2	25°	Sf-metam. rocks	27	10.76	42.74	36.50	10.00	6.05	5.36
3	28°	Sf-metam. rocks	25	4.64	59.92	24.88	10.56	5.66	4.65
4	29°	Sf-metam. rocks	50	9.19	50.80	26.36	13.65	5.42	4.81
5	33°	Mar-s sandstone	15	0.99	74.51	19.39	5.11	6.20	5.19
6	34°	Mar-s sandstone	15	3.12	76.59	13.75	6.54	8.00	7.70
8	32°	Mar-s sandstone	13	4.05	80.44	15.51	–	5.63	4.86
10	22°	Mar-s sandstone	5	–	76.69	19.50	3.81	6.22	5.20
11	18°	Sf-metam. rocks	40	3.21	43.01	44.51	9.27	6.30	5.50
12	21°	Ma-claystone	3	–	53.70	34.25	12.05	7.71	7.01

mesh screen was placed over the troughs to prevent material splashing out again. The troughs were placed flat on the ground; a drain was made at the upper edge to prevent sediment transported by overland flow from entering the troughs.

At each site 4 to 6 Gerlach troughs and 3 to 4 splash troughs were arranged "en echelon" on the slope at a downslope distance of about 2 metres. The slopes varied in length from 6 - 60 metres.

The Gerlach troughs and splash troughs were rather small in view of the great variation in the amount of sediment transport between certain spots on the slope. Distinct rills were not visible on these slopes.

4.   RESULTS AND DISCUSSION

Fig. 2 and table 2 give the mean splash transport in g mm^{-1} rain as a percentage of the mean total water erosion (= overland flow erosion + splash erosion, see fig. 1) measured over a period of 3 months. It is shown that the mean splash transport as a percentage of the total water erosion decreases with an increase of the mean amount of overland flow (in g mm^{-1} rain) produced on these plots. It is interesting to note that in the more or less natural landscape units (plots 1-8, in fig. 2) with slope lengths varying from 10-60 metres, the mean transport by splash alone, varies from 30% to 95% of the total transport by water erosion. This

Tab. 3:   continued

C	N	C/N	Exchangeable cations (meq/100 gr. soil)						base sat. pct.	aggregate stab. (McCalla) drops per 0.1 gram
			Ca	Mg	K	Na	Sum	CEC		
4.15	0.15	27.6	62.0	1.99	0.47	0.14	64.8	15.4	100	105.1
6.00	0.36	16.67	7.6	2.38	0.10	0.08	10.20	18.3	55.7	7.1
2.09	0.17	12.29	4.2	0.90	0.07	0.08	5.25	11.7	44.9	78.7
3.54	0.26	13.61	5.6	1.76	0.12	0.08	7.60	17.8	42.7	20.2
0.99	0.08	12.38	11.4	1.17	0.19	0.07	12.8	10.0	100	52.5
1.55	0.11	14.09	36.5	1.28	0.31	0.04	38.10	9.7	100	37.3
1.53	0.10	15.30	4.3	1.69	0.07	0.013	6.20	9.6	64.6	103.4
0.73	0.03	22.81	17.4	0.9	0.14	0.06	18.00	5.9	100	15.2
1.40	0.11	12.73	5.9	1.81	0.60	0.12	6.5	16.4	39.6	6.8
3.48	0.16	21.75	24.0	0.91	0.61	0.15	2.57	16.5	100	64.6

amount of sediment weight, which passes a unit of width of slope by passing through the air cannot be neglected and therefore in developing water erosion formulae for these areas one must take into account not only sediment transport formulae for overland flow erosion, but also sediment transport formulae describing the splash transport rate (see fig. 1).

Two explanations can be given for the relative importance of splash transport as part of the total water erosion transport:

1.   Splash transport can take place while there is still no overland flow. Especially in land units with low overland flow production (high infiltration capacity of the soil) splash erosion becomes relatively important over a given period of time.

2.   On the slopes (varying in length from 10 to 60 m) we could not establish a good relationship between the mean overland flow production and the slope length on different plots, nor could we correlate the mean overland flow erosion and slope length. This may form an indication that overland flow occurs locally on the slope. In that case the catchment area is limited, as it is for splash transport (DE PLOEY & SAVAT 1968, MOSLEY 1974). Splash transport rate may have therefore the same or approximately the same importance as overland transport rate on these natural slopes.

Fig. 2 shows that on two agricultural plots (no. 10 and no. 11) the amount of splash reduces to a percentage of 5-15% which is small compared to the total amount of overland flow erosion. This must be due to the relatively high overland flow production on these plots, and to the fact that on these bare loose freshly ploughed soils, detachment by overland flow

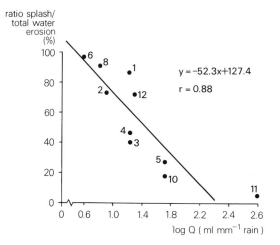

Fig. 2:
The ratio splash/total water erosion (%), related with the mean runoff (Q) measured in different land units over a period of 3 months. (The figures refer to the plot numbers described in table 2 and 3).

shear may occur, which will greatly increase the amount of sediment supply to the flow.

On plot 12, however, which is a freshly ploughed claystone soil, the mean contribution of splash to the total sediment transport is $\pm$ 87%. On these cohesive soils detachment by run-off shear is hardly possible, and run-off is low compared with that in the other units. This low run-off is caused by large fissures in the soil which develop each time the soil is drying out after a sunny period. We can conclude that on this agricultural plot with very low overland flow production, splash transport becomes the dominant process. For these soils an estimate of soil erosion by means of e.g. the Universal Soil Loss Equation may lead to serious errors since this empirical formula is based on the process of overland flow erosion.

In order to detect the two forms of sediment transport by overland flow, we correlate the sediment transport (S) with the run-off discharge (Q) (see fig. 3). The exponential values of Q are found by curve-fitting. The data from the measuring plots were taken together in two groups: the data of the more or less natural plots and the agricultural plots. The fairly high correlation coefficients show that differences in erodibility of the soil and vegetation density which influence the intercept of the graph are not too strong. Also the slope angles of the plots in these two groupes varying from 25° to 30° are assumed to be constant. The exponents of Q in fig. 3 can be compared with the exponents given in table 1.

From fig. 1 it appears that on the more or less natural plots the exponent of Q is significantly lower than on the agricultural plots. The exponent of Q on the agricultural plots has a value which approximates the exponential values of Q of the sediment transport formulae given in table 1, which have been developed for transport-limited conditions.

The differences in the exponential values of Q for the agricultural plots and the more or less natural plots may be explained by the differences in transport conditions for the overland flow, as was stated above. However, there might be other factors which explain the differences in the values of the exponent of Q. We shall discuss these factors first.

a.   Differences in the hydraulic conditions of the flow on the agricultural and the more or less natural plots: according to the experiment of SAVAT (1977), which tested the Manning equation for these overland flow films under rainfall, on smooth surfaces, the exponent of r (= flow depth) increases with decreasing Re-number. It can be inferred from the evaluation of the sediment transport formulae carried out by MORGAN (1980, 310-311, eq.

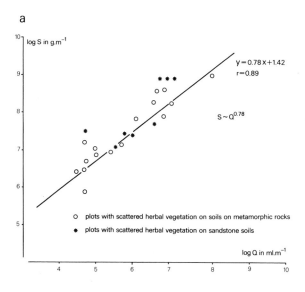

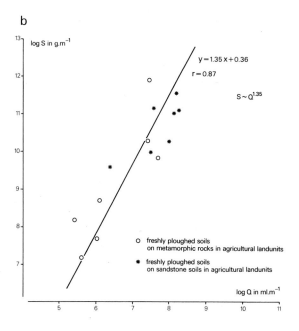

Fig. 3:   The relationship between overland flow (Q) and sediment transport (S) on a. plots with scattered natural vegetation and b. plots under recent agriculture.

(10), (11), (12), (13) and (14)) that in his sediment transport formulae higher exponents of r lead to a higher exponent of Q. Hence, an increasing Re-number leads, according to the work of SAVAT (1977) and MORGAN (1980), to a decreasing exponent of Q. From fig. 3 it can be inferred that according to the above-mentioned theory the Re-number for the more or less natural plots must be higher than that for the agricultural plots. We would expect, however, that for these bare agricultural plots, with high runoff, the Re-number would be higher than for the plots in the more or less natural units, where the surface cover of stones, litter and scattered herbal vegetation slows the velocity of the flow. Therefore, the differences in the Re-number for the various plots do not explain the difference in the exponential values of Q which was found by us.

b. In working out a sediment transport formula for transport-limited conditions, CARSON & KIRKBY (1972) argued on pp. 223-225 that flow through dense low vegetation (e.g. grass) is likely to produce lower exponents of Q than might be found on bare ground. According to them, exponents of Q might be lower in conditions, where the ratio of depth (r) to roughness (k) (r/k) actually decreases as water depth increases. This is the case if the plants of the vegetation cover branch strongly, so that "the number of immersed linear roughness elements increase as depth of water flow increases". The exponent of Q in that case may reach a minimum value of 1 (CARSON & KIRKBY 1972, 223).

As is shown in fig. 3 the exponent of Q for the more or less natural plots has decreased below 1. Therefore it cannot be solely the influence of branching vegetation on these natural plots which causes the lower coefficient of Q. Besides, it is doubtful whether there is in fact a strong influence of branching on these more or less natural plots. On these plots the vegetation cover is scarce and dots of herbal vegetation alternate with bare spots covered with litter and surface stones.

c. CARSON & KIKRBY (1972) also stated (on page 224) that on the basis of findings of ENGELUND & HANSEN (1967) the exponent is lowest when most of the sediment moves as bed load, and increases when the relative amount of suspended load increases. The exponent of Q given by CARSON & KIRKBY (1972) for conditions with mainly bed load are however larger than one, and therefore the values of the exponent of Q inferior to one are not explained by this theory.

The difference in the exponents of Q might, however, be explained by the fact that sediment transport can occur under two different types of conditions, as was stated above: transport-limited and detachment-limited conditions.

On the agricultural plots the exponential value of Q amounts to a value, which is comparable with coefficients of Q in sediment transport formulae worked out for overland flow erosion under transport-limited conditions. On these plots, the large production of overland flow and the low resistance of the soil obviously caused a high supply of sediment towards the flow by detachment via overland flow shear and splash impact. The amount of sediment detachment was probably such that in most cases the flow became fully saturated. MORGAN (1980) also found on his agricultural plots evidence that transport-limited conditions existed. However, he also found indications that in some cases overland flow could transport much more material than was actually available for removal; therefore detachment-limited conditions also occurred on these plots. For MORGAN (1980) this was the main reason why his sediment transport formula, which is based on transport-limited conditions, does not always give acceptable predictions.

The results of the measurements made on the more or less natural plots, which show exponential values of Q inferior to one (see fig. 3), indicate that on these plots detachment-limited conditions must have prevailed. The prevailing detachment-limited conditions in these plots are probably due to the great compactness and cohesiveness of the soils on these plots as compared to the freshly ploughed soils on the argicultural plots. Even though the runoff on these plots is relatively low (see table 2) the supply of sediment by splash detachment and possibly by runoff shear detachment is probably such that the flow does not become saturated. Probably with this low runoff, detachment by runoff shear does not even exist (DAVID & BEER 1975) and the sediment supply to the flow is regulated only by splash detachment. As was stated in section 1 this might explain that the exponential values of Q are lower than 1.

It is important to find out exactly under what circumstances transport-limited and detachment-limited conditions exist in the overland flow erosion process, since this will determine the type of transport formulae which have to be evaluated. Up till now most sediment transport formulae for overland flow erosion have been based on transport-limited conditions. The results on the more or less natural plots show that there is also a need for developing sediment transport formulae which are based on detachment-limited conditions and on the assumption that splash detachment is the main process.

5. CONCLUSIONS

The results of water erosion measurements in different land units in a Mediterranean area show that the splash erosion process cannot be neglected as an independent agent of sediment transport on slopes. It has been shown that in some representative more or less natural land units with relatively low run-off, splash transport is of about the same order of magnitude as overland flow transport. Therefore, sediment transport formulae for water erosion cannot be based simply on the process of sediment transport by overland flow erosion. Splash transport has to be considered as an independent agent and separate transport rate formulae have to be worked out.

Several sediment transport formulae are based on the maximum transport capacity of the flow. According to several authors, the exponent of Q in these formulae, varies from about 1.5 to 1.8. On the agricultural plots with freshley ploughed highly erodible soils, curve fitting showed an exponent of Q, which approximates these exponential values and we may conclude that on these plots transport limited conditions for overland flow erosion have dominated. On the more or less natural plots with more compact soils and lower run-off values the exponential value of Q is even smaller than one. This may indicate that on these plots detachment limited conditions prevailed.

ACKNOWLEDGEMENTS

The author is greatly indebted to Prof. Dr. J.H.J. Terwindt, Drs. G.F. Epema, Dr. H.Th. Riezebos and Drs. J.M. Roels for their constructive and critical remarks. Further he wishes to thank Mrs. E.M. Toppenberg-Smink for the drafting of the illustrations and Mrs. S.M. McNab (M.A.) for correcting the English text.

Financial supports for this study were given by the Dutch Organization for the Advancement of Pure Research (ZWO) and the Consiglio Nazionale delle Ricerche (CNR), Italy.

BIBLIOGRAPHY

AHNERT, F. (1977): Some comments on the quantitative formulation of geomorphological processes in a theoretical model. Earth Surface Processes 2, 191-201.

ASCH, Th.W.J. van (1980): Water erosion on slopes and landsliding in a Mediterranean landscape. Utrechtse Geografische Studies **20**. Geografisch Instituut R.U., Utrecht.

CARSON, M.A. & KIRKBY, M.J. (1972): Hillslope form and process. The University Press, Cambridge.

DAVID, W.P. & BEER, C.E. (1975): Simulation of soil erosion. Part 1: Development of a mathematical erosion model. Transactions of the American Society of Agricultural Engineers **18**, 126-199, 133.

ELLISON, W.D. (1944): Studies of raindrop erosion. Agricultural Engineering **25**, 131-136, 181-182.

GERLACH, T. (1966): Développement actuel des versants dans le bassin du Haut Grajcarek (Les Hautes Beskides – Les Carpates Occidentales). Wydawnictwa Geologiczne (Traveaux Géographiques) **52**. Warsawa.

KIRKBY, M.J. (1971): Hillslope process-response models based on the continuity equation. Transactions of the Institute of British Geographers, Special Publication **3**.

KOMURA, S. (1976): Hydraulics of slope erosion by overland flow. Journal of the Hydraulics Division, ASCE, **102** (HY 10), 1573-1586.

MEYER, L.D. & MONKE, E.J. (1965): Mechanics of soil erosion by rainfall and overland flow. Transactions of the American Society of Agricultural Engineers **8**, 572-577, 580.

MEYER, L.D. & WISCHMEIER, W.H. (1969): Mathematical simulation of the process of soil erosion by water. Transactions of the American Society of Agricultural Engineers **12**, 754-758, 762.

MORGAN, R.P.C. (1979): Recherches sur l'érosion des sols sableux en Bedfordshire, Angleterre. Proc. Seminar on Agricultural soil erosion in temperate non-Mediterranean Climates, l'Université Louis Pasteur, Strasbourg.

MORGAN, R.P.C. (1980): Field studies of sediment transport by overland flow. Earth Surface Processes **5**, 307-316.

MOSLEY, M.P. (1974): Rainsplash and the convexity of badland divides. Zeitschrift für Geomorphologie, N.F. Supplement Band **18**, 10-25.

MUTCHLER, C.K. (1971): Splash amounts from waterdrop impact on a smooth surface. Water resources Research **7**, 195-200.

PALMER, R.S. (1965): Waterdrop impact forces. Transactions of the American Society of Agricultural Engineers **8**, 69-70, 72.

PARK, S.W., MITCHELL, J.K. & BUBENZER, G.D. (1982): Splash erosion modeling: Physical analysis. Transactions of the American Society of Agricultural Engineers **25**, 357-361.

PLOEY, J. de, & MOEYERSONS, J. (1976): Quantitative data on splash erosion, simulated on unvegetated slopes. Zeitschrift für Geomorphologie, Supplement Band **25**, 120-131.

PLOEY, J. de, & SAVAT, J. (1968): Contribution à l'étude de l'érosion des sols par le splash. Zeitschrift für Geomorphologie N.F. **12**, 174-193.

SAVAT, J. (1977): The hydraulics of sheetflow on a smooth surface and the effect of simulated rainfall. Earth Surface Processes **2**, 125-140.

SAVAT, J. (1981): Work done by splash: laboratory experiments. Earth Surface Processes and Landforms **6**, 275-283.

Address of author:
Th.W.J. van Asch, Department of Physical Geography, Geographical Institute, State University of Utrecht, Heidelberglaan 2, 3508 TC Utrecht, The Netherlands

Jan de Ploey (Ed.):
Rainfall Simulation, Runoff and Soil Erosion
CATENA SUPPLEMENT 4, Braunschweig 1983

SOIL EROSION IN CENTRAL–JAVA (INDONESIA)
A COMPARATIVE STUDY OF EROSION RATES OBTAINED BY EROSION PLOTS AND CATCHMENT DISCHARGES

P. **van der Linden**, Amsterdam

ABSTRACT

The annual erosion rate from a tropical watershed in the Desel area of Central–Java has been estimated from both river load data and erosion plot measurements during and after rainstorms. The river load data comprised measurements of solutes, suspended and bedload material. Surface runoff and the consequent occurrence of soil erosion, including splash erosion, were measured by bounded runoff plots. Curve fitting analysis on each output variable and some erosivity indices allowed the determination of yearly material yields. Nearly 80% (177.0 tons) of the material transported yearly from the Desel area occurs as bedload. Suspended load accounts for about 20% (44.5 tons). The output of solute load, i.e., 33.6 kg/year, is negligible.

Grass-covered areas do not suffer serious erosion by surface runoff or rainsplash; their soils exhibit high infiltration capacities. Sites used for maize and/or cassava production are eroded at a rate of about 0.6 mm/year. Here, surface runoff occurs frequently due to the relatively low infiltration capacity of the soil, i.e., about 13 mm/hr. Bare soils (approx. 15% of the watershed) with final infiltration rates of 2 to 8 mm/hr, show a yearly erosion by surface runoff of 8.2 mm, while rainsplash causes a net yearly downslope transport of 267 g per meter of contour.

The high degree of correspondence between material yields obtained by applying two different techniques suggests that these estimates are correct indicators of the order of erosion magnitude for the marls and claystones of the Merawu Formation. However, these data differ from those of other authors by up to 500%. Excluding the occurrence of catastrophic events, the present erosion rate is no longer considered to attain maximum values because of the limited availability of erosion-susceptible material.

1. INTRODUCTION

Since the action of rain is the fundamental cause of soil erosion, studies should be aimed at how erosion is affected by different kinds of rain, and how the response varies with differing soil conditions. In other words, the amount of erosion depends on the combination of the rain's power to cause erosion (erosivity), and the ability of the soil to withstand rain (erodibility). Erosivity is defined as the potential ability of the rainfall to cause erosion. For given soil conditions, one storm can be compared quantitatively with another and a numerical scale of values of erosivity can be created. This aspect of rainfall erosion is governed by the physical characteristics of the rainfall. Erodibility, the vulnerability or susceptibility of the soil to erosion, is a function of both soil characteristics (physical, chemical and biological) and soil management.

Three approaches are commonly used in determining soil erodibility (EL–SWAIFY & DANGLER 1976). The first is based on actual measurements of soil-loss from selected natural sites over long periods of time in order to allow representation of a large variety of rainstorms and antecedent soil moisture and surface conditions (WISCHMEIER 1976). The second is based on measurements under simulated rainstorms (MEYER & MCCUNE 1958). The final approach is to compute soil erodibility by using prediction equations that contain, as independent variables, easily measureable basic soil parameters that are strongly correlated with erodibility (ROTH et al. 1974, WISCHMEIER et al. 1971). Most models used in soil erosion studies are of the parametric grey-box type. They are based on defining the most important factors, measuring them and relating them statistically to the measured values of soil-loss. In recent years it has been realized that this approach is not entirely satisfactory in meeting the important objective of creating a model, that is, to increase the understanding of how the erosion system functions and responds to changes in the controlling factors. Today, greater emphasis is being placed on developing white-box parametric and deterministic models (MORGAN 1979).

The objectives of this study were to apply a parametric grey-box type approach to measure inputs of water and solutes, and outputs of water, solutes and solids from a small tropical watershed during rainstorms. Synchronous monitoring of surface runoff and erosion processes at representative bounded plots within the watershed revealed part of the drainage basin's internal structure. Consequently, it turns the grey-box approach into a light-grey coloured one. Furthermore, the material transport measured at the watershed outlet is compared with the erosion rates obtained through extrapolation of the plot data.

2. THE FIELD AREA

The investigations were carried out in a small catchment (17.8 ha) in the Serayu Valley (Central–Java, Indonesia) drained by the Desel River, a first order tributary of the Urang River (Fig. 1). The study area experiences an Indo–Australian monsoon climate characterized by distinct wet and dry seasons. 90 percent of the mean annual precipitation of about 3,900 mm falls during the wet season from October to June, when the average daily precipitation is about 21 mm. During the dry season it is 13 mm. The temperature (yearly average of 23°C varies little and the relative humidity is high (yearly average of 84%). Winds are feeble, ranging from 1.4 to 2.3 m/sec. Their northwest direction during the wet season changes to southeast at the beginning of the dry season (BRAAK 1929, ISNUGROHO 1975).

In and around the research area outcrop claystones and marls of the Marine Facies of the Merawu Formation (SPEELMAN 1979), a Miocene formation geomorphologically characterized by the presence of denuded hills and slopes with severe mass wasting (VAN ZUIDAM et al. 1978). Very large mudflows with single and multiple scars adjoin rotational slumps and slides. Some of the large mudflows move gradually and fractionally while locally more rapid movements and gullying occur in the loose debris as well as in the soft fractured rocks. Depth of the mobile zone depends on the terrain slope (SPEELMAN 1979) and varies in thickness from 0.5 m on slope of 8° to 4 m on slopes of 22°. Streams draining this area, such as the Urang and Merawu Rivers, contribute considerably to the load of the Serayu River. The mean annual denudation rate is probably higher than the mean value of 1.6 mm for the Serayu River basin quoted by RUTTEN (1917), it is thought to be at least 5 mm (SMEC 1973).

The Desel catchment is situated at about 700 to 800 m above mean sea-level and has a mean wateshed slope of approximately 19°. Part of the area is used for shifting cultivation while only a few rainfed rice fields are present (MALINGREAU 1977). Some former agricul-

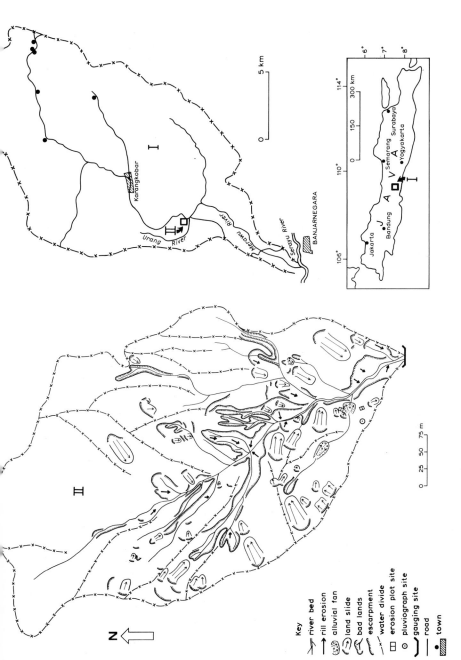

Fig. 1: Location and a geomorphological sketchmap of the Desel River basin.

Tab. 1: LAND COVER DISTRIBUTION OF THE DESEL RIVER BASÍN AND ANNUAL MATERIAL YIELD BY SURFACE RUNOFF

land cover	area				annual reosion rate by surface runoff (tons)
	including bare soil hard rock exposures		bare soil hard rock exposures estimated separately		
	(ha)	(%)	(ha)	(%)	
rice	0.7	4	0.7	4	negligible
maize	0.2	1	0.2	1	1.2
cassava and widely scattered banana trees	5.2	29	4.4	25	26.6
cassava, widely scattered banana trees and 'alang-alang'	4.6	26	3.9	22	negligible
'alang-alang', widely scattered bushes and grass	1.5	9	1.3	7	negligible
widely scattered bushes and grass	4.5	25	3.8	21	negligible
'alang-alang'	1.1	6	0.9	5	negligible
bare soil	-	-	2.6	15	212.3
total	17.8	100	17.8	100	240.1

tural areas have already been devastated by accelerated soil erosion, with much bedrock exposed and large areas of bare, truncated soils. These eroded areas are randomly distributed over the Desel catchment excluding the rainfed rice fields and cover about 15% of the basin (Table 1).

Due to the high erosion rates, most soils can be classified as Troporthents with only Chromusterts occurring at stable sites.

3. METHODOLOGY

Discharge of the Desel River was determined at a sharp-crested V-notch weir (1.0 m wide), located within a rectangular concrete weir 8.5 m wide (Fig. 2a) and equipped with an automatic water level recorder. At stages higher than 17 cm flow velocity was measured by means of a Pitot tube.

River water samples were collected at regular time intervals during single rainstorm events to determine the concentration of suspended and dissolved load. Suspended matter concentration was quantified by filtration and weighing. The main solute constituents analyzed were: Ca, HCO_3, Cl and $CaCO_3$ (titrimetric), Na and K (flamephotometric), SO_4 (colorimetric), NO_3 and SiO_2 (spectrophotometric), Mg and Total Dissolved Load (calculated, the latter based on electrical conductivity).

Before each rainstorm three bedload traps (0.5 × 0.5 × 0.5 m, covered with screening wire with mesh 0.075 mm) were placed in the gauging section at regular intervals (Fig. 2a). After the storm, material trapped was weighed and sampled to determine specific gravity, moisture content and grain-size distribution.

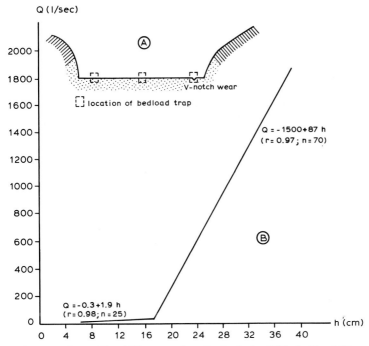

Fig. 2:   a. Cross section at Desel River gauging site (scale 1 : 190); b. Desel River rating curve.

Photo 1:   Grass-covered erosion plots in the Desel River basin.

Tab. 2:   EROSION PLOT PROPERTIES

				soil properties			
plot	area (m^2)	slope (degrees)	land cover	%C	%(0-2 μm)	%(2-50μm)	%(<50μm)
I	10.8	18	grass	0.81	24	30	46
II	10.6	20	cut grass	0.81	25	33	42
III	11.0	17	maize/cassava	1.48	24	31	45
IV	11.4	19	bare	0.68	14	34	52

At the bounded runoff plots of known area, slope steepness and length, soil type and cover, runoff and soil-loss were monitored. Although these plots probably give the most reliable data on soil-loss per unit area, several errors can occur in their use (HUDSON 1957). These include maintenance of a constant level between the soil surface and lip of the trough leading to the collector, runoff collecting along the plot boundaries forming rills (which would otherwise not develop), and the plot being a partially closed system isolated from the input of material and water originating upslope. Due to financial and material limitations only four plots (without replication) could be constructed. Standardized plots (22 m long and 1.8 m wide) appeared to give many problems, such as the complexity of slopes affected by mass wasting. Active rotational slides often resulted in inverse slope directions. The plots finally used were 5 m long and approximately 2 m wide with edges made of sheet metal, pushed about 5 cm into the soil (Photo 1). After two months of data collection two plots were seriously damaged by mass wasting processes but they were restored in order to continue the series of measurements.

The erosion plots were located on slopes typical of the average for the area, had similar soil properties and land cover also typical for the basin. Although site selection procedures may lead to errors when plot measurements are extrapolated and average erosion values calculated for the total watershed, the plots are invaluable for comparison with the results of the Desel's input–output analysis procedure.

Water and eroded material from the plots were channelled into a collecting reservoir with a 220 litre capacity, from which only 10% of the overflow was allowed to pass into a second reservoir, thereby permitting collection of all surface runoff caused by an imaginary rainstorm of 240 mm when infiltration is considered negligible. During rainstorms the total amount of runoff within the first reservoir, and when needed in the second, was measured every three minutes. As soon as precipitation and surface runoff had ceased, the contents of the first reservoir were thoroughly mixed by stirring. A two litre sample was extracted, dried and weighed in the laboratory to determine the amount of soil-loss.

Material transported both down and upslope by rainsplash was caught by traps 30 cm wide, as described by VAN DER LINDEN (1978), placed parallel to the contours at an upslope site in each erosion plot. At plot boundaries perpendicular to the slope an equilibrium exists between in and outsplashing particles. This excludes the placing of traps at these locations.

Rainfall was measured with a float type recording gauge (Fig. 1). During rainstorms standard rainfall collectors positioned near the plots and the gauging site were read every three minutes.

4. RESULTS

4.1. CATCHMENT INPUT: RAINFALL AND ITS SOLUTE LOAD

The amount of rainfall alone does not reveal the information necessary to quantify rainfall erosivity (MORGAN 1979, SOIL CONS. SOC. OF AM. 1977). The total force applied to the soil surface by individual raindrops can best be expressed by the momentum of the rainstorm involved. To calculate this variable, information must be available about the intensity and duration of the rainstorm, size and velocity of individual raindrops, and the drop-size distribution. Because of the many problems involved in determining these rainfall properties, several investigators heve developed erosivity indices, mostly representing a measure of rainfall kinetic energy.

Due to the fact that at most Indonesian meteorological stations only daily rainfall amount is measured, this variable has been included in the present study as a measure of erosivity.

WISCHMEIER & SMITH (1958) presented an erosivity index which can be derived from the rainfall intensity and duration:

$$EI_{30} = [(13.32(p) + 9.78(\log i) \, I_{30} \, (10^{-2})$$

where, EI_{30} = erosivity index of Wischmeier & Smith (J/m^2)
   p = partial rainfall (cm) with constant intensity i
   i = rainfall intensity (cm/hr)
   I_{30} = twice the greatest amount of rainfall received in any
       30-minute period (cm/hr).

For Java and Madura (Indonesia), BOLS (1978) presented a measure of rainfall kinetic energy (BI), based on the total amount of rainfall per storm (R in cm):

$$BI = 2.467 \, R^2 / (0.0727 \, R + 0.725) \quad (J/m^2)$$

The EI_{30} index of Wischmeier & Smith was determined for 38 rainstorms which occurred in the Desel area during the research period (September–December, 1978). Curve fitting analysis on R and EI_{30} resulted in:

$$EI_{30} = 2.60 \, R^{1.87},$$
with $r = 0.83$ at a significance level $< 1\%$.

In areas with a monsoon regime daily rainfall usually occurs as one storm. Consequently, it can be assumed that the monthly rainfall divided by the number of rainy days in that month provides a reasonable measure of the average amount of rain falling during one storm in that particular month. This property and the above mentioned relationships between EI_{30} and R, and between BI and R have been applied in calculating the monthly and yearly amounts of EI_{30} and BI (Table 3).

Rainfall data from the stations closest to the research area, Banjarnegara and Karangkobar, were used (Banjarnegara–Desel: ca. 16 km; Karangkobar–Desel: ca 8 km).

The average rainfall solute composition measured at the Desel River basin is given in Table 4 and appeared to be constant throughout the field observation period.

Tab. 3: EROSIVITY DATA PER RAINY DAY (R = amount of rainfall; n = number of rainy days; R = mean amount of rainfall per rainy day; EI_{30} = mean Wischmeier's erosivity index per rainy day; BI = mean Bols' erosivity index per rainy day).

	erosivity									
	based on Banjarnegara rainfall data					based on Karangkobar rainfall data				
period	R (cm)	n	R (cm)	EI_{30} (J/m^2)	BI (J/m^2)	R (cm)	n	R (cm)	EI_{30} (J/m^2)	BI (J/m^2)
Jan	53.1	20	2.7	16.7	19.5	54.1	27	2.0	9.5	11.3
Feb	38.1	16	2.4	13.4	15.8	45.6	21	2.2	11.4	13.5
Mar	60.2	22	2.7	16.7	19.5	53.8	23	2.3	12.4	14.6
Apr	50.3	17	3.0	20.3	23.5	38.9	22	1.8	7.8	9.3
May	26.0	11	2.4	13.4	15.8	26.2	16	1.6	6.3	7.5
Jun	10.3	6	1.7	7.0	8.4	9.7	7	1.4	4.9	5.9
Jul	6.1	3	2.0	9.5	11.3	6.3	5	1.3	4.3	5.1
Aug	5.3	3	1.8	7.8	9.3	8.3	6	1.4	4.9	5.9
Sep	6.6	4	1.7	7.0	8.4	9.2	8	1.2	3.7	4.4
Oct	20.4	9	2.3	12.4	14.6	32.8	17	1.9	8.7	10.3
Nov	46.2	16	2.9	19.1	22.2	47.6	22	2.2	11.4	13.5
Dec	60.1	20	3.0	20.3	23.5	59.6	26	2.3	12.4	14.6
year	382.7	146	2.6	13.6	18.3	392.1	201	2.0	8.1	11.3

Tab. 4: SOLUTE CONTENTS OF RAIN, GROUND AND RIVER WATER
(i = rainfall intensity; TDL = total dissolved load).

	solute content in ppm						
item	rain water	ground water	river water collected t minutes after the rainstorm started (i = 20 mm/hr, duration = 35 min)				
			t= 0	t= 15	t= 20	t= 35	t= 120
SiO_2	1.2	4.2	5.0	6.0	6.0	6.5	5.5
Fe	0.0	0.2	0.2	0.2	0.2	0.1	0.2
Ca	2.0	25.0	25.0	20.0	22.0	19.0	23.5
Mg	1.2	22.0	24.0	10.0	18.3	15.8	22.8
Na	0.8	39.3	40.0	35.0	30.8	20.0	40.5
K	0.1	0.6	0.9	0.8	0.9	0.7	0.9
HCO_3	12.0	262.0	274.0	265.0	250.0	155.0	270.0
SO_4	2.0	52.0	50.0	60.0	47.0	40.0	55.0
Cl	3.6	8.5	7.5	5.0	2.5	2.5	7.0
NO_2	0.0	0.0	0.0	0.0	0.0	0.0	0.0
NO_3	0.4	0.6	0.8	0.7	0.6	0.6	0.7
TDL	25.0	460.0	690.0	680.0	650.0	600.0	680.0
pH	5.0	6.0	7.5	5.0	5.5	6.0	7.5
stage (cm)			13.0	20.0	21.0	23.0	14.0

4.2. CATCHMENT OUTPUT: WATER

A rating curve was determined for the Desel River (Fig. 2b). Although it is well-known that this stage-discharge relationship is logarithmic, more significant results were obtained by distinguishing two linear sections within the curve. The maximum discharge observed during field measurements was 3,162 l/sec. To determine the proportions of quick and delayed flow with respect to total water input by rainfall, hydrograph analysis according to Barnes (ILRI 1973) was applied. This resulted in a mean groundwater recession curve represented by $Q_t = 1.22 \, \bar{e}^{0.0461t}$, with a recession constant of $K = 0.95$.

Table 5 shows the proportions of quick and delayed flow as percentages of total rainfall, with the amount of water not discharged by these means indicated as storage. Evapotranspiration losses are assumed to be negligible during and shortly after rainstorms. Serious discrepancies between the hydrologic and topographic divides are considered unlikely.

Tab. 5:   INPUT AND OUTPUT DATA FOR THE DESEL RIVER CATCHMENT
(R = amount of rainfall; EI_{30} = Wischmeier's erisivity index; BI = Bols' erosivity index; QF = water discharge by quickflows as a percentage of rainfall; DF = water discharge by deleyed flow as a percentage of rainfall; ST = water storage in the catchment as a percentage of rainfall; BL = amount of bedload transported from the basin; DL = amount of suspended load transported from the basin; DL = amount of dissolved load transported from the basin).

R (cm)	EI_{30} (J/m^2)	BI (J/m^2)	QF (%)	DF (%)	ST (%)	BL (kg)	SL (kg)	DL (g)
1.37	7.5	5.6	70	20	10	490	249	145
1.67	10.5	8.1	42	25	33	575	272	118
1.16	8.0	3.9	33	23	44	634	197	272
1.73	5.4	8.6	45	22	33	1100	223	93
2.80	29.3	20.8	41	21	38	3170	421	450
0.68	0.1	1.5	54	20	26	251	90	159
0.42	5.0	0.6	60	25	15	151	71	76
0.10	0.1	0.0	65	24	11	0	40	60
0.15	0.1	0.1	57	25	18	0	55	29
0.45	0.6	0.7	54	24	22	0	82	90
0.77	1.0	1.9	42	24	34	0	93	145
9.88	118.5	166.9	52	22	26	3493	1139	1070
0.90	5.4	2.5	55	21	24	340	134	39
6.10	76.8	78.6	70	20	10	3260	977	390
0.22	0.2	0.2	46	25	29	0	74	66
0.55	0.7	1.8	53	25	22	276	89	87
0.20	0.1	0.1	52	23	25	0	73	4

4.3.   CATCHMENT OUTPUT: SOLUTE LOAD

The mean solute content of groundwater (Table 4) during base flow conditions varies little. During rainfall, however, the concentration of river water solute load decreases rapidly, both in total and per constituent due to the effect of precipitation dilution.

Depending on the duration and perhaps also the intensity of the rainstorm, chemical composition of the dissolved load returns to its initial level within 2½ hours after cessation of the rainfall. An exception to this general rule is the amount of dissolved silica. During all te observed rainstorms concentration of SiO_2 increased from 4 or 5 to 7 or 8 ppm at peak flow conditions, with a subsequent decrease. An example of the variation in solute load during rainstorms is given in Table 4.

Analysis of river water samples collected at regular time intervals during each rainstorm resulted in determination of the total amount of solute load per rainstorm transported out of the Desel catchment. This is shown in Table 5. Curve fitting analysis on the erosivity indices R, EI_{30} and BI, and output of dissolved load (DL) gave:

DL (g) $= 32.1 + 0.94$ R (cm)   (r $= 0.94$, sign. level $< 1\%$);
DL (g) $= 77.4 + 7.3$ EI_{30} (J/m^2)   (r $= 0.93$, sign. level $< 1\%$);
DL (g) $= 93.9 + 5.6$ BI (J/m^2)   (r $= 0.93$, sign. level $< 1\%$).

4.4.   CATCHMENT OUTPUT: SUSPENDED LOAD

Water samples taken at regular time intervals during each rainstorm were also collected to determine the amount of suspended load carried out from the research area. The concentration of suspended matter varied from 0 at base flow conditions to 63,095 mg/l at peak discharges and always showed a similar pattern. Shortly after the storm started the concentration increased and reached its maximum value at maximum water stage. After that, the concentration decreased gradually.

The concentration of suspended matter at known river discharges allows the determination of total suspended load catchment output from each rainstorm (Table 5). Results of the fitting analysis on the erosivity indices R, EI_{30} and BI, and output of suspended matter

(SL) per rainstorm were:
SL (kg) $= 36.0 + 12.8$ R (cm)   (r $= 0.98$, sign. level $< 1\%$);
SL (kg) $= 98.1 + 9.7$ EI_{30} (J/m^2)   (r $= 0.98$, sign. level $< 1\%$);
SL (kg) $= 124.6 + 7.3$ BI (J/m^2)   (r $= 0.95$, sign. level $< 1\%$).

4.5.   CATCHMENT OUTPUT: BEDLOAD

Because of the problem of determining the amount or concentration of bedload per time-unit or discharge volume the total amount of bedload transported from the catchment per rainstorm has been ascertained. Due to the large volumes of this output variable, 0.125^3 bedload traps were placed at only three sites (Fig. 2a). Grain-size analysis on bedload samples collected after each rainstorm did not reveal any significant difference with respect to composition. Particles exceeding 23 mm in diameter were not observed. D_{50} amounted to 4.5 mm.

To obtain the total amount of bedload discharge it was assumed that this variable is distributed linearly within the river cross-section at the sampling site with zero transport at the banks. Results are shown in Table 5 and curve fitting analysis on the erosivity indices R, EI_{30}

and BI, and bedload output per rainstorm (BL) were:
BL (kg) $= 37.5$ R$^{1.08}$ (R in cm)   (r $= 0.95$, sign. level $< 1\%$);
BL (kg) $= 506.6 + 30.6$ EI_{30} (J/m^2)   (r $= 0.87$, sign. level $< 1\%$);
BL (kg) $= 214.1$ BI$^{0.62}$ (BI in J/m^2)   (r $= 0.95$, sign. level $< 1\%$).

4.6.   THE EROSION PLOTS

Comparison of erosion plot properties (Table 2) with data indicated in Table 1 shows that the land cover of plots I and II represent 55% of the Desel River basin – grass or alang-alang possibly combined with cassava or widely scattered banana trees or bushes. Since grass

Tab. 6: INPUT AND OUTPUT DATA FOR FOUR EROSION PLOTS (R = amount of rainfall; EI_{30} = Wischmeier's erosivity index; BI = Bols' erosivity index; nd = not determined).

R (cm)	EI_{30} (J/m²)	BI (J/m²)	runoff as a percentage of rainfall on plot				soil-loss (g) by surface runoff from plot				net downslope splashed material (g) from plot			
			I	II	III	IV	I	II	III	IV	I	II	III	IV
1.3	nd	5.1	0	0	18	52	0	0	18	506	0	0	1.56	5.94
2.0	nd	11.3	0	0	32	38	0	0	21	498	0	0	1.86	3.18
2.4	nd	15.8	0	0	34	43	0	0	29	464	0	0	0.66	4.80
1.8	9.3	8.9	0	0	21	46	0	0	21	758	0	0	0.60	2.70
1.7	9.9	8.4	0	0	25	66	0	0	23	405	0	0	3.60	3.66
1.8	5.0	8.9	0	0	19	53	0	0	32	710	0	0	1.80	4.08
1.2	nd	4.4	0	0	15	55	0	0	13	138	0	0	0.00	0.00
2.5	30.1	17.0	0	0	39	64	0	0	40	850	0	0	1.80	4.80
0.9	2.2	2.3	0	0	12	53	0	0	15	218	0	0	0.00	0.00
2.8	nd	20.8	0	0	35	62	0	0	53	688	0	0	1.56	3.54
0.6	0.3	1.2	0	0	0	11	0	0	0	25	0	0	0.00	0.00
1.2	nd	4.4	0	0	17	56	0	0	15	128	0	0	0.00	0.00
0.4	0.8	0.5	0	0	11	22	0	0	12	6	0	0	0.00	0.00
2.4	nd	15.8	0	0	32	62	0	0	39	396	0	0	5.58	3.84
0.8	2.1	2.0	0	0	13	13	0	0	12	171	0	0	0.00	0.00
1.6	7.0	7.5	0	0	16	62	0	0	24	232	0	0	2.94	2.76
6.5	155.8	87.0	5	10	46	72	14	42	181	1659	0	0	1.86	1.98
0.3	0.2	0.3	0	0	0	32	0	0	0	9	0	0	0.00	0.00
0.8	0.2	2.0	0	0	0	51	0	0	0	178	0	0	0.00	0.00
3.5	30.0	30.8	3	17	39	67	3	25	132	927	0	0	0.60	1.14
0.6	0.4	1.2	0	0	12	24	0	0	13	35	0	0	0.00	0.00

Tab. 7: RESULTS OF POWER CURVE FITTING ANALYSIS ON EROSION PLOT OUTPUT VARIABLES AND EROSIVITY INDICES (R = amount of rainfall (cm); EI_{30} = Wischmeier's erosivity index (J/m²); BI = Bols' erosivity index (J/m²); RO = runoff percentage; SL = soil-loss (gr); SP = net amount of downslope splashed material (gr); r = correlation coefficient; n = sample size).

plot	dependent variable	independent variable	numerical constant	regression coefficient	r	n	significance level of r
III	RO	R	16.02	0.66	0.94	18	< 1%
IV	RO	R	37.08	0.48	0.67	21	< 1%
III	SL	R	16.27	1.05	0.89	18	< 1%
IV	SL	R	121.65	1.87	0.91	21	< 1%
IV	SP	R	5.36	− 0.60	0.58	12	< 5%
III	RO	EI_{30}	11.91	0.29	0.94	11	< 1%
IV	RO	EI_{30}	31.38	0.20	0.65	14	< 5%
III	SL	EI_{30}	11.81	0.48	0.89	11	< 1%
IV	SL	EI_{30}	76.36	0.72	0.83	14	< 1%
IV	SP	EI_{30}	4.63	− 0.18	0.44	7	< 5%
III	RO	BI	10.76	0.36	0.93	18	< 1%
IV	RO	BI	27.84	0.26	0.67	21	< 1%
III	SL	BI	8.77	0.56	0.88	18	< 1%
IV	SL	BI	39.45	1.01	0.92	21	< 1%
IV	SP	BI	8.04	− 0.34	0.58	12	< 5%

is often used for fodder, the grass of plot II was cut once per week in order to obtain representative runoff and soil-loss data.

Plot III is comparable with the area where land cover comprises maize and cassava, the latter combined with widely scattered banana trees. Truncated soils are found in bare areas, i.e., at the main scarp of rotational slides or in areas suffering a high erosion rate through surface runoff, these are represented by plot IV.

4.7. EROSION PLOT OUTPUT

During the field observation period surface runoff was recorded only twice from plots I and II, i.e., during storms of 3.5 and 6.5 cm. Soil-loss due to these events appeared to be limited (Table 6).

The bare erosion plot and that where maize and cassava form the land cover are characterized by a frequent occurrence of surface runoff. Runoff percentages vary from 0 to 46 at plot III (average, 21%) while bare soil exhibits values of 11 to 72% (average, 48%). The quantity of soil-loss from the crop-covered plot varies from 0 to 181 g, and that from plot IV from 6 to 1,659 g: high runoff percentages correspond with high soil-losses.

Splash erosion does not occur on the grass-covered plots. At plots III and IV it varies from 0 to 5.58 g and 0 to 5.94 g respectively. From Table 6 it appears that the total amount of net downslope splashed soil particles is relatively low when the runoff coefficient is high.

Table 7 shows results of curve fitting analysis on the erosivity indices R, EI_{30} and BI, and plot output variables. For plot III no significant relationship (5% significance level) could be established between net amount of splashed particles and any erosivity index.

4.8. INFILTRATION AT THE EROSION PLOTS

The infiltration capacities of soils in plots I and II were exceeded by rainfall intensity on only two occasions. This suggests a relatively high infiltration capacity, but because of the minor occurrence of surface runoff at these locations no detailed information about the infiltration rate of grass-covered soils can be presented.

Figures 3 and 4 show some characteristic infiltration curves for plots III and IV during different rainstorms. Plot III exhibits a final infiltration rate of about 13 mm/hr, though both higher and lower infiltration rates occurred during the preceding periods. The bare soil of plot IV shows a final infiltration rate lower than that for plot III. depending on antecedent plot conditions and rainfall intensity it varies from 2 to about 8 mm/hr. In contrast with plot III, the infiltration capacity during a storm always decreases to a final value.

4.9. YEARLY OUTPUT: DESEL RIVER CATCHMENT

Annual material discharge quantities were determined using the mean erosivity per rainy day (Table 3) and the derived relationship between R, EI_{30} and BI, and the output of solute, suspended and bedload per rainstorm (Table 8). These mean discharge values were 33.6 kg solute load, 44.5 tons suspended load and 177.0 tons bedload (0.0, 20.1 and 79.9% of total load respectively). The data result in a yield of 1,244.4 tons/km^2/year.

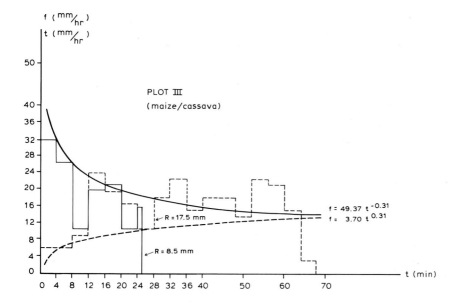

Fig. 3:   Infiltration rate (f) and rainfall intensity (i) during two different rainstorms at plot III.

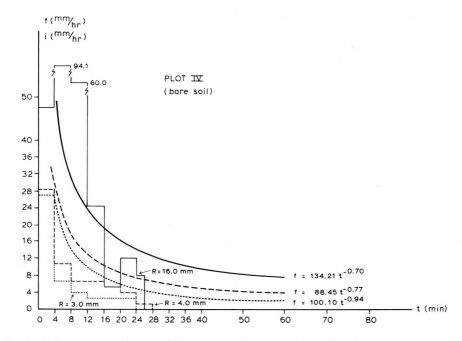

Fig. 4:   Infiltration rate (f) and rainfall intensity (i) during three different rainstorms at plot IV.

Tab. 8: ANNUAL CATCHMENT AND PLOT OUTPUT VALUES (R = amount of rainfall; EI_{30} = Wischmeier's erosivity index; BI = Bols' erosivity index).

		output						
		bases on Banjarnegara erosivity data			based on Karangkobar erosivity data			mea:
	item	R (cm)	EI_{30} (J/m^2)	BI (J/m^2)	R (cm)	EI_{30} (J/m^2)	BI (J/m^2)	
yearly catchment output	solute load (kg)	40.9	28.5	29.2	43.8	28.4	31.3	33.(
	suspended load (tons)	54.5	37.2	38.2	57.6	38.0	41.3	44.
	bedload (tons)	187.7	146.7	191.9	187.2	159.1	189.4	177.(
yearly soil-loss (kg) by surface runoff from plot	III	6.6	6.5	6.6	6.6	6.9	6.7	6.'
	IV	109.0	82.1	111.6	88.1	76.2	90.5	93.
yearly soil loss (kg) by rainsplash from plot	IV	0.4	0.4	0.4	0.7	0.6	0.7	0.

4.10. YEARLY OUTPUT: EROSION PLOTS

Yearly plot soil-losses were derived from mean erosivity values per rainy day (Table 3) and the significant (level † 5%) power relationships between erosivity indices and plot output (Table 8).

Plot III shows a mean annual erosion rate by overland flow of 605 g/m^2, while from plot IV the value is 8,164 g/m^2.

Per meter contour splash erosion causes a net downslope material transport of 267 g/year for soil and cover conditions represented by plot IV. On grass-covered sites soil-loss by surface runoff is negligible and splash erosion does not occur. Areas covered by crops suffer some soil-loss by splash erosion, but the absence of significant relationships between erosivity and the amount of splashed material does not allow reliable estimates.

5. DISCUSSION

5.1. CATCHMENT OUTPUT: WATER

According to the data in Table 5 an approximately constant proportion of rainfall is discharged from the basin as delayed flow. Storage capacity is very limited and the maximum observed value is 2.6 cm. No trend of decreasing water storage capacity from the start of the wet monsoon was observed. Antecedent soil moisture conditions in the Desel catchment explain only the differences in water storage per subsequent rainstorm if the time lapse between these storms is limited. High runoff percentages characterize the Desel area. Rainstorms less than 0.5 cm show discharges by quick flow which vary from 46 to 65% of precipitation input and the maximum value observed was 70%. In view of this it is clear that during storms a constant quantity of rainfall is discharged as delayed flow, uninfluenced by the soil moisture conditions, rainfall intensity or duration. This quantity of water (20-25% of the rainfall) represents that part of the rainfall which infiltrates directly or indirectly into the soil at an approximately constant rate and reaches the Desel River as subsurface flow. Part of the remaining rainfall (10-44%) replenishes the storage reservoir of the basin while the major part is discharged as quick flow.

5.2. CATCHMENT OUTPUT: SOLUTE LOAD

Although relatively large quantities of calcium and magnesium are carried, sodium (Table 4) is the principle cation present in the ground and river water of the Desel catchment. This cation composition is characteristic for water draining hydrolyzate sedimentary areas. The fine-grained claystones and marls of the Merawu Formation are partly composed of colloidal clay, including clay minerals and other particulate matter (MOHR 1938). These clay minerals have high cation exchange capacities and, in combination with the rapid supply of soluble material by erosion, may exert a considerable influence on the proportional contents of different cations in water associated with them. For the Desel River catchment, where water circulation is rapid, the direct solution of hydrolyzate minerals is very significant.

The quantity of river water dissolved constituents clarly reflects the effect of dilution by precipitation. All decrease in concentration except SiO_2, which increases. According to MOHR (1906) sedimentary rocks of the Merawu Formation are largely composed of fine quartz grains with an average diameter of 20 to 50 μm. These grains are responsible for the typical white colour of the river water originating from these areas. Seriously eroded terrains of fine-grained sediments provide a constantly renewable source of soluble matter as the insoluble detritus is mechanically removed by water running from the exposed soil and rock surfaces. Fresh surfaces containing soluble material mixed with the insoluble components are exposed for future solution. Such a source is at least partly responsible for the increase in silica concentration during rainstorms while the relatively high sulphate content may also be ascribed to the same process (HEM 1975).

The data from Table 8 indicate that the very limited yearly output of solutes amounts to less than 0.1% of the annual suspended load. This figure does not agree with the general data known for tropical areas. According to e.g. VAN DER LINDEN (1978) the proportion of dissolved load to suspended solids generally varies from 30 to 50% in rivers draining such areas. However, shallow truncated soils and frequent occurrences of hard rock exposures in the Desel River basin permit only a very short residence time of precipitation water in the soil or hardly weathered hard rock. Moreover, because of these shallow soils and with respect to rain water the rather impermeable bedrock, the quantity of soluble material which can be reached by infiltrated rain water is limited.

5.3. CATCHMENT OUTPUT: SUSPENDED LOAD

Table 8 shows yearly average output of material from the Desel River catchment as suspended matter to be 44.5 metric tons (250 tons/km^2/year). It must be stressed that this figure is at best an order of magnitude indication and is thought to be on the low side. Two obvious reasons why this value is an underestimate are: (a) the assumption that the mean amount of rainfall per rainy day falls in only one storm, and (b) the suspended material concentration measured at the water surface during high river stages results in concentration values which are too low because of a decrease in suspended matter with increasing distance from the bed.

The general empirical equation developed by FOURNIER (1960) gives annual suspended load discharge of 2,416 tons and 2,148 tons based on rainfall data from Banjarnegara and Karangkobar respectively. MOHR (1906) estimated the total amount of discharged suspended load from the outcropping Merawu Formation as 11,800 tons/km^2/year (2,100 tons/year for the Desel basin). SMEC data (1973) indicate a yearly discharge of 13,900 tons/km^2 (about 2,475 tons/year in the Desel catchment). These figures are all higher than the present estimated value for the Desel River basin.

5.4. CATCHMENT OUTPUT: BEDLOAD

Due to the high runoff percentages, the frequent occurrences of hard rock exposures and shallow truncated soils, and the active mass wasting processes, supply of relatively coarse material to the Desel River will be abundant during rainstorms. This explains the high proportion of material discharged as bedload, i.e., about 80% of the total yearly output (Table 8). The figure emphasizes the importance of mechanical weathering in this tropical environment.

Bedload material transported during rainstorms is composed of particles smaller than 23 mm in diameter. Although larger rock fragments do reach the river, disintegration occurs quickly during fluvial transport. This rapid disintegration process is caused by low internal coherence of the fine-grained marls and claystone, possibly favoured by the absorption of water by clay minerals present in this rock type.

5.5. EROSION PLOT OUTPUT: SURFACE RUNOFF AND SOIL EROSION INVOLVED

Considering surface runoff and the consequent occurrence of soil erosion at the runoff plots, the collected data clearly show the important role that the kind and degree of soil cover plays in determining erosion quantity.

The grass-covered plots, both the undisturbed and that frequently visited for fodder cutting, are characterized by such high infiltration values that soil erosion by surface runoff rarely occurs. Only long-duration rainstorms and possibly also storms exhibiting extremely high rainfall intensities result in the appearance of overland flow, leading to modest amounts of soil-loss. The plot where soil is covered by maize and cassava is eroded at a rate of about 0.6 mm/year (Table 8). The maximum rate was measured at plot IV which is characterized by bare soil. Here, the mean surface lowering amounts to 8.2 mm/year. In obtaining these figures the specific gravity of eroded material was assumed to be 2.0 g/cm^3.

When the erosion plots are regarded as spatially representative sites within the catchment the yearly material yield for Desel River basin is 240.1 tons (Table 1). This figure does not reach the high values found by RUTTEN (1917), SMEC (1973) or MEIJERINK (1977) and the exclusion of soil-loss by mass wasting and river bed, river bank and gully erosion may be responsible for this relatively low rate. However, the shallow soils and frequent bedrock exposures limit the availability of erosion susceptable material. VAN ZUIDAM et al. (1978) mentioned the presence of planation surfaces within the area where Marine Facies of the Merawu Formation outcrop. On the other hand, colluvial deposits in the Desel basin might even cause an overestimation of actual erosion rate.

5.6.   EROSION PLOT OUTPUT: RAINSPLASH

Rainsplash is greatly dependent on the input of momentum or energy, resistance of the exposed soil to this force, and on site factors such as slope and vegetation. The input of momentum or energy during a particular storm is determined by its intensity, drop-size distribution, and the size and velocity of individual raindrops. Resistance of a soil surface to splash erosion will be influenced in the first instance by the type of soil cover. Protection against splash erosion increases with increasing density of vegetation, thus giving a decreased energy input (HUDSON 1973). However, the precise effect depends on the nature and height of vegetation cover. The effectiveness of splash erosion is also influenced by the site slope. On an extended horizontal surface material splashed outward from a given point is balanced by that splashed inward from surrounding points, resulting in zero net soil-loss. However, on a sloping surface vertically falling raindrops hit the soil at an angle and tend to carry more particles in a downslope than in an upslope direction, resulting in a net downslope transport of soil material.

Rainsplash measurements at the runoff plots express only the effect of land cover on the amount of splashed material, as all other rainsplash influencing variables are similar. Soils covered by grass do not exhibit any transport of soil particles since the protecting influence of the grass-cover appears to be sufficient to oppose rainsplash erosion. The process of creep mentioned by MOSLEY (1974) and KWAAD (1976), generated by raindrops hitting a sloping soil surface, could not be observed with the field equipment available.

Where agriculture is practiced soils did not have a permanently equal degree of vegetation cover. Measurements by means of runoff plots were performed during the first three months of the wet season. Consequently, the maize and cassava plants offered an inreasing protection to the soil from the start of observations. This resulted in the absence of any significant relationship between erosivity and the net amount of splashed material determined at this site. On plot IV, where changing site properties influencing rainsplash were absent, a significant relationship (level † 5%) between erosivity and splashed material was apparent. Table 8 indicates that 534 g of soil material per year are transported downslope for a 2.0 m wide segment. It must be understood, however, that calculations relating to yearly soil-loss by rainsplash cannot be made in the same way as those for soil-loss by surface runoff. During storm events a continuous movement of material through the air is taking place on a slope due to raindrop impact. For an uniform slope of given length and a width of 1.0 m, net downslope ttransported material amounts to 267 g/year when site properties correspond with those of erosion plot IV. This amount actually represents soil-loss from the upper part of the slope where soil-loss by rainsplash is not replaced by material splashed down from upslope locations. Consequently, this process leads to the formation of convex slope forms as recognized by DAVIS in 1892.

5.7.   INFILTRATION AT THE EROSION PLOTS

Infiltration plots for the bare soil of plot IV are given in Figure 4. The final infiltration rate does not attain the same values but decreases with decreasing erosivity of the rainstorm. This can probably be attributed to the effect of falling raindrops since they expend part of their energy in compacting the soil and another part in detaching and removing the soil particles. Rainstorms of high erosivity cause the surface soil to be compacted to a relatively high degree but, soil detachment increases even more rapidly. The soil of plot III showed rather peculiar features in that at times the infiltration rate increased after the start of a rainstorm (Fig. 3). This is probably caused by the presence of a soil crust which originates from a prior rainstorm when fine soil material sealed the soil and raindrop impact caused compaction. A crust formed in this way will decrease splash processes and cause surface ponding during the next rainstorm. After the soil has been wettened the crust may be eroded by the high degree of turbulence of the ponded water and/or by the impact of falling raindrops. That fact that raindrop impact is greater on already wettened soil has already been noted by LOW (1954). When conditions do not favour the formation of a new crust these processes will lead to an increase in infiltration rate to an asymtotic value as is illustrated in Figure 3.

Soil infiltration capacity also increases with increasing vegetative cover. This may occur either directly or indirectly, e.g., by decreasing raindrop impact thus preventing serious soil particle detachment and crust formation, or by increasing organic matter content and porosity of the surface soil.

6. CONCLUSIONS

There are significant, generally linear relationships between erosivity indices (R, EI_{30} and BI) and discharges involved of dissolved, suspended and bedload material from the Desel catchment. Based on these relationships and the assumption than in a monsoon area daily rainfall usually falls during one storm, yearly outputs of these loads have been determined as 33.6 kg, 44.5 tons and 177.0 tons respectively. Nearly 80% of the annual material transport occurs as bedload. Suspended load accounts for about 20% and solute load is negligible.

Vegetative cover exerts a major influence on runoff and soil erosion. Grass-covered sites are characterized by relatively high infiltration capacities while crop-covered sites show final infiltration rates of about 13 mm/hr. At the latter erosion by surface runoff amounts to about 0.6 mm/year. Due to the changing degree of cover by crops no significant relationship between erosivity and net amount of splashed soil particles could be determined. Consequently, reliable estimates of erosion rate by rainsplash cannot yet be given for these areas. Final infiltration capacity of bare soil material varies from 2 to about 8 mm/hr, dependent on the degree of soil compaction by raindrop impact; the yearly erosion rate amounts to 8.2 mm, while splash erosion causes a net downslope transport of 267 g soil material per meter contour per year.

Total annual material discharge based on input-output analysis of the Desel catchment is 221.5 tons, while that based on erosion plot research amounts to 240.1 tons. The discrepancy between these yearly yields is explained by the fact that suspended load has been underestimated. It can also be assumed that about 20 tons of material eroded from the slopes is trapped by irregular topography resulting from mass movements before reaching the discharge measuring site. Furthermore, material supply to the Desel River by mass wasting processes is not incorporated in the plot data as it is in the river load data, thus causing an even greater discrepancy between the derived yields. Some alluvial and colluvial deposits have also been recognized locally at the Desel area.

Because of the high degree of correspondence between results obtained for the yearly erosion rates it seems acceptable to consider the estimates as correct indications of the order of magnitude for erosion rate in the Desel River catchment. The data presented by other investigators (RUTTEN 1917, MOHR 1906, SMEC 1973, MEIJERINK 1977), however, indicate higher values. This can be ascribed to the fact that present erosion rates no longer attain maximum values, since bedrock exposures occur frequently and the remaining soils are shallow. This has resulted in a reduced availability of erosion-susceptible material. In addition, planation surfaces can be recognized in areas where the Merawu Formation outcrops. Finally, mean erosion rates are highly influenced by the occurrence of catastrophic events – floods of high return period may move more material in a few days than average floods in several years.

ACKNOWLEDGEMENTS

The research was made possible by the financial support of the Netherlands Universities Foundation For International Cooperation (NUFFIC) which is greatfully acknowledged.

The Faculty of Geography, Gadjah Mada University (Yogyakarta, Indonesia), is thanked for the willing cooperation with respect to field and laboratory facilities.

Dr. Ir. E. Seyhan and Prof. Dr. Th. Levelt are thanked for critically reading the manuscript.

Thanks are also due to drs. Joko Cahyono and drs. Supriyadi, who collected the field data within the framework of their doctoral thesis research. Finally, I would like to thank Prof. Dr. I. Simmers and CATENA's reviewing experts who suggested ways of improving the original version.

REFERENCES

BOLS, P.L. (1978): The iso-erodent map of Java and Madura. Belgian Technical Assistance Project ATA 105, Soil Research Institute, Bogor, Indonesia, 39 pp.

BRAAK, C. (1929): The climate of the Netherlands Indies. Proc. Royal Magn. Meteorol. Obs., Batavia, part I and II.

DAVIS, W.M. (1892): The convex profile of badland divides. Science **20**.

EL–SWAIFY, S.A. & DANGLER, E.W. (1977): Erodibilities of selected tropical soils in relation to structural and hydrologic parameters. In: Soil Erosion: Prediction and Control. Proc. Nat. Conf. Soil Erosion, Indiana, Spec. Publ. **21**, 393 pp.

FOURNIER, F. (1960): Climat et érosion: la relation entre l'érosion du sol par l'eau et les précipitations atmospheriques. Paris, 201 pp.

HEM, J.D. (1975): Study and interpretation of the chemical characteristics of natural water. Geol. Survey Water Supply Paper **1493**, 363 pp.

HUDSON, N.W. (1957): Erosion Control Research. Pr. Rep. on exp. Henderson Res. St., 1953-1956. Rhodesian Agr. Journal **54**, 4, 297-323.

HUDSON, N.W. (1973): Soil Conservation. B.T. Batsford Limited, London, 320 pp.

ILRI (International Institute for Land Reclamation and Improvement) (1973): Drainage Principles and Applications. ILRI Publ. **16**, vol. II, Theories of field drainage and watershed runoff, Wageningen.

ISNUGROHO (1975): Tersedianya air tahunen fungsi meteorologi di daerah Kali Serayu. M.Sc. thesis, Fakultas Geografi, Universitas Gadjah Mada, Yogyakarta, 113 pp.

KWAAD, F.J.P.M. (1977): Measurements of rainsplash erosion and the formation of colluvium beneath deciduous woodland in the Luxembourg Ardennes. Earth Surface Processes **2**, 2/3, 161-173.

LOW, A.J. (1954): Measurement of the stability of moist soil aggregates to falling water drops according to Low. J. of Soil Sc. **5**, 57-78.

MALINGREAU, J.P. (1977): A proposed landcover/land use classification and its use with remote sensing data in Indonesia. The Ind. J. of geography 7, 33, 5-29.

MEYER, L.D. & MCCUNE, D.L. (1958): Rainfall simulator for runoff plots. Agr. Eng. **39**, 10, 644-648.

MEIJERINK, A.M.J. (1977): A hydrological reconnaissance survey of the Serayu River basin. Serayu Valley Project, Final Report 2, ITC, Enschede, 25-55.

MORGAN, R.P.G. (1979): Soil Erosion. Topics in applied geography. Longman, London–New York, 113 pp.

MOHR, E.C.J. (1906): Verslag eener Excursie naar Bandjarnegara in Verband met het Slibgevaar veroorzaakt door eenige Rivieren in 't Serajoe-Dal. Jaarb. Dep. Landb., 13 pp.

MOHR, E.C.J. (1938): De Bodem der Tropen in het algemeen en die van Nederlandsch-Indië in het bijzonder. Kon. Ver. Kol. Inst. Amsterdam, med. **XXXI**, 12.

MOSLEY, M.P. (1974): Rainsplash and the convexity of badland divides. Zeitschrift für Geom., N.F., Suppl. Bd. **18**, 10-25.

ROTH, C.B., NELSON, D.W. & ROMKENS, M.J.M. (1974): Prediction of subsoil erodibility using chemical, minealogical and physical parameters. EPA Tech. Series 660/2-74-043, Env. Prot. Ag., Washington.

RUTTEN, L.M.R. (1917): Over Denudatiesnelheid op Java. Versl. Kon. Ac. van Wetensch., Amsterdam, 920-930.

SMEC (Snowy Mountains Engineering Cooperation) (1974): Serayu River Basin Study **4**, Hydrology, Dir. Gen. of Waterres. Div., Jakarta.

SOIL CONSERVATION SOCIETY OF AMERICA (1977): Soil Erosion: Prediction and control. Proc. Nat. Conf. Soil Erosion, Indiana, Spec. Publ. **21**, 393 pp.

SPEELMAN, H. (1979): Geology, hydrogeology and engineering geological features of the Serayu River basin (Central–Java, Indonesia). Serayu Valley Project, Final report **4**, Free University, Amsterdam, 155 pp.

WISCHMEIER, W.H. & SMITH, D.D. (1958): Rainfall energy and its relationship to soil-loss. Trans. Amer. Geoph. Union **39**, 2, 285-291.

WISCHMEIER, W.H., JOHNSON, C.B. & CROSS, B.V. (1971): A soil erodibility nomograph for farmland and construction sites. J. Soil Water Cons. **26**, 5, 189-193.

WISCHMEIER, W.H. (1976): Use and misuse of the universal soil-loss equation. J. Soil Water Cons. **31**, 1, 5-9.

VAN DER LINDEN, P. (1978): Contemporary soil erosion in the Sanggreman River basin related to the Quaternary landscape development. A pedogeomorphic and hydro-geomorphological case study in Middle–Java, Indonesia. Serayu Valley Project, Final Report **3**, University of Amsterdam, 110 pp.

VAN ZUIDAM, R.A., MEIJERINK, A.M.J. & VERSTAPPEN, H.Th. (1977): A geomorphological survey of the Serayu River basin. Serayu Valley Project, Final Report **2**, ITC, Enschede, 3-25.

Address of author:
P. van der Linden, Institute of Earth Sciences, Free University of Amsterdam,
De Boelelaan 1085, 1081 HV Amsterdam, The Netherlands

Jan de Ploey (Ed.):
Rainfall Simulation, Runoff and Soil Erosion
CATENA, SUPPLEMENT 4, Braunschweig 1983

SLOW PARTICULATE FLOW IN CONDENSED MEDIA AS AN ESCAPE MECHANISM :

MEAN TRANSLATION DISTANCE

W.E.H. **Culling**, London

SUMMARY

Mass transport in particulate media is the outcome of the interaction between activity on the part of the individual particles and the restraints on their movement imposed by the structure of the medium. Provided the medium can be regarded as statistically homogenous then transport phenomena can be sub-divided into a series of elementary interactions between particles and their environment. Each interaction con be idealised as the escape of particles from one equilibrium position to another across a potential surface. By analogy with chemical kinetics the saddle point on the intervening potential surface is identified with the activation energy. In chemical physics the distribution of kinetic energy possessed by the particles obeys a Maxwell-Boltzmann law and the activation energy is a constant. In order that the concept be applied to geomorphology both parameters need to be generalised and the analysis is given for the case where both are represented by a gamma distribution. Application to soil creep enables the determination of expressions for the mean drift velocity and thereby the diffusion and drift coefficients of the macroscopic transport equations.

1. INTRODUCTION

The major part of the landscape as studied by geomorphologists depends for its precise form on the outcome of the behaviour of particulate media. The constituent particles in such cases are taken to possess to a greater or lesser degree the power of acting independently. The springs of action in such media can be resolved into two agencies: the activity or possession of kinetic energy on the part of the particles and the structural constraints upon the motion that would result from the free play of that kinetic energy. On both counts a random character is imparted to the movement of individual particles as a direct consequence of the particulate nature of the medium. Landscape forming processes studied at the particle level are inevitably stochastic.

Apart from the occasional mention of possible applications elsewhere this paper is concerned solely with the soil mass on hillside slopes as an example of a particulate medium. Even then we are concerned only with flow phenomena viewed from a particular standpoint. Here we regard the flow mechanism as a pure phenomenon and are not concerned with its contribution to the shaping of the landscape. For this we refer to our earlier papers (CULLING 1963, 1965), for a particular aspect, once again from a rather 'pure' standpoint and to the papers by KIRKBY (1971) and HIRANO (1975) for its setting in a more general scheme and to the relevant chapters in CARSON & KIRKBY (1972) and YOUNG (1972).

Activity represented by the possession of kinetic energy on the part of the particle is manifest characteristically in the possession of momentum. In some cases immediately, but in all cases eventually, this is inhibited by the reaction of neighbouring particles, in which case part of the mechanical energy is transmitted, part possibly converted into some form of internal energy and certainly part lost to the dynamical system as heat. Structural constraint is thus imposed by the presence of other particles arranged in a relatively close-packed but irregular array. Particles are in contact with one or more of their fellows in the sense that forces can be transmitted across contact zones which even though partly constituted by films of water act essentially as solids. Because of their differing shapes and sizes particles are separated by interstitial space occupied mostly by air or water and so each particle occupies a cell formed by its neighbouring (cell) particles and in turn forms part of the cell wall for each of its neighbours. From this viewpoint the soil mass is abstracted as an irregular three dimensional array of cells within which soil particles can oscillate in response to the possession of kinetic energy with varying shades of freedom and if the activity and opportunity coincide can escape from one cell to another. It is this escape mechanism we wish to explore. In this connection we use the term translation in a restricted sense to refer to the result of a successful escape from one equilibrium position in the initial cell to another in an adjacent cell and not to the mere oscillatory motion undertaken entirely within one cell and about the neighbourhood of the initial equilibrium position.

Activity on the part of the particle is brought about by processes operating within the soil mass, either internally or externally to the local dynamical system, and termed (by achaeologists) turbatory. These include physical, chemical, faunal and floral agencies. Physical examples include, thermal expansion and contraction, feeze and thaw of interstitial water, variations in pore water pressure and in the local velocity of throughflow, electrical and magnetic phenomena, Van der Waals' forces and gravity; chemical examples include solution and precipitation, hydration and dessication, crystallisation and reactions leading to rearrangement, changes in temperature and volume and in the nature of the chemical bonds. Biologic contributions are harder to assess. It has been customary to discount them but this is now seen to be short-sighted. The classical work of Darwin means that the annelida alone make a significant contribution. Burrowing animals assist in the denudation of Luxembourg catchments (IMESON 1976, 1977); isopods and porcupines disturb the Negev soil (YAIR & LAVEE 1981) and in Sierra Leone the topmost layers of the soil have been thoroughly worked over by termites and left in a friable state with considerable increase in free volume (MILLINGTON 1981, and personal communication).

Certain of the displacing forces such as gravity, hydraulic throughflow or the hydration cycle present a systematic directed component (or in the latter case two); but in all cases there exists a random component when referred to an external frame of reference. At the particle level the random component is that component left after the subtraction of the directed component. This random component arises on the one part from the intermittent and independent character of the turbatory forces and on the other, upon the irregular and transmutable nature of the soil structure.

As in the collision of gas molecules we are not in a position to monitor each event in a significant macroscopic happening. Such large scale behaviour in which we are interested and which alone we can measure directly involves large numbers of individual units. Unlike a gas, the motion of individual particles though a matter of experimental difficulty, is within the limits of direct observation but because of the random nature of individual particle trajectories the derivation of macroscopic flow parameters is an indirect process and depends upon assumptions of a probabilistic character. This fundamental imperfection in our knowledge has several important consequences. First we are led to a statistical mechanical approach as appropriate to the very large numbers involved and to the incomplete nature of our knowledge. Secondly our knowledge is 'statistical' in the sense that we deal with the more general random variable and derive statements about probability distributions rather than exact values. Thirdly, in so far as we make macroscopic measurements we deal with time and spatial averages and therefore assume that they exist; which in turn involves some fairly deep assumptions of a statistical mechanical and ergodic nature. On the other hand we cannot conveniently as yet measure microscopic behaviour in the field directly but must rely upon indirect theoretical predictions (CULLING 1981).

A further consequence of immediate relevance to the matter in hand is that a fundamental assumption of a probabilistic nature has to be made about the elemental behaviour of the individual units. An assumption of this nature is inescapable in a statistical mechanical approach and in effect builds in the required irreversibility in an otherwise reversible phenomenon. Apart from the special directed components, which by definition are parallel, it is postulated that the displacing forces have no preferred direction. This is equivalent to the assumption of molecular chaos in the kinetic theory of gases. A similar assumption has to be made about the void structure of the soil.

Over short time scales soil particles are able to react elastically and so transmit externally imposed forces. It follows from the irregular structure of the soil that particle contact zones have variably oriented planes of contact and that the transmission of stress through the particulate medium of the soil results in an independent resolution of the force at each and every contact. There is no restriction on the partition between components and so an external force directed normally at a boundary can be transformed into an exclusively shear stress at an internal contact and vice versa with all partitions in between possible. The isotropy implicit in the assumption as to soil structure means that after the abstraction of a systematic component equivalent to the mean applied deviator stress at the boundary we are left with a random component with a spherically symmetrical distribution. Thus the random nature of internally induced turbatory forces is compounded by the successive resolution of directed forces applied externally to the local particle system.

As well as being subject to a random distribution of displacing forces the particle is presented at each event with an independent distribution of surrounding void space. The effective free volume of the soil mass is something more than the existing voidage at any one time; it also includes all the space a particle may command given its kinetic energy and the local configuration, ie. it includes space made available by dilatancy. The soil mass, at least to start with, is assumed statistically homogenous and isotropic so that the centre of gravity of a particle lies at the centre of a spherically symmetrical distribution of void space.

Given the irregular particulate nature of the soil mass some form of movement idealised as random motion appears inevitable. The random nature of the applied force merely compounds this randomicity. This principle is limited only in those cases in which the soil fails to act as a particulate medium such as the parallel motion on the part of all particles involved in a landslip. The random component though always present may, of course be negligible or in certain circumstances or from a particular viewpoint may be conveniently transformed into a mean motion.

Compaction with depth and other like phenomena are for the moment neglected or at least taken as negligible provided we take sufficiently thin layers of soil. They are, together with the whole question of density dependent motion more profitably taken up at a later stage of the investigation, at the macroscopic level of the appropriate differential equations.

The outcome of the random nature of both the activity of the particle and of the structure of the soil is that the individual particle executes a three-dimensional random walk. Upon this is superimposed any drift due to the presence of a general directed force. This behaviour at the particle level promotes a diffusive character to the macroscopic motion of the soil mass. The transport of soil material across the landscape by this means is of a kind with the flow of current in transmission lines; the actual motion being made up of minute displacements of flow units (electrons, particles), each consisting of a directed and a random component. Soil particles displaced and in motion constitute a 'particle gas' moving through an irregular lattice and as in a conductor only a very small proportion of all particles are in motion at any one time.

The mathematical theory given in the earlier papers (CULLING 1963, 1965), formalises the foregoing arguments and provides a fairly rigorous link between the elemental reversible behaviour of individual particles and the irreversible and systematic macroscopic flow pattern observable in the landscape. We can claim only a 'fairly' rigorous development because there exist some well known paradoxes associated with the irreversible behaviour of dynamical systems.

The stochastic theory of soil creep as presented in the earlier papers was couched in general terms and shared some of the characteristics of an existence theorem. In this paper we discuss one approach, derived ultimately from atomic physics, to the derivation of the precise nature of the drift and diffusion coefficients and finish up with formulations of a similar nature to those common in physical theory. But before we do so we outline as a preliminary an abstraction of the soil structure as a blurred crystal lattice.

2. BLURRED CRYSTAL MODEL OF SOIL STRUCTURE

Natural soil aggregates share some of the properties of solids in fairly obvious ways. To impulsive forces their immediate response is elastic; a free surface can exist and they are capable of maintaining a structure that will bear a substantial load. On the other hand they possess properties normally associated with liquids, in particular fluidity. The parallel between soil creep and liquid flow is fairly transparent at the macroscopic level. A more profound link exists via the theory of Brownian motion between soil creep as the expression of random reversible behaviour by the soil particles and Kirkwood's derivation of the diffusion coefficient from statistical mechanical principles (KIRKWOOD 1946, CULLING 1963).

Flow in the soil mass as in a liquid depends upon the free volume provided by holes (voids). This notion, though ancient, has had to await a belated rejuvenation during the last few decades. It was discussed by Aristotle (Physics IV. vi-ix) and was stated in these very terms by Theophrastus (De Sensibus). Contemporary approaches to liquid structure treat each molecule as acting in a local free volume and subject to the several or averaged interaction of neighbouring molecules. This is to treat a liquid as a dense gas. Alternatively a liquid can be regarded as a degenerate solid. This viewpoint characterising the 30's and 40's followed upon the discovery of vestiges of regularity and short range order in simple liquids and of the evidence of disorder and imperfection in crystalline structures. This approach associated with the name of FRENKEL (1926, 1946), although now superseded, brought great insight into transport processes in liquids (FISHER 1964, 2-3).

In seeking for geomorphologic parallels we look at the soil aggregate as a solid but through the eyes of a student of the liquid state. We are interested in those properties of the solid state that are shared by or exist on a continuum with the liquid state. We leave the complementary liquid/gas viewpoint for a future occasion.

In looking at the soil from the solid state viewpoint we equate soil particles with the particles of solids; atoms and molecules, ions and electrons as appropriate. In so doing we make great simplifications on both sides. Not only do we regard atoms as hard rigid spheres we almost make the same abstraction in the case of soil particles. Without some such simplification we can hope for little progress in the understanding of mass transport phenomena. The natural soil is far too complex to be tackled in a straightforward naive manner. Instead we adopt the ways of the theoretical physicist and postulate invisible simplicity to explain visible complexity (PERRIN 1908, 513, NYE 1972, 131).

The advantages of studying the crystalline state are threefold. The regular lattice structure provides a conceptual basis of relative simplicity from which to launch the investigation of the bewildering irregularity of natural soil aggregates. Several properties of crystal structures, notably the imperfections, throw light on similar properties in soil structures. This parallel has been exploited recently by PUSCH & FELTHAM (1980), based upon earlier work by FELTHAM (1973) on the translocation of crystal imperfections as a stochastic process. Finally, the solid state, though by no means completely understood, provides an interim approach to the less completely understood but ultimately more fundamental parallel with the statistical mechanical theories of the liquid state.

Our interest lies in the breakdown of the crystal lattice rather than its regularity and with such phenomena as self-diffusion, internal evaporation and fusion. The amount and distribution of free volume, the importance of holes and interstitial sites, the fundamental importance of oscillatory behaviour and the possibility of escape and the consequent mobility of particles all have their counterpart in the soil aggregate (FRENKEL 1946, SHEWMON 1965, MANNING 1968, ZIMAN 1972). The kinetic theory of crystals introduced the idea of atoms oscillating in thermal motion about equilibrium positions arranged or rather providing the lattice. This in turn led to the notion of particle escape, to wandering atoms, the electron gas and hole currents. In liquids this vibration-diffusion behaviour is more pronounced. As fusion point is approached, from the one side solids show increased free volume, intensified oscillation and loss of form, while from the other side, liquids show signs of increased local order. Computor simulations of the approach to fusion are given by ALDER & WAINWRIGHT (1939a, 1939b).

Unlike thermal motion which at a frequency 10^{12} per sec is virtually continuous with respect to any direct measurement, the oscillation imparted to a soil particle by turbatory agencies is pronouncedly intermittent. Under normal geomorphic conditions a particle spends most of its time at rest. Each oscillation is therefore separated by an interval long in comparison with the time the particle is actually in motion or to the relaxation time required for the dissipation of internal or thermal energy imparted during the disturbance, so that each disturbance can be regarded as statistically independent.

Resting upon classical statistical mechanical arguments but relying on some tenuous assumptions it can be shown that the most probable distribution for the mechanical energy transmitted to a particle at any one event is distributed according to a Maxwell-Boltzmann type law. It is hoped to be able to make this result rigorous and to estimate how probable is 'most probable'. In the meantime we develop the argument to encompass the more general gamma distribution; one that will probably cover the majority of natural examples and which includes the Maxwell-Boltzmann distribution as a special case.

The interval between successive oscillations is also sufficiently long enough for changes to take place in the local configuration. Thus at a subsequent disturbance, not only does the displacing force differ in direction, the particle is also likely to be confronted with a different configuration of cell space. If this were all the soil would be structured and in many respects behave like an amorphous solid at very low temperatures. Particle trajectories would trace (Gaussian) spikes and perform a slow diffusion consequent upon particles not returning exactly to the initial equilibrium position because of rotation and the possible re-arrangement of the local environment. Soil particles are more active than this on two counts. Like atoms in a crystal lattice opportunity exists for escape. Secondly the transmutability of the structure consequent upon particle escape and migration itself enhances the opportunity to escape. The resistance offered to a would be escaping particle can be idealised as a potential barrier in a manner that is a commonplace in physical theory. Unlike normal physical theory we will treat the barrier height as a random variable which, together with the random nature of the particle displacement energy, will ensure that the eventual translation of the particle is almost sure in the strict probabilistic sense, ie of probability one.

The trajectory of a particle over a long period is visualised as a set of spikes connected by translation tracks. We have already referred to the computor simulations of Alder and Wainwright; another pertinent illustration in the literature is the schematic diagram (fig. X.4) of BENSON (1960, 216), in which a particle bounces around a roughly spherical cell and eventually manages to escape.

The blurred crystal model of soil structure raises many questions of which only one can be followed up here, namely, the interaction between particle activity and soil structure, idealised as an escape mechanism, leading to a random walk on the part of individual particles and to a general diffusive type flow by the soil mass as a whole.

3. ESCAPE MODEL – GENERAL PRINCIPLES

The probability of a particle exceeding the bounds of stability and escaping over the potential barrier from its initial equilibrium neighbourhood depends upon certain aspects of the physical setting that we idealise as sets of random variables, each set characterising one major factor of the dynamic system:

A) W_r: the displacement energy; the kinetic energy possessed by the particle and available for the surmounting of the given potential barrier opposing escape from the initial neighbourhood.

B) E_r: the activation energy; the energy level associated with the potential surface and representing the saddle point of the minimum (local) passage across the potential divide separating two equilibrium neighbourhoods.

The terms potential surface and activation energy derive from the activation-complex or rate process theory of chemical kinetics (EYRING 1935, GLASSTONE et al. 1941, LAIDLER 1969).

The difference $W_r - E_r$, provides a further set of random variables, say S_r, which represents the excess of displacement energy over the presented activation energy. Summing over all positive values will then give a measure of the proportion of total particle displacements that are successful in escaping.

In general there exists a further set of random variables; the energy increment due to an applied external field of force, F. This is not due to any inherent variation in the force field but because the incremental energy is a function of the distance over which the force is applied, in this case the distance from the equilibrium position to the saddle point, which in general will be a variable. However, in this paper we will not explore this more general case but will content ourselves with treating the distance as a mean value, $\frac{1}{2}\bar{r}$, leaving to a sequel the case for variable distance to the barrier. Inherent variation in F, with distance or with time, is best left until the differential equation stage but even then is unlikely to yield to analytical solution.

We have then,

C) $\frac{1}{2}\bar{r}F$:   increment in energy due to an external field and superimposable upon the activation energy.

An example of an external field of force is that supplied by gravity. Other possible candidates include the throughflow of water, directed physical or chemical agencies and preferred directions in the activities of biologic agents. The downslope acceleration due to gravity on moderate slope angles (*less than* 30°) is an example of a weak force in the sense that unaided it is incapable of promoting particle translation, but in the presence of a strong turbatory oscillation it is able to impart a directed component to the resultant motion. Soil creep in such cases is an activated process with obvious parallels to thermally activated metal creep.

The probability of particle escape rests upon the relationship,

$$S_r \ = \ W_r \ - \ (E_r \ \pm \ \tfrac{1}{2}\bar{r}F) \tag{1}$$

This is fundamental equation for the particle escape mechanism. The analysis is developed in two stages. First only the displacement energy is regarded as a random variable; the bracketed term being taken as a (mean) constant. This constraint is then removed to take account of variable activation energies.

3.1.   VARIABLE DISPLACEMENT ENERGY

W_r is taken to be of Gaussian distribution, $N(m_1, \sigma_1^{2})$, in the first instance as this greatly simplifies the analysis. In the case where E_r degenerates to a constant value, E_0, and in the absence of an external force it is possible to evaluate the probability of escape immediately by integrating the density function $f(w)$ of W_r for all values greater than the barrier height. Hence

$$G \ = \ \frac{1}{\sigma_1(2\pi)^{\frac{1}{2}}} \int_{E_0}^{\infty} e^{\frac{-(w-m_1)^2}{2\sigma_1^2}} \ dw \ = \ \tfrac{1}{2}\,\mathrm{erfc}\,\frac{(E_0 - m_1)}{\sigma_1(2)^{\frac{1}{2}}} \tag{2}$$

where *erfc* (x) is the complementary error function

$$\mathrm{erfc}\,(x) \ = \ \frac{2}{(\pi)^{\frac{1}{2}}} \int_{x}^{\infty} e^{-t^2}\,dt \ = \ 1 \ - \ \mathrm{erf}\,(x)$$

and gives the proportion of all displacements that possess a displacement enegy equal to the activation energy of the potential barrier and therefore the upper bound to the proportion that successfully escape *ie* we notice but henceforth ignore the possibility of a particle perching on the saddle point.

If E_r the effective barrier height can take two values and out of a large number of events the proportions to be expected are p at height E_1 and q at height E_2, $(p + q = 1)$, then with the same distribution of W_r as before,

$$G = \frac{1}{2} \left\{ p \; erfc \; \frac{(E_1 - m_1)}{\sigma_1 (2)^{\frac{1}{2}}} + q \; erfc \; \frac{(E_2 - m_1)}{\sigma_1 (2)^{\frac{1}{2}}} \right\} \tag{3}$$

and this result can easily be extended to any finite discrete set for E_r. Such a case would be applicable to a regular crystal lattice provided some estimate can be made as to the relative proportions of occurrence and the mean activation energies of the various interstitial escape routes. In a regular lattice the interstitial sites are also in a regular array and in simple cases the values of occurrence for E_r can be taken from tables such as that of PRINS & PETERSEN (1936, 150), abridged in FRENKEL (1946, 113).

Where an external force is applied we take a cross section of the symmetrically disposed potential barrier through the centre of gravity of the particle as origin. In the usual convention we represent this in fig. 1 as a sine curve of wave length equal to the mean inter-equilibrium distance, $\bar{r}$. A variety of specific forms to the shape of the potential well have been studied (COLE 1967, 231, BARTON 1974, 95), but we are not at present concerned with how a particle reaches the barrier, the model is concerned solely with the kinetic energy a particle possesses at the saddle point. A more precise but less informative illustration of the case in hand would represent the barrier by a Dirac function.

Transforming the external force F into energy terms, namely $\frac{1}{2} \bar{r} F$, where $\frac{1}{2} \bar{r}$ is the distance over which the force is applied, then we can simply add the resulting increment to the activation energy, the increment being negative in the direction of the force. The applied potential gradient due to the external field is represented in fig 1 by the dotted line. The excess proportion of particles that are successful in escaping in the positive direction is in the case represented by (2),

$$g = \frac{1}{2} \left\{ erfc \; \frac{(E_0 - \frac{1}{2} \bar{r} F - m_1)}{\sigma_1 (2)^{\frac{1}{2}}} - erfc \; \frac{(E_0 + \frac{1}{2} \bar{r} F - m_1)}{\sigma_1 (2)^{\frac{1}{2}}} \right\} \tag{4}$$

The mean drift velocity in the direction of the external force is then given by

$$\bar{v} = \bar{r} N g \tag{5}$$

for we assume that the barrier is symmetrically disposed about the crest and where N is the number of particle displacements per unit time. Thus more explicitly

$$\bar{v} = \frac{1}{2} N \bar{r} \left\{ erfc \; \frac{(E_0 - \frac{1}{2} \bar{r} F - m_1)}{\sigma_1 (2)^{\frac{1}{2}}} - erfc \; \frac{(E_0 + \frac{1}{2} \bar{r} F - m_1)}{\sigma_1 (2)^{\frac{1}{2}}} \right\} \tag{6}$$

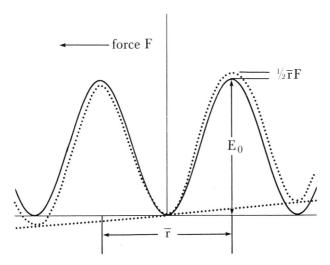

Fig. 1:   Potential barrier about an equilibrium position in the presence of a directed force.

For small values of F and provided the difference between the two means, $H = E_0 - m_1$, is also small

$$\bar{v} \simeq \frac{N\bar{r}^2 F}{\sigma_1 (2\pi)^{\frac{1}{2}}} \tag{7}$$

For large values of F there is an asymptotic expansion but it is no improvement upon (6).

Looking at other candidates for the distribution of particle energy we notice first the exponential distribution,

$$f(w) = \lambda e^{-\lambda w} \qquad\qquad 0 \leqslant w < \infty \tag{8}$$

where for a barrier height of E_0 ,

$$G = \lambda \int_{E_0}^{\infty} e^{-\lambda w}\, dw = e^{-\lambda E_0} \tag{9}$$

With the same notation as before the mean drift velocity is given by

$$\bar{v} = N\bar{r}e^{-\lambda E_0} \left| e^{\lambda \frac{1}{2}\bar{r}F} - e^{-\lambda\frac{1}{2}\bar{r}F} \right| = 2N\bar{r}e^{-\lambda E_0}\, \sinh \tfrac{1}{2}\lambda\bar{r}F \tag{10}$$

If $\bar{r}F$ is large,

$$\bar{v} \simeq N\bar{r}e^{-\lambda(E_0 + \frac{1}{2}\bar{r}F)} \tag{11}$$

whereas if $\bar{r}F << 1$,

$$\bar{v} \simeq N\bar{r}^2 F \lambda e^{-\lambda E_0} \tag{12}$$

Consequent upon the exponential form of the Maxwell-Boltzmann distribution this particular case is of great theoretical importance and the above analysis is a commonplace in the physical literature, where it is the custom to assume that the activation energy is a constant.

Generalising to the gamma distribution,

$$f(w) = \frac{\lambda^m}{\Gamma(m)} e^{-\lambda w} w^{m-1} \qquad 0 \leqslant w < \infty \qquad 0 < m, \ 0 < \lambda \tag{13}$$

$$G = \frac{\lambda^m}{\Gamma(m)} \int_{E_0}^{\infty} e^{-\lambda w} w^{m-1} dw = e^{-\lambda E_0} \left[1 + \lambda E_0 + \frac{1}{2}\lambda^2 E_0^2 + \ldots \right.$$

$$\left. \ldots + \frac{\lambda^{m-1} E_0^{m-1}}{(m-1)!} \right] \tag{14}$$

$$= 1 - P(m, E_0) \tag{15}$$

where $P(m, h)$ is the incomplete gamma function for which tables are available (ABRAMOWITZ & STEGUN 1965, 260, 941).

With the same conditions and notation as before the mean drift velocity is

$$\bar{v} = N\bar{r} \left| P(m, E_0 - \tfrac{1}{2}\bar{r}F) - P(m, E_0 + \tfrac{1}{2}\bar{r}F) \right| \tag{16}$$

Returning to (14) and taking terms up to the second order in $\bar{r}F$, we find that

$$\bar{v} = 2N\bar{r}e^{-\lambda E_0} \left| \sinh \tfrac{1}{2}\lambda\bar{r}F \left[1 + \lambda E_0 + \tfrac{1}{2}\lambda^2 (E_0^2 + \tfrac{1}{4}\bar{r}^2F^2) \right] - \right.$$

$$\left. - \cosh \tfrac{1}{2}\lambda\bar{r}F \left[\tfrac{1}{2}\lambda\bar{r}F + \tfrac{1}{2}\lambda^2\bar{r}E_0F \right] \right| \tag{17}$$

For large $\bar{r}F$,

$$\bar{v} \simeq N\bar{r}e^{-\lambda(E_0 - \tfrac{1}{2}\bar{r}F)} \left[1 + \lambda(E_0 - \tfrac{1}{2}\bar{r}F) + \tfrac{1}{2}\lambda^2(E_0 - \tfrac{1}{2}\bar{r}F)^2 \right] \tag{18}$$

and for small $\bar{r}F$,

$$\bar{v} \simeq \tfrac{1}{2}N\bar{r}^2\lambda^3 F E_0^2 \ e^{-\lambda E_0} \tag{19}$$

The gamma distribution includes both the previous examples as special cases. If $m = 1$, then (13) degenerates into the exponential distribution (8) and (16) to (10). For $0 < m \leqslant 1$, the graph of the density function is J-shaped. For $m > 0$ the graph is uni-modal with mean $\frac{m}{\lambda}$ and variance $\frac{m}{\lambda^2}$. As m increases above $m = 1$ the graph detaches from the zero ordinate and at first is markedly skew. As m continues to increase the bulk of the distribution shifts to the right becoming in the process more symmetrical approaching asymptotically a Gaussian form. From (14) as $m \rightarrow \infty$, $G \rightarrow 1$, no matter what the value of E_0 might be. For if m is sufficiently large then it is almost certain that an event will be of greater value than E_0.

The gamma distribution should cover reasonably well the kinds of distribution of particle energy expected to occur naturally and provided we remain content with the assumption of significant mean values for both activation energy and translation length, as is common in physical and chemical theory, then our treatment is in a sense complete. However, we lack the kind of theoretical and empirical infrastructure that the physicist can command and so cannot derive the values of parameters from existing knowledge nor at the persent can we hope to measure the distribution of particle energy directly.

3.2.   VARIABLE BARRIER HEIGHT

Relaxing the constraint on barrier height implies the addition and subtraction of random variables. To do this in general we need characteristic function theory. Here we work in the Fourier domain and in particular use the well known 'equivalence' between the addition of random variables, the convolution of their distribution functions and the product of their corresponding characteristic functions (denoted by $c.f.$) Furthermore if the $c.f.$ of Z_r is $f_z(t)$ then the $c.f.$ of $-Z_r$ is $f_z(-t)$.

More precisely, if to the random variables, S_r, W_r, E_r and F_r, there correspond the distribution functions F_s, F_w, F_E and F_F and the $c.f.s f_s(t), f_w(t), f_E(t)$ and $f_F(t)$ respectively, then to the relationship

$$S_r = W_r - (E_r + F_r)$$

there corresponds

$$f_s(t) = f_w(t)\, f_E(-t)\, f_F(-t) \tag{20}$$

and provided $f_s(t)$ is continuous, where

$$f_s(t) = \int_{-\infty}^{\infty} f(s)\, e^{its}\, ds \tag{21}$$

$$f(s) = \frac{1}{2\pi} \int_{-\infty}^{\infty} f_s(t)\, e^{-its}\, dt \tag{22}$$

gives the corresponding distribution of excess of displacement energy over barrier height (CRAMER 1936, 37, TITCHMARSH 1967, 4).

Let the barrier height be represented by the step function

$$F(u) = \begin{cases} 0 & u < E_1 \\ p & E_1 \leqslant u \leqslant E_2 \\ 1 & E_2 < u \end{cases} \tag{23}$$

The corresponding $c.f.$ is the Stieltjes integral

$$f_E(t) = \int_{-\infty}^{\infty} f(u) \, e^{itu} \, du = p \, e^{itE_1} + q \, e^{itE_2} \qquad (p + q = 1) \tag{24}$$

With a Gaussian distribution of particle displacement energy, $\mathcal{N}(m_1, \sigma_1^2)$,

$$f_w(t) = \frac{1}{\sigma_1 (2\pi)^{\frac{1}{2}}} \int_{-\infty}^{\infty} e^{\frac{-(w - m_1)^2}{2\sigma_1^2} + it\omega} \, dw = e^{m_1 it - \frac{1}{2}\sigma_1^2 t^2} \tag{25}$$

From (20) it follows that the $c.f.$ of the distribution function relating to particle escape is given by

$$f_s(t) = \left(p e^{-itE_1} + q e^{-itE_2} \right) e^{m_1 it - \frac{1}{2}\sigma_1^2 t^2} \tag{26}$$

Inverting

$$f(s) = \frac{1}{2\pi} \int_{-\infty}^{\infty} f_s(t) \, e^{-its} \, dt = \frac{1}{\sigma_1 (2\pi)^{\frac{1}{2}}} \left| p e^{\frac{-(s - m_1 + E_1)^2}{2\sigma_1^2}} + \right.$$
$$\left. + q e^{\frac{-(s - m_1 + E_2)^2}{2\sigma_1^2}} \right| \tag{27}$$

The proportion of successful escapes is then given by

$$G = \int_0^{\infty} f(s) \, ds = \frac{1}{2} \left| p \, \text{erfc} \, \frac{(E_1 - m_1)}{\sigma_1 (2)^{\frac{1}{2}}} + q \, \text{erfc} \, \frac{(E_2 - m_1)}{\sigma_1 (2)^{\frac{1}{2}}} \right| \tag{28}$$

which is in accord with our previous result.

An immediate extension can be made to the case for v barrier elevations E_i, with probability of occurrence, p_i, $(i = 1, 2, \ldots v)$ and with $\sum p_i = 1$. Thus

$$G = \frac{1}{2} \sum p_i \, \text{erfc} \, \frac{(E_i - m_1)}{\sigma_1 (2)^{\frac{1}{2}}} \tag{29}$$

By a further straightforward piece of analysis the number of salt i can be increased in such a manner that in the limit the distribution of activation energy is of Gaussian form.

For the Gaussian/Gaussian case, then, we have

$$f_s(t) = \left(e^{m_1 it - \frac{1}{2} \sigma_1^2 t^2} \right) \left(e^{-m_2 it - \frac{1}{2} \sigma_2^2 t^2} \right) \tag{30}$$

where the distribution of barrier height is $N(m_2, \sigma_2^2)$. Then

$$f(s) = \frac{1}{\sigma (2\pi)^{\frac{1}{2}}} e^{\frac{-(s-M)^2}{2\sigma^2}} \tag{31}$$

where we have put $M = m_2 - m_1$ and $\sigma^2 = c_1^2 + \sigma_2^2$, and

$$G = \frac{1}{2} erfc \frac{M}{\sigma (2)^{\frac{1}{2}}} \tag{32}$$

follow on from the simple 'addition law' applicable to the convolution of Gaussian random variables.

To gauge the effect of a superposed external force in these latter cases we follow similar lines to those treated previously. If $\bar{r}$ is the mean translation distance, assumed distributed symmetrically about the centre of gravity of the particle, then the energy expended on the particle is $\frac{1}{2} \bar{r} F$ as before. Insertion into (30) gives

$$f_s(t) = \left(e^{m_1 it - \frac{1}{2} \sigma_1^2 t^2} \right) \left(e^{-(m_2 \pm \frac{1}{2} \bar{r} F) it - \frac{1}{2} \sigma_2^2 t^2} \right) \tag{33}$$

$$f(s) = \frac{1}{\sigma (2\pi)^{\frac{1}{2}}} e^{\frac{-(s - M \pm \frac{1}{2} \bar{r} F)^2}{2\sigma^2}} \tag{34}$$

then

$$G = \frac{1}{2} erfc \frac{(M \pm \frac{1}{2} \bar{r} F)}{\sigma (2)^{\frac{1}{2}}} \tag{35}$$

$$\bar{v} = \frac{1}{2} N \bar{r} \left\{ erfc \frac{(M - \frac{1}{2} \bar{r} F)}{\sigma (2)^{\frac{1}{2}}} - erfc \frac{(M + \frac{1}{2} \bar{r} F)}{\sigma (2)^{\frac{1}{2}}} \right\} \tag{36}$$

$$\simeq N \frac{\bar{r}^2}{\sigma (2\pi)^{\frac{1}{2}}} F \tag{37}$$

As to be expected this latter expression is similar to (7) for the earlier result is included in the latter when the uniform barrier height is regarded as a degenerate Gaussian distribution, $N(m_2, 0)$.

We now generalise to the gamma/gamma case. For the distribution of particle displacement energy we have

$$f(w) = \frac{\lambda_1^p}{\Gamma(p)} e^{-\lambda_1 w} w^{p-1} \qquad\qquad 0 \leqslant w < \infty \qquad\qquad (38)$$

$$p > 0, \ \lambda_1 > 0$$

and for the barrier height (activation energy)

$$f(u) = \frac{\lambda_2^q}{\Gamma(q)} e^{-\lambda_2 u} u^{q-1} \qquad\qquad 0 < u < \infty \qquad\qquad (39)$$

$$q > 0, \ \lambda_2 > 0$$

The convolution $S_r = W_r - E_r$ bears the $c.f.$

$$f_s(t) = \frac{\lambda_1^p}{\Gamma(p)} \int_0^\infty e^{itw - \lambda_1 w} w^{p-1} \, d\omega \cdot \frac{\lambda_2^q}{\Gamma(q)} \int_0^\infty e^{-itu - \lambda_2 u} u^{q-1} \, du =$$

$$= \frac{1}{(1 - \frac{it}{\lambda_1})^p (1 + \frac{it}{\lambda_2})^q} \qquad\qquad (40)$$

From which we derive

$$f(s) = \frac{\lambda_1^p \lambda_2^q}{2\pi} \int_{-\infty}^\infty \frac{e^{-its}}{(\lambda_1 - it)^p (\lambda_2 + it)^q} \, dt \qquad\qquad (41)$$

If we put $(\lambda_1 - it) = -\frac{z}{s}$ and $\lambda = \lambda_1 + \lambda_2$,

$$f(s) = \frac{\lambda_1^p \lambda_2^q}{2\pi i \lambda^q} e^{-\lambda_1 s} s^{p-1} \int_{-\lambda_1 s - i\infty}^{-\lambda_1 s + i\infty} \frac{e^{-z}}{(-z)^p (1 + \frac{z}{\lambda_s})^q} \, dz \qquad\qquad (42)$$

The Whittaker confluent hypergeometric function $W_{k, m}(z)$ is defined by the integral

$$- \frac{1}{2\pi i} \Gamma(k + \tfrac{1}{2} - m) e^{-\frac{1}{2}z} z^k \int_\infty^{(0+)} (-t)^{-k - \frac{1}{2} + m} (1 + \tfrac{t}{z})^{k - \frac{1}{2} + m} e^{-t} \, dt \qquad\qquad (43)$$

where the path of integration starts at 'infinity' on the real axis, circles the origin in a positive direction and returns to the starting point, making sure that the point $t = -z$ is outside (WHITTAKER & WATSON 1927, 245, 338).

We then deform the contour in (42) and write

$$- \frac{1}{2\pi i} \int_{\infty}^{(0+)} \frac{e^{-z}}{(-z)^p \left(1 + \frac{z}{\lambda_s}\right)^q} \, ds \qquad (44)$$

$$= \frac{e^{\frac{1}{2}\lambda_s}}{\Gamma(p)} (\lambda_s)^{\frac{1}{2}(q-p)} W_{\frac{1}{2}(p-q), \frac{1}{2}(1-p-q)}(\lambda_s)$$

Since $W_{k,m}(z) = W_{k,-m}(z)$ we may re-write (42) in the form

$$f(s) = \frac{\lambda_1{}^p \lambda_2{}^q}{\Gamma(p) \lambda^{\frac{1}{2}(p+q)}} \, e^{-s(\lambda_1 - \frac{1}{2}\lambda)} \, s^{\frac{1}{2}(p+q)-1} \, W_{\frac{1}{2}(p-q), \frac{1}{2}(p+q-1)}(\lambda s) \qquad (45)$$

(KULLBACK 1934, 286. 1936).

Although the initial density functions $f(w)$ and $f(u)$ are defined over $(0, \infty)$, the density function for $f(s)$ is defined over $(-\infty, \infty)$ and in the application of (45) care has to be taken over the domain and sign of λ_s, otherwise we may suffer the embarrassment of trying to deal with Fourier transforms of distribution functions that do not exist.

Whittakers confluent hypergeometric function $W_{k,m}(z)$ is related to Kummer's confluent hypergeometric function $M_{k,m}(z)$ by the formula

$$W_{k,m}(z) = \frac{\Gamma(-2m)}{\Gamma(\frac{1}{2} - m - k)} M_{k,m}(z) + \frac{\Gamma(2m)}{\Gamma(\frac{1}{2} + m - k)} M_{k,-m}(z) \qquad (46)$$

(provided $2m$ is not an integer), and which in turn can be expressed as an hypergeometric series,

$$M_{k,m}(z) = z^{\frac{1}{2}+m} \, e^{-\frac{1}{2}z} \, {}_1F_1(\tfrac{1}{2} - k + m, 1 + 2m, z)$$

where

$${}_1F_1(\alpha, \beta, z) = 1 + \frac{\alpha}{1.\beta} z + \frac{\alpha(\alpha+1)}{\beta(\beta+1) 2!} z^2 + \cdots \qquad (47)$$

$$= \sum_{r=0}^{\infty} \frac{(\alpha)_r}{(\beta)_r \, r!} \, z^r$$

$$= M(\alpha, \beta, z)$$

where $(\alpha)_r = \alpha(\alpha + 1)(\alpha + 2) \ldots \ldots (\alpha + r - 1)$

and and $(\alpha)_0 = 1$; and similarly so for $(\beta)_r$, and it is $M(\alpha, \beta, z)$ that is available in tables (ABRAMOWITZ & STEGUN 1965, 503-536, JANKE & EMDE 1945, 275-282).

Whittaker functions are expectionally rich in properties and by selecting appropriate values of α, β or z most of the functions common in mathematical physics can be expressed in terms of confluent hypergeometric functions. In his original memoir Whittaker lists five general classes of functions (WHITTAKER 1904) and ABRAMOWITZ & STEGUN (1965, 509) list 20 specific examples.

For instance, if we put $p = q$, (45) becomes

$$f(s) = \frac{(\lambda_1 \lambda_2)^p}{\Gamma(p) \lambda^p} e^{-s(\lambda_1 - \frac{1}{2}\lambda)} s^{p-1} W_{0, p-\frac{1}{2}}(\lambda s) \tag{48}$$

Now

$$W_{0, p-\frac{1}{2}}(\lambda s) = (\frac{\lambda s}{\pi})^{\frac{1}{2}} K_{p-\frac{1}{2}}(\frac{1}{2}\lambda s)$$

where $K_{p-\frac{1}{2}}(z)$ is the modified Bessel function of the second kind and of order $p - \frac{1}{2}$. We have then

$$f(s) = \frac{(\lambda_1 \lambda_2)^p}{\Gamma(p)\pi^{\frac{1}{2}} \lambda^{p-\frac{1}{2}}} e^{-s(\lambda_1 - \frac{1}{2}\lambda)} s^{p-\frac{1}{2}} K_{p-\frac{1}{2}}(\frac{1}{2}\lambda s) \tag{49}$$

If we now put $p = q = 1$,

$$f(s) = \frac{\lambda_1 \lambda_2}{\pi^{\frac{1}{2}} \lambda^{\frac{1}{2}}} e^{-s(\lambda_1 - \frac{1}{2}\lambda)} s^{\frac{1}{2}} K_{\frac{1}{2}}(\frac{1}{2}\lambda s) \tag{50}$$

$$K_{\frac{1}{2}}(z) = (\frac{\pi}{2z})^{\frac{1}{2}} e^{-z} = K_{\frac{1}{2}}(-z)$$

we finally arrive at

$$f(s) = \begin{cases} \dfrac{\lambda_1 \lambda_2}{\lambda_1 + \lambda_2} e^{-s\lambda_1} & s \geqslant 0 \\[4mm] \dfrac{\lambda_1 \lambda_2}{\lambda_1 + \lambda_2} e^{s\lambda_2} & s \leqslant 0 \end{cases} \tag{51}$$

This result for $p = q = 1$ is for the exponential/exponential case but it requires careful substantiation. Heuristically, if we write,

$$f_s(t) = \frac{1}{(1 - \dfrac{it}{\lambda_1})(1 + \dfrac{it}{\lambda_2})}$$

in the form

$$f_s(t) = \cfrac{1}{(1 + \frac{\lambda_1}{\lambda_2})(1 - \frac{it}{\lambda_1})} + \cfrac{1}{(1 + \frac{\lambda_2}{\lambda_1})(1 + \frac{it}{\lambda_2})}$$

we can see that it takes the form expected of the $c.f.$ of

$$\cfrac{\lambda_1}{(1 + \frac{\lambda_1}{\lambda_2})} e^{-\lambda_1 s} + \cfrac{\lambda_2}{(1 + \frac{\lambda_2}{\lambda_1})} e^{\lambda_2 s} \tag{52}$$

which with due attention to domain can be re-arranged to give (51).

The result is plausible physically. Unfortuneately owing to the behaviour of e^x at infinity the Fourier transform of $f(s)$ does not exist. A rigorous derivation is available, however, if use is made of Titchmarsh's generalised Fourier transforms (TITCHMARSH 1967, 4, TRANTER 1966, 8-11).

A graph of the density function (51) is given in fig 2 and is seen to comprise the two initial density functions arranged appropriately as to sign and subject to the factor

$$\frac{\lambda_1 \lambda_2}{\lambda_1 + \lambda_2}$$

Finally the probability of an event where the displacement energy is in excess of the barrier height is

$$G = \frac{\lambda_1 \lambda_2}{\lambda_1 + \lambda_2} \int_0^\infty e^{-\lambda_1 s} ds = \frac{\lambda_2}{\lambda_1 + \lambda_2} \tag{53}$$

Although on theoretical grounds an exponential distribution is a strong contender for the distribution of particle displacement energy it is not so for the distribution of activation energy. In this latter intance it is more likely to be distributed uni-modally about a well defined mode, possibly symmetrically (Gaussian) but more generally skew and reasonably well represented by a gamma distribution. So before we move on to deal with the general gamma/gamma case we detail the important exponential/gamma case wherein the activation energy is represented by a gamma distribution with $q > 0$ but otherwise unrestricted, although the most likely values appear to be $q > 1$.

If we insert the vaue $p = 1$ into (38) and (45) we get

$$f(s) = \frac{\lambda_1 \lambda_2^q}{\lambda^{\frac{1}{2}(q+1)}} e^{-s(\lambda_1 - \frac{1}{2}\lambda)} s^{\frac{1}{2}(q-1)} W_{\frac{1}{2}(1-q), \frac{1}{2}q}(\lambda s) \tag{54}$$

Applying (46) we find that the first term vanishes (provided $2q$ is not an integer),

13

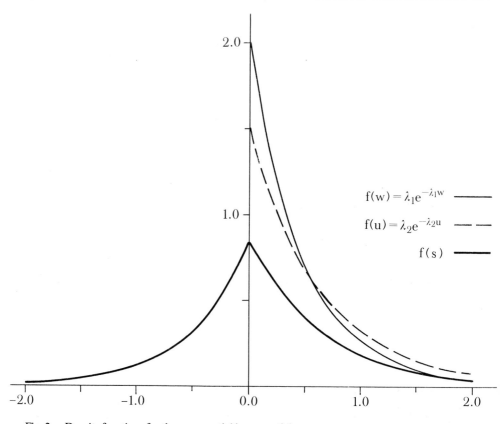

Fig. 2:   Density functions for the exponential/exponential case.

$$f(s) \;=\; \frac{\lambda_1 \lambda_2{}^q}{\lambda^{\frac{1}{2}(q+1)}} \; e^{-s(\lambda_1 - \frac{1}{2}\lambda)} \; s^{\frac{1}{2}(q-1)} \; M_{\frac{1}{2}(1-q),\, -\frac{1}{2}q}(\lambda s) \qquad (55)$$

Expressing the confluent hypergeometric function in series form

$$M_{\frac{1}{2}(1-q),\, -\frac{1}{2}q}(\lambda s) \;=\; e^{-\frac{1}{2}\lambda s} \, (\lambda s)^{\frac{1}{2}(1-q)} \, M(0,\, 1-q,\, \lambda s) \qquad (56)$$

and inerting into (55)

$$f(s) \;=\; \frac{\lambda_1 \lambda_2{}^q}{\lambda^q} \; e^{-\lambda_1 s} \, M(0,\, 1-q,\, \lambda s) \qquad (57)$$

Making use of Kummer's transformaton,

$$M(a, b, z) \;=\; e^z \, M(b-a, b, -z)$$

we find that

$$M\,(0,\,1\,-\,q,\,\lambda\,s)\;=\;e^{\lambda\,s}\,M\,(1\,-\,q,\,1\,-\,q,\,-\,\lambda\,s)$$

$$=\;e^{\lambda\,s}\cdot e^{-\,\lambda\,s}\;=\;1$$

Hence quite simply

$$f\,(s)\;=\;\frac{\lambda_1\,\lambda_2{}^q}{\lambda^q}\,e^{-\,\lambda_1\,s}\qquad\qquad s\,\geqslant\,0 \tag{58}$$

The same considerations as to domain and sign apply as in the previous example and therefore

$$f\,(s)\;=\;\frac{\lambda_1\,\lambda_2{}^q}{\lambda^q}\,e^{\lambda_2\,s}\qquad\qquad s\,\leqslant\,0 \tag{59}$$

Summing for all cases in which the displacement energy is equal to or greater than the activation anergy,

$$G\;=\;\frac{\lambda_1\,\lambda_2{}^q}{\lambda^q}\int_0^\infty e^{-\,\lambda_1\,s}\,ds\;=\;(\frac{\lambda_2}{\lambda_1\,+\,\lambda_2})^q \tag{60}$$

If q degenerates to unity then (60) reduces to (55) as required.

When using (45) to calculate the proportion of successful escapes it is always advantageous, if possible, to select values of p and q that provide elegant simplifications to well known or easily integrable functions, as is the case in the two examples considered. Where this is not possible the Whittaker function is expanded according to (46) and (47), but this is not always possible. The rule is, if p and q cannot be chosen to give simplification then they must be chosen non-integers.
Thus

$$G\;=\;\int_0^\infty f\,(s)\,ds\;=\;\frac{\lambda_1{}^p\,\lambda_2{}^q}{\Gamma(p)\,\lambda^{\frac{1}{2}(p\,+\,q)}}\int_0^\infty e^{-\,s(\lambda_1\,-\,\frac{1}{2}\lambda)}\,s^{\frac{1}{2}(p\,+\,q)\,-\,1}\,W_{\frac{1}{2}(p\,-\,q),\,\frac{1}{2}(p\,+\,q\,-\,1)}(\lambda\,s)\,ds\;=$$

$$=\;\frac{\lambda_1{}^p\,\lambda_2{}^q}{\Gamma(p)}\left\{\frac{\Gamma(1\,-\,p\,-\,q)}{\Gamma(1\,-\,p)}\int_0^\infty e^{-\,\lambda_1\,s}\,s^{p\,+\,q\,-\,1}\,{}_1F_1\,(q,\,p\,+\,q,\,\lambda\,s)\,ds\;+\right.$$

$$\left.+\;\lambda^{1\,-\,p\,-\,q}\,\frac{\Gamma(p\,+\,q\,-\,1)}{\Gamma(q)}\int_0^\infty e^{-\,\lambda_1\,s}\,{}_1F_1\,(1\,-\,p,\,2\,-\,p\,-\,q,\,\lambda\,s)\,ds\right\} \tag{61}$$

If we put $p\,=\,q\,=\,1$ and apply the recurrence relationship,

$$(1\,+\,a\,-\,b)\,M(a,\,b,\,z)\,=\,a\,M(a\,+\,1,\,b,\,z)\,-\,(b\,-\,1)\,M(a,\,b\,-\,1,\,z)$$

and ten the Kummer transformation we can eventually arrive at (53) but only by assuming that the first component in (61) vanishes. We return to this matter later.

The task of evaluating (61) term by term consists of integrating a series of terms with the general form

$$A \int_0^\infty e^{-\lambda_1 s} s^n \, ds \tag{62}$$

where A is a complicated coefficient in powers of p, q and λ. The whole business is rather cumbersome and to avoid tedious repetition we defer the detail until (74-80).

In considering the effect of an external force we return once again to the case for $p = q = 1$, (exponential/exponential). The density function for barrier height is now

$$f(u) = \lambda_2 \, e^{-\lambda_2 (u \pm u_0)} \qquad\qquad (u \pm u_0) \geqslant 0 \tag{63}$$

where $u_0 = \frac{1}{2} \, \bar{r} \, F$. For the negative direction the $c.f.$ is

$$f_u(t) = \lambda_2 \int_{u_0}^\infty e^{-\lambda_2 (u - u_0) + itu} \, du =$$

$$= \lambda_2 \int_0^\infty e^{-\lambda_2 y + it(y + u_0)} \, dy = \frac{e^{itu_0}}{\left(1 - \dfrac{it}{\lambda_2}\right)} \tag{64}$$

Quite generally, if $f(t)$ is the $c.f.$ of $f(z)$ then $e^{it\tau} f(t)$ is the $c.f.$ of $f(z - \tau)$. It follows that for the negative direction

$$f_s(t) = \frac{e^{-itu_0}}{\left(1 - \dfrac{it}{\lambda_1}\right)\left(1 + \dfrac{it}{\lambda_2}\right)} \tag{65}$$

and

$$f_-(s) = \begin{cases} \dfrac{\lambda_1 \lambda_2}{\lambda_1 + \lambda_2} \, e^{-\lambda_1 (s + u_0)} & (s + u_0) \geqslant 0 \\[4mm] \dfrac{\lambda_1 \lambda_2}{\lambda_1 + \lambda_2} \, e^{\lambda_2 (s + u_0)} & (s + u_0) \leqslant 0 \end{cases} \tag{66}$$

While for the positive direction

$$f_+(s) = \begin{cases} \dfrac{\lambda_1 \lambda_2}{\lambda_1 + \lambda_2} \, e^{-\lambda_1 (s - u_0)} & (s - u_0) \geqslant 0 \\[4mm] \dfrac{\lambda_1 \lambda_2}{\lambda_1 + \lambda_2} \, e^{\lambda_2 (s - u_0)} & (s - u_0) \leqslant 0 \end{cases} \tag{67}$$

The probability of excess displacement energy is, for the negative direction

$$G_- = \frac{\lambda_1 \lambda_2}{\lambda_1 + \lambda_2} \int_0^\infty e^{-\lambda_1(s + u_0)} \, ds = \frac{\lambda_2}{\lambda_1 + \lambda_2} e^{-\lambda_1 u_0} \tag{68}$$

and for the positive direction

$$G_+ = \frac{\lambda_1 \lambda_2}{\lambda_1 + \lambda_2} \left[\int_{u_0}^\infty e^{-\lambda_1(s - u_0)} \, ds + \int_0^{u_0} e^{\lambda_2(s - u_0)} \, ds \right] =$$

$$= \frac{\lambda_1 \lambda_2}{\lambda_1 + \lambda_2} \left\{ \frac{1}{\lambda_1} + \frac{1}{\lambda_2} \left[1 - e^{-\lambda_2 u_0} \right] \right\} \tag{69}$$

The net excess in the positive direction is then

$$g = \frac{\lambda_1 \lambda_2}{\lambda_1 + \lambda_2} \left\{ \frac{1}{\lambda_1} \left[1 - e^{-\lambda_1 u_0} \right] + \frac{1}{\lambda_2} \left[1 - e^{-\lambda_2 u_0} \right] \right\} \tag{70}$$

Graphs of the density functions (66) and (67) and of (70) are illustrated in fig. 3.

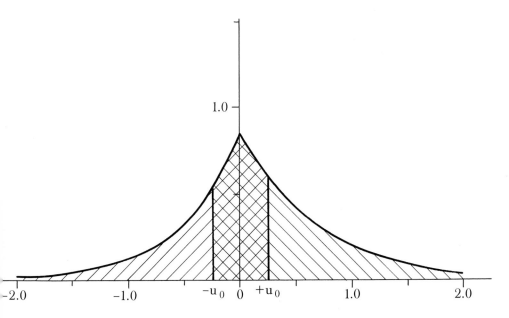

Fig. 3: Density functions for the positive and negative directions and the net excess in the positive direction.

In the gamma/gamma case the distribution of barrier height is represented by

$$f(u) = \frac{\lambda_2{}^q}{\Gamma(q)} \, e^{-\lambda_2 (u \pm u_0)} \, (u \pm u_0)^{q-1} \, du \qquad (u \pm u_0) \geqslant 0 \qquad (71)$$

and the $c.f.$ of displacement energy excess is

$$f_s(t) = \frac{e^{\pm i t u_0}}{(1 - \frac{it}{\lambda_1})^p \, (1 + \frac{it}{\lambda_2})^q} \qquad (72)$$

Repeating the analysis of (40-45),

$$f(s) = \frac{\lambda_1{}^p \lambda_2{}^q}{\Gamma(p) \, \lambda^{\frac{1}{2}(p+q)}} \, e^{-(s \pm u_0)(\lambda_1 - \frac{1}{2}\lambda)} \, (s \pm u_0)^{\frac{1}{2}(p+q)-1} \, \cdot$$

$$\cdot \; W_{\frac{1}{2}(p+q), \frac{1}{2}(p+q-1)} (\lambda[s \pm u_0]) \qquad (73)$$

Expanding the Whittaker function, (for positive values of $s \pm u_0$),

$$f(s) = \frac{\lambda_1{}^p \lambda_2{}^q}{\Gamma(p)} \, e^{-\lambda_1 (s \pm u_0)} \left| (s \pm u_0)^{p+q-1} \right.$$

$$\cdot \; \frac{\Gamma(1-p-q)}{\Gamma(1-p)} \; {}_1F_1 (q, p+q, \lambda(s \pm u_0)) \; +$$

$$\left. + \; \lambda^{1-p-q} \frac{\Gamma(p+q-1)}{\Gamma(q)} \; {}_1F_1(1-p, 2-p-q, \lambda(s \pm u_0)) \right|$$

$$(74)$$

provided $(1 - p - q)$ is not an integer.

For the exponential/gamma case by substituting $p = 1$ (q not an integer),

$$f(s) = \frac{\lambda_1 \lambda_2{}^q}{\lambda^q} \, e^{-\lambda_1 (s \pm u_0)} \, {}_1F_1(0, 1-q, \lambda(s \pm u_0)) =$$

$$= \frac{\lambda_1 \lambda_2{}^q}{\lambda^q} \, e^{-\lambda_1 (s \pm u_0)} \qquad (s \pm u_0) \geqslant 0 \qquad (75)$$

and for negative values of $(s \pm u_0)$

$$f(s) = \frac{\lambda_1 \lambda_2{}^q}{\lambda^q} \, e^{\lambda_2 (s \pm u_0)} \qquad (s \pm u_0) \leqslant 0 \qquad (76)$$

Returning to the general formula (74), for the negative direction we need to integrate a series of integrals of the form

$$\int_0^\infty f_-(s)\, ds = \int_0^\infty e^{-\lambda_1(s + u_0)} (s + u_0)^n\, ds = \int_{u_0}^\infty e^{-\lambda_1 y}\, y^n\, dy \tag{77}$$

and for the positive direction

$$\int_0^\infty f_+(s)\, ds = \int_{u_0}^\infty e^{-\lambda_1(s - u_0)} (s - u_0)^n\, ds + \int_0^{u_0} e^{\lambda_2(s - u_0)} (s - u_0)^n\, ds =$$

$$= \int_0^\infty e^{-\lambda_1 y}\, y^n\, dy + \int_{-u_0}^0 e^{\lambda_2 y}\, y^n\, dy =$$

$$= \int_0^\infty e^{-\lambda_1 y}\, y^n\, dy + \int_0^{u_0} e^{-\lambda_2 y}\, y^n\, dy \tag{78}$$

The net excess in the positive direction consists of a series of integrals of the form

$$\int_0^{u_0} e^{-\lambda_1 y}\, y^n\, dy + \int_0^{u_0} e^{-\lambda_2 y}\, y^n\, dy \tag{79}$$

In series form the expression for the net excess in the positive direction reads,

$$g = \frac{\lambda_1^p \lambda_2^q}{\Gamma(p)} \int_0^{u_0} (e^{-\lambda_1 y} + e^{-\lambda_2 y}) \left\{ \frac{\Gamma(1 - p - q)}{\Gamma(1 - p)}\, y^{p + q - 1} \cdot \right.$$

$$\cdot \left[1 + \frac{q}{p + q}\, \lambda y + \frac{q(q + 1)}{(p + q)(p + q + 1)}\, \tfrac{1}{2}\lambda^2 y^2 + \cdots \right] +$$

$$+ \lambda^{1 - p - q}\, \frac{\Gamma(p + q - 1)}{\Gamma(q)} \left[1 + \frac{(1 - p)}{(2 - p - q)}\, \lambda y + \right.$$

$$+ \frac{(1 - p)(2 - p)}{(2 - p - q)(3 - p - q)}\, \tfrac{1}{2}\lambda^2 y^2 + \cdots \left. \right] \right\}\, dy \tag{80}$$

If we attempt to put $p = q = 1$ in order to retrieve (70) we discover that $(1 - p - q) = -1$ and $(1 - p) = 0$. Now

$$\lim_{z \to n} \frac{1}{\Gamma(-z)} = \frac{1}{(-n-1)!} = 0 \qquad n = 0, 1, 2 . .$$

and is a simple zero. Therefore the ratio

$$\lim_{z \to n} \frac{\Gamma(-z-1)}{\Gamma(-z)} = \frac{1}{(-n-1)} \qquad n = 0, 1, 2 . .$$

and is finite. However, if in

$$\frac{\Gamma(1-p-q)}{\Gamma(1-p)}$$

we adopt the stratagem of letting p approach unity much faster than q, then we ensure that the ratio of gamma functions behaves like,

$$\frac{\Gamma(-1 + \varepsilon)}{\Gamma(0)} = 0$$

and we may then safely ignore the first component in (80). We then find that the second component reduces to

$$g = \frac{\lambda_1 \lambda_2}{\lambda_1 + \lambda_2} \int_0^{u_0} (e^{-\lambda_1 y} + e^{-\lambda_2 y}) \, dy \qquad (81)$$

which does agree with (70).

The cases covered should encompass most expected physical conditions. If this should not be so and further refinement becomes necessary we may turn to a series of gamma distributions

$$a_1 f_1(x) + a_2 f_2(x) + . . . \qquad . . + a_n f_n(x) \qquad (82)$$

where the $a_i > 0$ and $\sum a_i = 1$ and $f(x)$ is a distribution of form (38) with parameters λ_i and m_i, (ROBBINS & PITMAN 1949). Or laternatively to a series such as Edgeworth's based on terms of the form

$$H_r(x) \, \alpha(x) \qquad (83)$$

where $H_r(x)$ is an Hermitian polynominal and $\alpha(x) = N(m, \sigma^2)$ (KENDALL & STUART 1958, 157).

4.   DERIVATION OF THE COEFFICIENTS

Random walk behaviour on the part of individual particles induces diffuse flow in the aggregate as a whole in which the flow vectors across planes normal to the co-ordinate axes, per unit area, per unit time are

$$- D_i \; \frac{\partial W}{\partial x_i} \;\; + \;\; c_i W$$

For an external force field in the x-direction only, the diffusion equation takes the form

$$\frac{\partial W}{\partial t} \;\; = \;\; - c_x \; \frac{\partial W}{\partial x} \;\; + \;\; D \nabla^2 (W) \tag{84}$$

where we assume isotropy $(i.e. \; D_x = D_y = D_z = D)$. The fundamental solution of (84) is

$$W(R) \;\; = \;\; (2 \pi Dt)^{-\frac{1}{2}} \; exp \left[- \frac{(x \, - \, c_x t)^2}{4 Dt} \;\; - \;\; \frac{y^2}{4 Dt} \;\; - \;\; \frac{z^2}{4 Dt} \right] \tag{85}$$

expressing the radially symmetric Gaussian dispersion of particles as the square of the time superimposed upon the dirft in the x direction directly proportional to time.

The mean translation distance is assumed given, derived empirically or semi-empirically from the observed structure of the soil. The use of a constant mean value greatly simplifies the derivation of the drift and diffusion coefficients from the fundamental postulates of the stochastic theory of soil creep and the particle escape model. Once the net drift in the direction of the external force has been formulated the mean particle velocity can be arrived at quite simply by multiplying this quantity by the mean number of translations per unit time, n. This latter is related to the number of particle displacements N, by the probability of a successful escape, G. Thus the drift coefficient is given by

$$c \;\; = \;\; n \bar{r} \;\; = \;\; N G \bar{r} \tag{86}$$

G which will necessarily have a value between 0 and 1 is available from the appropriate formulation of the particle escape model.

The diffusion coefficient can be determined given the mean translation length, $\bar{r}$, and the mean residence time τ from the formula

$$D \;\; = \;\; \frac{1}{6} \; \frac{\bar{r}^2}{\tau} \tag{87}$$

This well known expression is similar to that derived by Einstein for Brownian motion and is valid for any Brownian type movement in which two successive displacements are uncorrelated as to direction. It therefore applies to random walks on a crystal lattice or a blurred crystal structure. Fundamentally it reflects the relationship between activity (in this case the reciprocal of the mean residence time) and structure (mean square displacement length).

The mean residence time is the reciprocal of the probability of translation on the part of the particle. If v_m is the mean frequency of particle oscillation

$$v_0 = v_m G \tag{88}$$

gives the frequency of particle translations per particle and the reciprocal is the mean residence time

$$\tau = \frac{1}{v_0} \tag{89}$$

Multiplying by $\bar{r}$ gives an equivalent relationship to (86). We have explicity,

$$D = \frac{1}{6} v_0 \bar{r}^2 = \frac{1}{6} v_m G \bar{r}^2 \tag{90}$$

The factor of $\frac{1}{6}$, which is customary, arises from the so called Joule classification of direction and the method used in the original determination of the self-diffusion coefficient of gases by Meyer (JEANS 1925, 307).

The relationship between R_n, the distance between the origin and the position of a particle after exactly n steps and the distance the particle actually travels is given, in the absence of drift, by

$$\overline{R_n^2} = n\bar{r}^2 \tag{91}$$

This important relationship can be established in a non-rigorous fashion by quite simple and straight-forward arguments and because it exemplifies the advantage of basing the analysis upon regular lattice structures and then generalising to the irregular (blurring the crystal), we give the derivation and follow in the main the treatment of SHEWMON (1963, 48-49).

For a Markov process on a regular lattice the vector R_n connecting the origin and the position of a particle after just n displacements can be resolved, quite generally, into the sum of the n vectors comprising the individual displacements,

$$\underset{\sim}{R}_n = \underset{\sim}{r}_1 + \underset{\sim}{r}_2 + \cdots \qquad \cdots + \underset{\sim}{r}_n \tag{92}$$

Squaring both sides

$$\underset{\sim}{R}_n \cdot \underset{\sim}{R}_n = \underset{\sim}{r}_1 \cdot \underset{\sim}{r}_1 + \underset{\sim}{r}_1 \cdot \underset{\sim}{r}_2 + \cdots \qquad \cdots + \underset{\sim}{r}_1 \cdot \underset{\sim}{r}_n$$

$$+ \underset{\sim}{r}_2 \cdot \underset{\sim}{r}_1 + \underset{\sim}{r}_2 \cdot \underset{\sim}{r}_2 + \cdots \qquad \cdots + \underset{\sim}{r}_2 \cdot \underset{\sim}{r}_n$$

$$\cdots \cdots \qquad \cdots \qquad \cdots \cdots$$

$$+ \underset{\sim}{r}_n \cdot \underset{\sim}{r}_1 + \underset{\sim}{r}_n \cdot \underset{\sim}{r}_2 + \cdots \qquad \cdots + \underset{\sim}{r}_n \cdot \underset{\sim}{r}_n$$

$$= \sum_{i=1}^{n} \underset{\sim}{r}_i \cdot \underset{\sim}{r}_i + 2 \sum_{i=1}^{n-1} \underset{\sim}{r}_i \cdot \underset{\sim}{r}_{i+1} + 2 \sum_{i=1}^{n-2} \underset{\sim}{r}_i \cdot \underset{\sim}{r}_{i+2} + \cdots$$

$$= \sum_{i=1}^{n} \underline{r}_i^2 + 2 \sum_{j=1}^{n-1} \sum_{i=1}^{n-j} \underline{r}_i \cdot \underline{r}_{i+j} \tag{93}$$

The vector (dot) product is by definition

$$\underline{r}_i \cdot \underline{r}_{i+j} = |\underline{r}_i| \cdot |\underline{r}_{i+j}| \cos\theta_{i,i+j} \tag{94}$$

where $\theta_{i,i+j}$ is the angle between the two vectors $\underline{r}_i$ and $\underline{r}_{i+j}$. Whereupon

$$\underline{R}_n^2 = \sum_{i=1}^{n} \underline{r}_i^2 + 2 \sum_{j=1}^{n-1} \sum_{i=1}^{n-j} |\underline{r}_i| \cdot |\underline{r}_{i+j}| \cos\theta_{i,i+j} \tag{95}$$

This expression is completely general. No restriction has been placed upon the magnitude of the displacements, the allowable values of the angle θ, whether the displacements are patterned systematically or in random order and as to the number of dimensions of the vectors. In keeping with the restrictions we have accepted earlier, namely a constant displacement length, we consider a lattice with cubic symmetry and assume isotropy *i.e.* the eight possible avenues of escape are occupied with equal probability. We may then rewrite (95) as,

$$R_n^2 = nr^2 \left(1 + \frac{2}{n} \sum_{j=1}^{n-1} \sum_{i=1}^{n-j} \cos\theta_{i,i+j} \right) \tag{96}$$

To calculate the mean square, $\overline{R_n^2}$, consider a large number of realisations each of which is of n component displacements. Then by summing and averaging and then dividing by the number of realisations we reach the desired quantity. In each case the first term nr^2 has the same value. This is not so for the double sum term. Nevertheless we may write

$$\overline{R_n^2} = nr^2 \left(1 + \frac{2}{n} \overline{\sum_{j=1}^{n-1} \sum_{i=1}^{n-j} \cos\theta_{i,i+j}} \right) \tag{97}$$

Because of the inherent symmetry and isotropy the double sum term can be eliminated by detailed balancing. For any displacement there exists within the cubic symmetry a complementary displacement in the opposite direction of equal magnitude and probability of occurrence. The values of $\cos\theta_{i,i+j}$ can be paired and the average value of the double sum term for large n, is zero. We are left with

$$\overline{R_n^2} = nr^2 \tag{98}$$

or more conventionally,

$$(\overline{R_n^2})^{\frac{1}{2}} = n^{\frac{1}{2}} r \tag{99}$$

(the root mean square total displacement equals the square root of the number of displacements times the displacement length).

The argument of Shewmon can be extended in a non-rigorous manner to cater for the case where all directions are allowed instead of just a discrete regular set; also the constancy of displacement length can be relaxed. Provided symmetry is preserved, by a spherically uniform distribution or a Gaussian distribution, which may be ellipsoidal, then the detailed balancing can be carried out and

$$\overline{R_n^2} = n\overline{r}^2 \tag{100}$$

These results can be substantiated rigorously using more refined methods. In fact the results can be greatly extended. By a method, due originally to Markov, the distribution of R_n can be shown to tend asymptotically for large κ to a Gaussian form for a wide class of individual component distributions, not necessarily symmetrical about the origin, provided they are equivalent and independent. The results can be applied to give the same result for the much wider class in which the distribution law may differ from displacement to displacement, provided it satisfies the Liapounov criterion, which in effect means a finite absolute third moment to the particle displacement distribution. It is difficult to see how the distribution of natural soil particle displacements, however caused, can fail to fulfill this condition (CHANDRASEKHAR 1943, CULLING 1963, 1965).

The relationship is also of great practical importance. It is much easier to measure R_n than r. Then provided we have some estimate of $\overline{r}$ we can arrive at n, which will give the mean frequency of particle translation *i.e.* $v_m G$ in (85). Then from a knowledge of the frequency of particle oscillation v_m, we can arrive at a value for G, the probability of escape on the part of the particle. The frequency v_m should be controllable experimentally *eg.* for thermal or hydration cycles, and may be measureable for such cases in the field.

Then as a first stage, in appropriate cases, the activation energy would be assumed to be a constant so that by use of the theory developed in the section on variable displacement energy, we can test alternative hypotheses for the distribution of particle energy and the examples detailed in that section are the ones to start with. Armed with this knowledge or better still if we can gain some idea of the distribution of particle energy from some independent source, we will be in a position to measure the magnitude and variation in the activation energy. This information can then be used to test various ideas as to the nature of the activation energy.

The furtherance of such a research programme will require considerable time, ingenuity and patience but if successful it will put numbers to two fundamental parameters and provide a window on the microscopic behaviour of the soil.

The distribution of R_n in itself is even more important than the relationship and its investigation is logically prior. If turbatory forces exist, are strong, intermittent and have no preferred direction then R_n should adopt a Gaussian distribution in an homogenous medium. Evidence of diffusion should be sought, in the first instance, in the absence of any external force. But this is purely for observational convenience. If diffuse movements take place then they will do so in the presence of drift and particle movement is to be expected in the upslope direction. This may already have been encountered in the recorded observations of counter-slope creep which seems to provide for puzzlement (STATHAM 1981, 170). Such observations should be siezed upon for they could prove crucial.

Finally although surface movement provides a more convenient experimental and observational medium and is ostensibly a simplified sub-class of the three dimensional transport phenomena studied in this paper, in reality it brings certain difficulties in its train. We have assumed throughout that the axes can be rotated until any external force acts parallel to one of the co-ordinates. With surface phenomena this is not always convenient for the slope surface itself supplies the natural co-ordinate frame. This can lead in certain cases to the introduction of bias into the displacing mechanism but more importantly the very presence of the free hemisphere above the particle adds further complexity to the problem. For these reasons we have not covered surface movement but reserve its discussion for a future occasion, when we consider among other processes those of rain-drop impact, slope wash and in general, agencies where the nature of the free particle trajectory is important.

ACKNOWLEDGEMENTS

This work has been supported by a N.E.R.C. research Grant. Helpful discussions have taken place with Prof. J.B. Thornes and Dr M. Knott. The diagrams were drawn by Mrs J. Pugh.

BIBLIOGRAPHY

ABRAMOWITZ, M. & STEGUN, I.A. (1965): Handbook of mathematical functions. Dover. New York.
ALDER, B.J. & WAINWRIGHT, T.E. (1939a): Studies in molecular dynamics. I General method. Journal of Chemical Physics. 31, 459-466.
ALDER, B.J. & WAINWRIGHT, T.E. (1939b): Molecular motions. Scientific American. Oct. 1939, 3-10.
BARTON, A.F.M. (1974): The dynamic liquid state. Longmans. London.
BENSON, S.W. (1960): The foundations of chemical kinetics. McGraw-Hill. New York.
CARSON, M.A. & KIRKBY, M.J. (1972): Hillslope form and process. Cambridge University Press. London.
CHANDRASEKHAR, S. (1943): Stochastic problems in physics and astronomy. Reviews of Modern Physics. 15, 1-89.
COLE, G.H.A. (1967): The statistical theory of classical simple dense liquids. Pergamon. Oxford.
CRAMER, H. (1936): Random variables and probability distributions. Cambridge University Press. London.
CULLING, W.E.H. (1963): Soil creep and the development of hillside slopes. Journal of Geology. 71, 127-161.
CULLING, W.E.H. (1965): Theory of erosion on soil covered slopes. Journal of Geology. 73, 230-254.
CULLING, W.E.H. (1981): New methods in the measurement of slow particulate transport processes on hillside slopes. Erosion and Sediment Transport Measurement (Proceedings Florence Symposium) 1981. I.A.H.S. publication 133, 267-274.
EYRING, H. (1935): The activated complex in chemical reactions. Journal of Chemical Physics. 3, 107-115.
FELTHAM, P. (1973): A stochastic model of crystal plasticity. Journal of Physics. D. Applied Physics. 6, 2048-2056.
FISHER, I.Z. (1964): Statistical theory of liquids. University of Chicago Press. Chicago.
FRENKEL, J. (1926): Über die Wärmebewegung in festen und flüssigen Körpern. Zeitschrift für Physik. 35, 652-669.
FRENKEL, J. (1946): Kinetic theory of liquids. Oxford University Press. London. (Dover reprint) 1955.
GLASSTONE, S., LAIDLER, K. & EYRING, H. (1941): The theory of rate processes. McGraw-Hill. New York.
HIRANO, M. (1975): Simulation of developmental process of interfluvial slopes with reference to graded form. Journal of Geology. 83, 113-123.
IMESON, A.C. (1976): Some effects of burrowing animals on slope processes in the Luxembourg Ardennes. Geografiska Annaler. 58A, 115-125, 317-328.
IMESON, A.C. (1977): Splash erosion, animal activity and sediment supply in a small forested catchment. Earth Surface Processes. 2, 153-160.
JANKE, E. & EMDE, F. (1945): Tables of functions with formulae and curves. 4th edition. Dover. New York.

JEANS, J.H. (1925): Dynamical theory of gases. 4th edition. Cambridge University Press. London.

KENDALL, M. & STUART, A. (1958): The advanced theory of statistics. Vol. I Distribution theory. Griffin. London.

KIRKBY, M.J. (1971): Hillslope process-esponse models based on the continuity equation. In: Slopes: form and process. Ed. D. Brunsden. Institute of British Geographers. Special Publ. **3**, 15-30.

KIRKWOOD, J.G. (1946): The statistical mechanical theory of transport processes. I. General theory. Journal of Chemical Physics. **14**, 180-201.

KULLBACK, S. (1934): An application of characteristic functions to the distribution problem of statistics. American Journal of Mathematical Statistics. **5**, 263-307.

KULLBACK, S. (1936): The distribution laws of the difference and quotient of variables independently distributed in Pearson type III laws. American Journal of Mathematical Statistics. **7**, 51-53.

LAIDLER, K. (1969): Theories of chemical reaction rates. McGraw-Hill. London.

MANNING, J.R. (1968): Diffusion kinetics for atoms in crystals. Van Nostrand. London.

MILLINGTON, A.C. (1981): Relationship between three scales of erosion measurement on two small basins in Sierra Leone. Erosion and Sediment Transport Measurement (Proceedings Florence Symposium) 1981. I.A.H.S. Publ. **133**, 485-492.

NYE, M.J. (1972): Molecular Reality. MacDonald. London.

PERRIN, J. (1908): Peut-on peser un atom avec précision? Revue du mois. **6**, 513-514.

PRINS, J.A. & PETERSEN, H. (1936): Theoretical diffraction patterns corresponding to some simple types of molecular arrangement in liquids. Physica. **3**, 147-153.

PUSCH, R. & FELTHAM, P. (1980): A stochastic model of the creep of soils. Geotechnique. **30**, 497-506.

ROBBINS, H. & PITMAN, E.J.G. (1949): Applications of the method of mixtures to quadratic forms in normal variates. American Journal of Mathematical Statistics. **20**, 552-560.

SHEWMON, P.G. (1965): Diffusion in solids. McGraw-Hill. New York.

STATHAM, I. (1981): Slope processes. In: Geomorphological techniques. 156-177. Ed. A. Goudie. Allen & Unwin. London.

TITCHMARSH, E.C. (1967): Introduction to the theory of Fourier integrals. 2nd edition. Oxford University Press. London.

TRANTER, C.T. (1966): Integral transforms of mathematical Physics. 3rd edition. Methuen. London.

WHITTAKER, E. (1904): An expression of certain known functions as generalised hypergeometric functions. Bulletin of American Mathematical Society. **10**, 125-134.

WHITTAKER, E. & WATSON, G.N. (1927): A course of modern analysis. 4th edition. Cambridge University Press. London.

YAIR, A. & LAVEE, H. (1981): An investigation of the source areas of sediment and sediment transport by overland flow along arid hillslopes. Erosion and Sediment Transport Measurement (Proceedings Florence Symposium) 1981. I.A.H.S. Publ. **133**. 433-446.

YOUNG, A. (1972): Slopes. Oliver & Boyd. Edinburgh.

ZIMAN, J.M. (1972): Principles of the theory of solids. Cambridge University Press. London.

Address of author:
W.E.H. Culling, Bedford College, Regent's Park
London NW 1 4NS, Great Britain

Jan de Ploey (Ed.)
Rainfall Simulation, Runoff and Soil Erosion
CATENA SUPPLEMENT 4, Braunschweig 1983

RATE PROCESS THEORY
IN GEOMORPHIC SOIL CREEP

W.E.H. **Culling**, London

Rate process theory originates in physical chemistry but has manifold application to physical processes, in fact to any rearrangement of matter existing in a particulate form. Idealising
soil structure as a blurred crystal lattice rate process concepts can be applied to the translation
of individual soil particles. Soil creep is then seen to be a special extreme case of dry particulate
flow and rate process theory is employed to construct a unified theory. Geomorphic soil creep
is distinguished from rheologic creep as studied by soil engineers; the former takes place at the
particle level while the latter is essentially a molecular phenomenon but they are both manifestations of the same fundamental physical process. That is the escape of a particle over a con-
straining potential barrier by virtue of the possession of a kinetic energy that is partly intrinsic
but can be supplemented and given a preferred direction by the influence of external force
fields. Expressions are derived for various flow properties of the soil in a geomorphic setting
including (apparent) viscosity, diffusion and pressure variation. Relationships are traced via
the general theory to cases of accelerated flow including slurries, liquefaction and fluidised
phenomena.

1. INTRODUCTION

The transport of material within the landscape is currently regarded as a set of disjoint
processes. In this paper we set out to provide a unified theoretical basis employing the ideas
of rate process theory. At the core of this theory resides the simple idea of a particle or flow
unit escaping from its initial constraints, surmounting a potential barrier, finally coming to
rest in a fresh equilibrium position. The flow of the mass is made up of a very large number of
such elementary translations. This notion is so fundamental it can be applied in principle to
any rearrangement of matter conceived as a particulate medium. We cannot follow up all the
potential applications in geomorphology, instead we base our investigation upon soil creep
and for three reasons. Rate process theory presupposes a certain degree of structure and
idealisation and this is already to hand in the stochastic theory of soil creep set out in CULL-
ING (1963). Secondly granular flow, in so far as the rearrangement of matter is concerned is a
single phase phenomenon. Finally there is the need to distinguish between creep motions as
studied by soil engineers and soil creep as understood by geomorphologists.

In this latter connection we note that when in the 60s soil engineers applied rate process
ideas to the study of soil deformation there was initially some confusion as to the scale at
which the process operates. Early work (MURAYAMA & SHIBATA 1961, CHRISTENSEN
& WU 1964, and MITCHELL 1964) envisaged operation at the level of the soil particle but it
was eventually realised that the concepts of rate process theory as originally conceived by
EYRING (1935), are essentially molecular and this interpretation in the case of soil deformation was later verified by experimental results (MITCHELL 1969). Despite the
misgivings of MITCHELL (1976, 300) about the application of rate process theory to particle
phenomena this is the purpose of this paper. In doing so we are led to characterise soil creep

as understood by engineers as a rheologic process operating at the molecular level, while geomorphic soil creep is essentially a particle scale phenomenon. Nevertheless they are two manifestations of the same fundamental flow mechanism which can be described quite simply in terms of rate process theory.

The structure of the soil is extremely complicated. It possesses many of the properties of fractals (MANDELBROT 1977, CULLING 1982). Despite the adoption of a stochastic approach some idealisation is essential if any progress is to be made. A fruitful model can be developed which in essentials disrupts or blurrs the characteristic regularity of the crystal lattice. Instead of a periodic structure describable in naive Fourier terms

$$f(\underline{r}) \; = \; \sum_g A_g \, e^{i\underline{g} \cdot \underline{r}} \tag{1}$$

where g is the reciprocal lattice vector (ZIMAN 1972), the regularity is relaxed as in Frenkel's theory of fusion (FRENKEL 1935, 1946, 93). In place of a series of spikes the radial distribution function becomes blurred as individual spikes broaden in a Gaussian fashion and eventually merge,

$$f(\underline{r}) \; = \; \sum_n A_n \, e^{i\psi_n} \tag{2}$$

where the ψ_n are vectors with elements composed of a set of random numbers on $(0, 2\pi)$. The summation gives a Gaussian random function (RICE 1944).

In a crystal lattice each atom is normally resident in a potential cell formed by the combined force fields of its neighbours. This force field can be represented by a potential surface and the static picture is disturbed by the thermal oscillation of the atoms about their equilibrium positions and this in turn promotes local variation in the strength of the potential surface. Possible translation paths follow the spaces between particles and are marked by cols on the potential surface the saddle points of which give a measure of the escape or activation energy. Escape and consequent translation of the particle depends upon the existence of a suitable vacancy. Natural crystals are far from perfect and include a number of holes or vacancies as well as other imperfections. Translation of a particle means that the vacancy migrates in the opposite direction. In the absence of a superimposed force field resulting in a preferred direction the migrations are disposed randomly on the lattice and both particles and holes diffuse through the body of the material.

In regarding the soil as a blurred crystal structure we endow it with many properties of the liquid state; the presence of significant free volume, the absence of long range order and the possibility of mass flow of an irreversible nature due to the reversible motions of individual particles. Even the short range order of liquids finds a parallel as it is known that clay and sand particles in their differing ways are not completely random in orientation in natural soils. However, as in elementary theories of the liquid state these possibilities are neglected and we regard the local potential surface about a particle as a random function possessing a spherical distribution and therefore completely determined by a continuous radial distribution function.

Given such a concept models can be constructed in terms of either mean values or probability distributions for both the barrier height and of the inter-equilibrium distance. Rate process theory is satisfied with just these two values from the background structure of the medium. The form of the potential well is not taken into account nor is the dynamics of the approach to the saddle point. There is no call for doublet or triplet distributions or complicated correlation functions. This is both the strength and weakness of rate process theory.

The concept of the blurring of the crystal structure (structural diffusion) with increased thermal energy and the explanation of the increased mobility in terms of 'holes' is essentially that of the kinetic theory of liquids advanced by FRENKEL (1946). Further detail and one specific development of the blurred crystal model can be gained from a recent treatment of the escape mechanism from a fairly abstract point of view (CULLING 1983).

At the particle level, agencies within the soil (physical, chemical, floral and faunal) tend to displace particles the translations possessing a random and sometimes a systematic component. The application of rate process theory provides a measure of the rate constant of the process. The stochastic theory of soil creep goes on to describe the translatory behaviour of the particles as an intermittent and protracted Brownian motion and the motion of the soil mass as of a diffusive nature. Rate process theory supplies an explicit formulation of both the drift and diffusion coefficients.

It may be the case that superimposed drift dominates the diffusive tendencies and the soil mass exhibits hydrodynamic type flow or even in certain cases turbulent flow. Nevertheless the individual fluctuations of individual particles remain of the utmost importance as they provide the opportunity for the geomorphologically important force fields to operate. That is, we regard soil creep as an activated process dependent upon geomorphic displacing agencies, just as electron flow in a conductor is activated by thermal oscillations, as indeed is rheologic type soil deformation.

The typical external force field is that of the downslope component of gravity; it is ubiquitous, persistant and within reason constant; but it is weak and without activating agencies is inoperative. Other important cases occur in which the field is localised and time variant. They may be internal to the soil mass but can be regarded as external to the individual particle system. Cyclic agencies such as hydration, freeze-thaw, etc., which possess a directed component are of prime importance in mass movement of the slope cover (KIRKBY 1967). However, each phase of the cyclic motion can be regarded as a flow system in its own right with strongly marked dirft direction but also possessing a random component particularly during the relaxation phase when free volume is increased.

Details of the stochastic theory of soil creep are available in CULLING (1963, 1965). The setting within the wider erosive scene is given in KIRKBY (1971) and HIRANO (1975) and in the relevant chapters of YOUNG (1972) and CARSON & KIRKBY (1972). Observational work has proliferated since the pioneer studies of YOUNG (1960) and KIRKBY (1967); a relatively recent summary of results is to be found in YOUNG (1974). The techniques of soil creep measurements are covered by STATHAM (1981); the disadvantages of current methods being discussed in CULLING (1981).

2. RATE PROCESS THEORY

Rate process theory originated in physical chemistry and Henry Eyring's concept of the activation complex formulated in 1935 brought great simplification to the problem of reaction rates which in essence goes back to the classical work of ARRHENIUS (1885) and his celebrated relationship between the rate of inversion of sucrose and the temperature

$$\varkappa \ = \ A \, e^{-\frac{E}{RT}} \tag{3}$$

(EYRING 1935 a & b).

From quantum mechanical and statistical mechanical principles the rate of a reaction is given as

$$\varkappa = \frac{KT}{h} \; \theta \frac{F^*}{F_A F_B \dots} \; e^{-\frac{E_0}{KT}} \tag{4}$$

where F^+, F_A, F_B, etc., are the partition functions for unit volume for, respectively, the activation complex, reactants A, B, etc., E_0 is the difference at absolute zero between the energy per mole of the activation complex and the sum of the energies of the reactants i.e. the activation energy at absolute zero or in practical terms the height of the potential barrier. The factor KT/h, where K is Boltzmann's constant, h Planck's constant and T the temperature, constitutes Eyring's universal factor, dependent only on the temperature and indendent of the reaction and the reactants, ($KT/h \sim 6 \times 10^{12}$ at 300 K). A recent review for a non-specialist geological readership and which goes into further detail regarding partition functions and reaction co-ordinates is LASAGA (1981).

The activation complex is the critical intermediary in any rate process. It is the slowest link in the chain of events and therefore controls the rate of the process as a whole. In physical chemical terms this means that the system is at or very near to equilibrium and there is no shortage of flow units. In the soil this implies that the rate of primary oscillation of the particles is at least one order of magnitude greater than the chance of an escape so that the system is sensitive to variation in the activation energy.

The transmission coefficient θ, relates to the possibility of an immediate return to the initial configuration or more generally that the reaction having reached the saddle point fails to proceed further. This peculiarity is a recognised weakness of 'hole-and-lattice' theories as well as activated state theories (FRENKEL 1946, 21-22). Apart from MITCHELL (1976, 294) most students outside physical chemistry assume a value of unity. If we deal with just one reactant, as is the case in most physical applications and assume no rotational or vibrational partition functions, then the frequency factor simplifies to

$$A \simeq \frac{KT}{h} \tag{5}$$

(GLASSTONE et al. 1941, 189), implying that the frequency factor depends only on the thermal energy.

The resulting relationship

$$\varkappa = \frac{KT}{h} \; e^{-\frac{E_0}{KT}} \tag{6}$$

is widely used in the physical scienes as representing Eyring's activated complex theory, or transition state theory or as sometimes termed by chemists, the theory of absolute reaction rates but which we following the most common usage outside physical chemistry, will term rate process theory (RPT). The standard text summarising the work of Eyring and subsequent workers is GLASSTONE et al. (1941). A chronicle of the path from ARRHENIUS to EYRING is given in EYRING (1935b). Further historical background is available in GLASSTONE (1946, 1083-1111) and in LAIDLER (1969). The present state of the theory and applications is the subject of a memorial volume to Henry Eyring (HIRSCHFELDER &

HENDERSON 1971). However, we are not concerned with rate process theory as a physical chemical theory but in its applications to physical processes involving mass transfer and which all stem from the seminal paper on viscosity, diffusion and plasticity (EYRING 1936).

In the soil mass activation takes place at two levels, of the molecule and of the soil particle. At the molecular level it is thermal activation that supplies the facilitator for rheologic deformation of the soil. Larger objects than molecules do exhibit thermal motion but it is very small. TABOR (1979, 101) quotes for a cricket ball (5 ounces; 141.75 gm) as 10^{-10}m/s. Making the same calculation for a sand grain of 1 mm^3 and of $\sim 1.5 \times 10^{-3}$ gm, in thermal equilibrium with its surroundings, it will have a mean thermal motion of 1×10^{-8} which is undetectable. The role of facilitator at the particle level in geomorphic soil creep is taken over by the various agencies that tend to displace the particle. As in a crystal particles can translate from one equilibrium position to another provided they possess sufficient kinetic energy to negotiate the intervening passage which in the soil will be oriented at random and, of course, provided there exists a hole or void adequate to receive the particle.

To summarise, rate process theory is not merely a theory of the kinetics of chemical reactions; it can in principle be applied to any process involving a rearrangement of matter. Given the blurred crystal model of soil structure and the stochastic theory of particle behaviour, soil creep is a prime candidate. The rearrangement of mass is viewed as the activated translation of large numbers of small flow units from their initial equilibrium position over a saddle region of an intervening potential surface to a fresh equilibrium site. The essential components of the process are,

1)   oscillatory ground motion of the flow units characterised by a frequency and an intensity given by the distribution of kinetic energy.

ii)   an activation state or transition complex sited at the potential saddle point and determining the minimum level of kinetic energy required for escape.

iii)   an external field of force imposing a preferred direction upon an otherwise random activty.

A further factor not essential to rate process theory in general but highly germane to our enquiry is,

iv)   the availability of a vacant space to accommodate the dissolution of the activated state or in physical terms to accept the translating particle.

With two components to the first factor this gives five variables. If we regard each as mappable on R^1, then the general model exists over R^5 and different manifestations of particulate flow will occupy different regions of this space.

The potential barrier separating two adjacent equilibrium positions is assumed symmetrical. The presence of an external force field is accounted for in energy terms by raising or lowering the effective activation energy appropriate to direction (figure 1). The mean transport rate is given by the difference

$$\bar{v} = (\varkappa_+ - \varkappa_-)\lambda = 2\lambda \frac{KT}{h} e^{-\frac{E_0}{KT}} sinh \frac{f\lambda}{2KT} \qquad (7)$$

where f is the external force and λ the inter-equilibrium distance. For strong forces, $f\lambda >> 2KT$, as is the case for most soil mechanical applications,

$$\bar{v} \simeq \lambda \frac{KT}{h} e^{-\frac{E_0}{KT}} e^{\frac{f\lambda}{2KT}} \qquad (8)$$

On the other hand for weak forces, $f\lambda << 2KT$, which may be the case in some geomorphic applications,

$$\bar{v} \simeq \lambda^2 \frac{f}{h} \; e^{-\frac{E_0}{KT}} \tag{9}$$

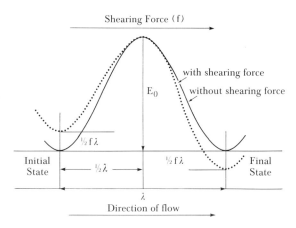

Fig. 1:   Potential energy curve for viscous flow

3.   RATE PROCESS THEORY IN SOIL MECHANICS

Applications of rate process theory outside physical chemistry are many and various and include flow and deformation in metals, crystals, ceramics, bitumen and polymers. Biochemical applications include the thermal stability of collagen and the release of acetyl-choline at synapses. More pertinent are the applications made by soil engineers. Improved understanding of creep phenomena in soils has followed upon a re-direction of attention away from observable qualities such as strength and deformation rate to more fundamental properties at the molecular level. A pioneering application of RPT to soil rheology was MURAYAMA & SHIBATA (1961), who envisaged a Bingham type flow. This was followed by CHRISTENSEN & WU (1964) and especially by MITCHELL (1964) and co-workers. The whole topic receives a detailed treatment in MITCHELL 1976, 292-339) and so we need refer later only to those aspects of prime relevance to our present purpose. An interesting soil mechanical viewpoint is that of WINTERKORN (1971), who like us seeks analogies between macromeritic behaviour and molecular properties.

For convenience, we give in outline the derivation of the Mitchell strain rate equation and of the explicit expression for the number of flow units. Then the experimental results are summarised preliminary to a discussion of the nature of the inter-particle contact.

If there are S flow units per unit length then from (7) the rate of axial strain is

$$\dot{\varepsilon} = 2S\lambda \frac{KT}{h} \; e^{-\frac{E_0}{KT}} \; sinh \frac{f\lambda}{2KT} \tag{10}$$

Now 'a conservative estimate of the least possible value for $f\lambda/2KT$ encountered in a natural soil system – is 3.36' (MITCHELL 1964, 34-38). Hence the basic equation takes the form

$$\dot{\varepsilon}_1 \; = \; S\lambda\frac{KT}{h} \; e^{-\frac{E_0}{KT}} \; e^{\frac{f\lambda}{2KT}} \tag{11}$$

Then

$$\ln\dot{\varepsilon}_1 \; = \; \ln\left(S\lambda\frac{KT}{h}\right) \; - \; \frac{E_0}{KT} \; + \; \frac{f\lambda}{2KT} \tag{12}$$

Taking mean values of f, to a first approximation as proportional to the deviator stress and inversely proportional to the number of flow unit contacts per unit area upon which stress distributes,

$$f \; = \; \frac{(\sigma_1 \; - \; \sigma_3)}{2S} \tag{13}$$

Substitution in (12) and re-arranging gives the Mitchell strain rate equation (MITCHELL 1964, p. 39 eq. 21),

$$(\sigma_1 \; - \; \sigma_3) \; = \; \frac{4SKT}{\lambda} \; \ln\dot{\varepsilon}_1 \; + \; \frac{4SE_0}{\lambda} \; - \; \frac{4SKT}{\lambda} \; \ln\left(S\lambda\left(\frac{KT}{h}\right)\right) \tag{14}$$

Putting

$$E \; = \; E_0 \; - \; \tfrac{1}{2}f \tag{15}$$

and denoting E the experimental activation energy, then

$$\dot{\varepsilon} \; = \; \frac{KT}{h} \; e^{-\frac{E}{KT}} \tag{16}$$

Following standard procedure for an Arrhenius plot (LAIDLER 1972),

$$\frac{\dot{\varepsilon}}{T} \; = \; \frac{K}{h} \; e^{-\frac{E}{KT}} \tag{17}$$

$$\ln\left(\frac{\dot{\varepsilon}}{T}\right) \; = \; \ln\left(\frac{K}{h}\right) \; - \; \frac{E}{KT} \tag{18}$$

and

$$\frac{\partial\left(\ln\frac{\dot{\varepsilon}}{T}\right)}{\partial\left(\frac{1}{T}\right)} \; = \; -\frac{E}{K} \tag{19}$$

Thus the experimental activation energy can be determined from the slope of the plot of

$\ln(\dot{\varepsilon}/T)$ versus ($1/T$), (MITCHELL et al. 1968, 1223, MITCHELL 1976, 295).

Provided we remain within the range wherein stress is large enough to ensure the safety of the approximation (8) but not large enough to induce tertiary creep, the logarithm of strain rate varies directly as the deviator stress. So that

$$\frac{\partial(\sigma_1 - \sigma_3)}{\partial(\ln \dot{\varepsilon})} = \frac{4SKT}{\lambda} \qquad (20)$$

from which the number of flow units can be estimated.

From his and co-workers results and from other sources Mitchell has collected values for the activation energy for several kinds of soil and for a variety of other materials. From the tabulated results (MITCHELL et al. 1968, 1228, repeated in MITCHELL 1976, 296) we note that:

i)   activation energies are relatively high for soils and range over (25-40 Kcal/mole; 105-168 KJ/mole). Similar values are found for undisturbed clay samples;

ii)   corresponding values are, for viscous flow of water (4-5 Kcal/mole; 16.8-21 KJ/mole), for plastics (7-14 Kcal/mole; 29.4-58.8 KJ/mole), for concrete (54 Kcal/mole; 226.8 KJ/mole) and for metals (50 + Kcal/mole; 210 + KJ/mole);

iii)   frozen soil has the very high value of (94 Kcal/mole; 394.8 KJ/mole);

iv)   suspensions and soil pastes where the water content is so high that soil structure is completely destroyed give approximately the same values as for water.

The relatively high values for soils imply the rupture of some form of chemical bonding. Purely physical bonds (electrostatic, VAN DER WAAL's) characteristically show much smaller values (LAIDLER 1972, 344). For comparison the value of the covalent O-O bond in diatomic molecules is 33.2 Kcal/mole (139.44 KJ/mole) (PAULING 1960, 85). The fact that similar values are found for both wet and dry clays indicates that the presence of water either as adsorbed layers or as pore water in the neighbourhood of the contact is unlikely to be the agent responsible for or even contributing to the bonding. Further support for this contention comes from the fact that the activation energy is independent of both void ratio and bulk water content.

The structure of water is still far from completely understood. According to the ideas of BERNAL and co-workers (BERNAL & FOWLER 1933) water at low temperatures retains a great deal of the weak (2-10 Kcal/mole; 8.4-42 KJ/mole) hydrogen bonding similar to that of ice. At the other extreme the breaking of the O-H bonds in water requires, on average, for the two bonds in a water molecule have slightly different energies, the high value of 110.6 Kcal/mole (464.5 KJ/mole) (PAULING 1960, 84, 449).

The activation energy for soils is independent of consolidation pressure and comparable values are obtained from both clay and sand. This suggests that the activation energy is related to individual bonds and that this bonding is brought about by a common chemical agency. This agency is believed to be that of covalent bonding between oxygen atoms on the surfaces of silicate minerals.

The second important area of experimental results concerns the number of flow units (bonds). The strength of a soil depends upon the number of bonds and this quantity is found to be directly proportional to the effective consolidation pressure. Dry clay is found to give a value approximately 100 times that of a corresponding wet sample. This is explained as the result of an increase in effective stress consequent upon the decrease of pore water pressure. The observation is crucial in the determination of the nature of the inter-particle bond for it is inconceivable that a change over two orders of magnitude could occur if the process operated at the particle level.

The inter-particle contact is the only significant region between soil particles at which effective transfer of normal or shear forces operates. According to the Terzhagi-Bowden and Tabor adhesion theory of friction the true area of contact is directly proportional to the effective normal stress and inversely proportional to the yield strength of the material (BOWDEN & TABOR 1950, 20). If the number of bonds is assumed roughly proportional to the area of contact then its magnitude will vary from contact to contact. The natural range of particle contact area seems to rule out any explanation at the particle level for the similar values found for experimental activation energies and for a relationship between strength and the number of bonds that is independent of sample, composition and condition of the soil.

4.   THE NATURE OF THE INTER–PARTICLE CONTACT

The soil mass is not one large crystal and soil deformation comprises the slipping of one particle past another as well as the make-and-break of chemical bonds as two silicate minerals work past each other. In this section we use the experimental results to provide an estimate of the time taken for inter-particle contact clearance. This involves, first of all, an estimate of the mean number of bonds per contact for various kinds of soil. In this we merely follow and extend the results of Mitchell. We find that, because of the small numbers involved in clay soils it is prudent to confine the investigation to sandy soils. The mean number of bonds per contact for such soils works out at $\sim 10^8$.

The time taken for particle clearance is calculated according to two models of bond rupture and renewal; the one due to Mitchell and following normal rate process concepts and the other, due to Murayama and Shibata, that once severed a bond is not repaired. It is found that the predicted time for clearance is totally at variance with experience. A fresh model is proposed intermediate in action and with the use of the correct analysis the times for clearance are brought down to reasonable dimensions. It is not suggested that this supplies a complete solution to the problems thereby posed for rheologic soil deformation but it is an essential prerequisite for the application of rate process theory to geomorphic soil creep, for it means that the rate of inter-particle clearance due to rheologic processes, though taking place during geomorphic creep, is not the controlling component in the process.

Though the mean inter-particle contact area is small the number of bonds is quite large. For San Francisco mud and remoulded illite, experiments conducted by MITCHELL and coworkers give values of $3.25 - 3.5 \times 10^{10}$ bonds per cm^2 under consolidation pressures of 1.0 kg/cm^2 and for Antioch sand under a confining pressure of 1.0 kg/cm^2 a value of 9.3×10^{10} per cm^2 of cross section. For illite the value varies from 5×10^{10} for a sample with 40% water content to 5×10^{12} per cm^2 for a completely dry sample, giving the hundredfold increase quoted (MITCHELL et al. 1969).

We follow the calculation of MITCHELL who from a representative range of $1 \times 10^{10} - 1 \times 10^{11}$ bonds per cm^2 for both sand and clay selects the value of 3.3×10^{10} for the purpose of an easy rough calculation. The number of particles per unit volume varies as d^{-3} and for sand with $d \sim 1$ mm and a void ratio of 1.0 there are approximately 1000 particles per c.c. (the corresponding values for clay (d $\sim$ 0.002 mm) and silt (d $\sim$ 0.02 mm) are given in Table 1a).

For sand a value of 6 contacts per particle is taken though perhaps from the work of Bernal five would have been a better figure. However, six gives 6000 contacts per cm^3 or $(6000)^{2/3}$ = 328.28 or roughly 330 per cm^3. Then quite simply for 3.3×10^{10} bonds per cm^2 we derive

Tab. 1:   INTER–PARTICLE CONTACTS FOR REPRESENTATIVE SOIL GRADES
(apart from silt grades, from MITCHELL et al. 1969, 1240)

Tab. 1a:CONTACTS PER cm^2

Grade	diameter mm	particles per cc	contacts per cc	contacts per cm^2
Sand	1	1×10^3	6×10^3	330
Silt	0.02	8×10^9	48×10^9	13.3×10^6
Clay (wet & dry)	0.002	8×10^{12}	48×10^{12}	13.3×10^8

Tab. 1b: BONDS PER CONTACT

Grade	Bonds per cm^2	Bonds per contact	Area of contact cm^2	Area of contact per sq cm, cm^2/cm^2
Sand	3.3×10^{10}	1×10^8	9×10^{-9}	2.87×10^{-5}
Silt	3.3×10^{10}	0.25×10^4	2.25×10^{-12}	2.97×10^{-5}
Clay (wet)	5×10^{10}	0.36×10^4	3.24×10^{-12}	4.5×10^{-5}
Clay (dry)	5×10^{12}	0.36×10^2	3.24×10^{-14}	4.5×10^{-3}

an average of 1×10^8 bonds per contact. The inter-equilibrium distance for oxygen atoms on the surface of soil silicates is 2.8 Å, taking this as 3×10^{-8} cm the area occupied by each oxygen atom and therefore each bond is 9×10^{-16} cm^2. The total contact area of bonded silicates per cm^2 of soil is therefore approximately 3×10^{-5} cm^2/cm^2 and an individual contact area roughly 9×10^{-8} cm^2.

For clay the value of 6 contacts per particle is adhered to although this is even more doubtful. However, with this value the results of similar calculations for wet (40% water) and dry clays are listed in Table 1b. We also supplement MITCHELL's calculations (MITCHELL et al. 1969, 1240-1) by including those for a silt grade.

The number of bonds per contact ranges from 1×10^8 for sand to 36 or 3600 (depending upon water content) for clay. Thus there are far less inter-particle contacts in sand soils but many more bonds per contact than for clays. This is in accord with intuition but the range is surprising. The values for clay samples are incredibly low. So much so that from henceforth we will be concerned with sand soils alone, hoping to return to the problem of clay soils at a later date.

The surface area of a spherical sand grain (d $=$ 1 mm) is 3.14×10^{-2} cm^2 and the ratio of the area of one contact to the surface area is 2.8×10^{-6}. Although not strictly comparable geometrically, the fraction of the apparent area between two steel plates $\sim$ 20 cm^2 and under a load of 1.0 kg/cm^2, actually in contact is 1×10^{-4}. For crossed steel cylinders under a load of 1 kg the area of contact was found to be 1.2×10^{-4} (BOWDEN & TABOR 1950, 28, 31).

We now perform some order of magnitude calculations on the rate of bond rupture and of the time taken for particle clearance according to the basic equation

$$v = \frac{KT}{h} \ e^{-\frac{E_0}{KT}} \ e^{\frac{f\lambda}{2KT}} \tag{21}$$

Assuming that bond rupture is a serial process (MITCHELL 1964, 34) and that there is no pre-conditioning of the bond so that under a shear stress ruptured bonds are renewed at an adjacent vacant site, the vacancy moving one inter-equilibrium distance in the opposite direction. Repetition of the process will result in the passage of the vacancy back through the contact so tending to work the particles past one another.

The applied external stress is taken as one half of the deviator stress. Then for a value of $1 \, kg/cm^2 \sim (1 \times 10^6 \, dynes/cm^2) \cong 0.1 J/cm^2, f = 0.5 \times 10^6 \, dynes/cm^2, (0.05 \, J/cm^2)$. For the individual bond $f_d = 1.515 \times 10^{-5}$ dynes, $(1.515 \times 10^{-12} \, J)$ and for the average inter-particle contact of 1×10^8 bonds, $f_c = 1.515 \times 10^3$ dynes $(1.515 \times 10^{-4} \, J)$. The values of K and h are standard and λ is taken as the inter-atomic distance between oxygen atoms on the surface of silicates.

$K = 1.381 \times 10^{-16}$ dynes/cm K^{-1} $(1.381 \times 10^{-3} \, JK^{-1})$
$h = 6.626 \times 10^{-27}$ erg sec $(6.626 \times 10^{-34} \, Jsec)$
$N_A = 6.022 \times 10_{23}$ per mole
$\lambda = 28 \times 10^{-8}$ cm

In addition we take into account the possible effect of hot spots. This possibility has previously been overlooked and from the results with metals (BOWDEN & TABOR 1950, 40), we select a value of ~ 100 K for the increase.

Confining ourselves to sand grains we take the value of 1×10^{-8} as the average number of bonds per inter-particle contact as suggested by the previous calculations in which we followed MITCHELL (1964). For a rough order of magnitude calculation we assume the molecules in close array and arranged in a square. To make the passage from one boundary to the opposite a vacancy will have to traverse $\sim 1 \times 10^4$ bond sites. For a complete clearance of the contact area, assuming no dislocations, misalignments and no rolling or deformation and above all an 'instantaneous' renewal of any ruptured bond, then no less than 10^{12} bonds need to be severed.

Prompted by the value for the O-O covalent bond we select for the activation energy a value of $E_0 = 2.5 \times 10^{-12}$ erg/molecule (35.85 Kcal/mole; 150.55 KJ/mole). Then at 300 K the time for one vacancy traverse is $\sim 1.4 \times 10^{17}$ secs and for a complete clearance 1.4×10^{25} secs. If we consider the possibility of hot spots ~ 400 K then the values become, respectively, 1.14×10^{11} secs and 1.14×10^{19} secs. As the biblical span is $\sim 2 \times 10^9$ secs and 2×10^{16} secs takes us back to the Cambrian, these calculated values are quite at variance with observation.

If we take the very low value of 1×10^{-12} ergs/molecule (14.34 Kcal/mole; 60.22 KJ/-mole), appropriate to plastics, although the traverse time comes down to less than a second (0.26 sec) for 300 K, the complete clearance takes approximately 300 days and for 400 K this latter is reduced to 2.25 days. These values are still too large. A reasonable value would fall within the range $10^{-2} - 10^2$ sec with a mean ~ 1 sec, as is suggested on other grounds (PUSCH & FELTHAM 1980).

Clearly, in attempting to explain soil deformation while remaining within the aegis of RPT some explanation has to be forthcoming as to why the calculated values are so much at variance with observation. Similar discrepancies have been found in other materials, notably crystals. It is as if we need another 'steric' factor.

Various possibilities arise. Some, including stochastic variants of rate process theory and the possibility of bad sites, pre-conditioning and other forms of interaction between bond sites will not be touched on in this instance. Instead, we confirm ourselves to just two; the relative rate at which bonds are renewed and the deployment of the external force over the bond sites of the contact zone.

In the previous analysis we have taken an extreme case in which bonds are renewed instantaneously. In addition, it has been assumed that the contact has perfect bonding to start with and so vacancies can only arise at the margin and doggedly work their way across the contact zone site by site. In reality there will be mis-alignment, dislocations and interior vacancies so speeding up the process but not to the magnitudes required. Also, problems arise in that once existing imperfections have worked their way out of the contact zone there is a return to perfect bonding. This is part of a large problem still to be resolved (TABOR 1979, 192).

The other extreme arises when once a bond is severed it is not renewed. In which case as the number of bonds decreases the shear stress over the contact zone is distributed over fewer and fewer sites. This idea of the progressive concentration of the external force is adumbrated in CHRISTENSEN & WU (1964), being applied to particle contacts as a whole but it is equally applicable at the molecular level.

The view that once a bond is severed it is never made good is adopted by MURAYAMA & SHIBATA (1961) who propose

$$-\frac{dN}{dt} = N \frac{KT}{h} e^{-\frac{E_0}{KT}} e^{\frac{f\lambda}{2NKT}} \tag{22}$$

for the rate of change of sound bonds, where N is the number of bonds. By expanding the exponentials (twice), an approximate expression is derived for the time to failure, t_f , when the number of bonds has fallen to zero,

$$\ln t_f = \ln \frac{h}{KT} + \frac{E_0}{KT} - \frac{f\lambda}{2N_0 KT} \tag{23}$$

where N_0 is the initial number of bonds. The progressive concentration of external force is accounted for by the inclusion of N in the denominator of the second exponential factor. Unfortunately the method of solution adopted tends to nullify the important multiplier effect.

A more realistic choice of model will take on an intermediate stance with the rate of bond renewal lying somewhere between the two extremes. To this end we develop (22) in the form

$$-\frac{dN}{dt} = \frac{KT}{h} e^{-\frac{E_0}{KT}} \left\{ N e^{\frac{f_s\lambda}{2NKT}} - (N_0 - N) e^{-\frac{\varepsilon_0}{KT}} e^{\frac{f_n\lambda}{2N_0 KT}} \right\} \tag{24}$$

where f_s is the shear force acting as the external force in the rate process scheme, tending to disrupt the bonds, and f_n the normal stress at the contact tending to the renewal of severed bonds and it is assumed that this normal stress is distributed over all bond sites throughout, hence N_0 in the final exponential. The ε_0 represents the extra energy of activation associated with bond creation. Extra energy is involved because the making of a bond requires the expenditure of additional (steric) kinetic energy to get the atoms into alignment. That the axial approach gives the minimal saddle point is brought out beautifully in the calculated potential energy surface for the approach of a hydrogen atom to a rigid hydrogen molecule by HIRSCHFELDER (GLASSTONE et al. 1941, 94, figure 13, HIRSCHFELDER 1971, 83).

Even for the extreme case (22) wherein the retarding effect of bond renewal is neglected, the calculated time to failure is still too great. However, the expansions of the exponentials to derive (23) are unwarranted as the external force is assumed large. A numerical solution of

(22) or (24) will correct this and bring the time of particle contact clearance down to more manageable proportions. Instead of a linear solution, an artefact of the exponential approximations, a numerical solution gives results to be expected from the progressive concentration of the external force upon fewer and fewer bonds i.e. linear at small values, increasing exponentially, finally becoming precipitous. However, unless the activation energy is low or the external force large (within our previous frame of reference), the exponentiation is slow to take off but once in operation, the multiplier effect brings the whole process to a close in short order for the external force acting upon each of the remaining bonds will eventually approach 10^8 times its initial value.

For some order of magnitude calculations; with $E_0 = 1.75 \times 10^{-2}$ ergs/molecule (105.38 KJ/mole), $f = 1.515 \times 10^3$ dynes (1.515×10^{-4} J) per contact and $T = 300$ K, a complete inter-particle contact clearance (assuming no renewal of bonds) is brought down to $\sim 3.67 \times 10^2$ secs. If the external force is doubled, to ~ 0.5 sec. On the other hand if hot spots raise the temperature to 400 K, down to $\sim 4.5 \times 10^{-2}$ secs.

When bond renewal is considered, if we regard the normal stress as distributed over all bond sites, then unless the stress is inordinately large there is very little effect upon the time to failure. In the same token, however, the stress so distributed acts upon the sound bonds as well as the vacant bond sites. The normal stress, or a component of it, will act to oppose the passage of the flow unit across the saddle point leading to bond rupture, i.e. it will act to supplement the activation energy in a similar manner to the effect of an external force acting to raise the activation energy in the opposite direction (7). Thus

$$E_{act} = E_0 + \frac{f_n\lambda}{2N_0}$$

(25)

so that the final form of (24) is

$$-\frac{dN}{dt} = \frac{KT}{h} e^{-\frac{E_0}{KT}} \left\{ Ne^{-\frac{f_n\lambda}{2N_0KT}} e^{\frac{f_s\lambda}{2NKT}} - (N_0 - N)e^{-\frac{\varepsilon_0}{KT}} e^{\frac{f_n\lambda}{2N_0KT}} \right\}$$

(26)

The effective increase in the activation energy for bond rupture is far more influential in protracing the time to failure than the effect on vacant bond sites.

We have taken N_0 as a constant; in reality it will be a variable. The equation of f_s and f_n with the macroscopic mean shear and normal stress is a simplification. As particles meet and then roll and slide past one another the relationship between the normal and shear stress at the contact pass through a cycle and the number of relevant bond sites does likewise. This is too complicated to model analytically but we may eventually be able to simulate particulate flow from first principles as has been done for the solid and liquids states (ALDER & WAINWRIGHT 1959).

Though by no means the whole story the notion of the progressive concentration of shear force developed from an amalgam of the ideas of MURAYAM & SHIBATA (1961) and CHRISTENSEN & WU (1964), brings the time of particle clearance and therefore of the passing of soil particles past one another down from geological values. The problems that remain are those of RPT as a physical theory and for the present we can leave its shortcomings to the physicists, metallurgists, and physical chemists. For our purposes we have brought the values down below what might be termed the geomorphic time scale. This means that in applications to geomorphic soil crept it is the geomorphic processes that are the slowest and govern the rate.

5.   RATE PROCESS THEORY OF GEOMORPHIC SOIL CREEP

Soil creep as understood by the engineer is directed, presistent and strong, and operates at the molecular level. Geomorphic creep is random, intermittent and weak, and is a particulate phenomenon. It is also characteristically much slower by at least an order of magnitude. A typical value from the engineering point of view is measured in cm/yr (CHOWDHURY 1978, 302); whereas values for geomorphic creep approximate 1-10 mm per annum (YOUNG 1972, 56).

Rate process theory is pre-supposed at the molecular level. The serial nature of bond rupture as vacancies migrate back across inter-particle contacts, implies that the activation energy for the severance of chemical bonding is the same at the particle level as at the molecular. There is the possibility of bad sites due to contaminants. Bad sites being of stronger bonding control the rate process as they do at metal contacts. If this is so, then the activation energy will vary from contact to contact. To take this possibility into account will demand a stochastic variant of rate process theory.

So far we have been concerned with chemical bonding but reasons are given later to suggest that in addition there is a mechanical contribution to the activation energy. This comes about because in making a translation a particle has to forge a passage and in some cases the space for the final equilibrium position.

The basic equation governing geomorphic soil creep is of the familiar Arrhenius form and each term in (7) has its counterpart but now at the particle level.

The inter-equilibrium distance λ' is of the order of particle diameters and not a few angstroms. The frequency term v_m is to be measured in hours or days and not determinable from quantum theory ($KT/h \sim 6 \times 10^{12}$ sec). Geomorphic agencies can supply the external force at the molecular level for the contact zone of an individual particle. At the particle level these become the oscillatory forces of frequency v_m. The true external forces at the particle level may be persistent and ubiquitous as is the force field of gravity, intermittent but systematically distributed like the agents of seasonal creep or variable in time and space as is the throughflow of water.

Finally the structure must be taken into account. It will supply two components; one will be the void ratio V_0/V giving the probability of a vacant space. Unlike crystal lattices both particles and vacancies vary irregularly in shape and size. Thus, a further term is required to give the probability that an adjacent vacancy if present is adequate to accommodate the given particle. The simplest model would be to choose two Gaussian distributions. If so, the term would be the integral over all positive values of the convolution of the difference of the two distribution functions and will be a complementary error function. So

$$S = \frac{V_0}{V} \tfrac{1}{2} erfc \left(\frac{M}{\sigma(2)^{\frac{1}{2}}} \right) \tag{27}$$

where M is the difference in the means and σ^2 the sum of the variances. The model assumes sufficient elasticity or plasticity to allow of passage between vacancies.

The basic equation is therefore

$$v = v_m S e^{-\beta E_0} e^{\frac{1}{2} f \beta \lambda'} \tag{28}$$

We have put β^{-1} in place of KT. They both describe a statistical mechanical temperature; at the particle level the 'temperature' is a measure of the kinetic energy of the particles. Some rather tenuous arguments suggest that a Maxwell-Boltzmann distribution is the most probable for the distribution of mechanical energy in a particulate medium but the probability is unlikely to be high. Alternatively, other models can be hypothesised; as already noted the activation energy itself may be a random variable. If this is the case and the relevant Fourier transforms are tractable, e.g. as for gamma functions representing skew unimodal distributions, then the exponential distribution of the Maxwell-Boltzmann term is replaced by a Whittaker confluent hyper-geometric function in the general case. For special values these latter functions assume the guise of well known functions and the exponential is one of these (CULLING 1983). We reserve the discussion of such stochastic variants to a future occasion.

In the presence of an external force a similar equation to (7) applies,

$$\bar{v} = 2\lambda' v_m S e^{-\beta E_0} \sinh \tfrac{1}{2} f \beta \lambda' \tag{29}$$

For a strong force

$$\bar{v} \simeq \lambda' v_m S e^{-\beta E_0} e^{\frac{1}{2} f \beta \lambda'} \tag{30}$$

and a weak force

$$\bar{v} \simeq \lambda'^2 v_m S f \beta e^{-\beta E_0} \tag{31}$$

This latter is applicable to the downslope component of gravity. Although the force field is ever present it is weak i.e. the rate process is dominated by the frequency term. Thus, gravitational soil creep is seen to be an activated process like the drift of cinders in a shaken box.

viscosity – In viscous flow a local region is envisaged by RPT as two ordered layers of particles (EYRING 1936, GLASSTONE et al. 1941, 477-516, Figure 118). Flow takes place when one layer slides past the other under the application of a shearing force directed in the plane of the layers. This is engineered by molecules jumping from one equilibrium position to the next (provided it is vacant), or what amounts to the same thing, holes or vacancies migrate in the opposite direction. Without the vacancies no flow takes place.

Fluidity should therefore vary in proportion to the relative number density of the holes. That liquids flow because they contain holes was known to the Greeks (Aristotle: Physics II, Theophrastus: De Sensibus). The importance of free volume for the liquid behaviour of soils was certainly known to Reynolds and even by Galileo (WINTERKORN 1971). Densely packed soils expand under strong shear, while loosely packed samples collapse. In between is a zone of density, the critical void ratio, which is held to separate the 'solid' and 'liquid' states of soil.

The viscosity coefficient quantifies the relationship between the velocity gradient and the work done to achieve it,

$$\eta = \frac{f \lambda}{\Delta u} \tag{32}$$

The increment in velocity is the relative motion between two particle layers,

$$\Delta u \;=\; \lambda'^2 v_m S\beta f e^{-\beta E_0} \tag{33}$$

if for intance gravity is the external agent. Then the apparent viscosity is

$$\eta_\alpha \;=\; \frac{1}{\lambda' s v_m \beta}\; e^{\beta E_0} \tag{34}$$

The shear force itself does not enter the expression and we have Newtonian flow. This result depends upon the validity of the approximation for a weak external force, i.e. flow under small shear as is the case for typical liquids. Unless the activation energy is lowered considerably or the frequency factor correspondingly increased Newtonian flow in a soil is a very slow business.

If the force is strong then (30) is to be used,

$$\eta_\alpha \;=\; \frac{f}{S v_m}\; e^{\beta E_0}\, e^{-\frac{1}{2} f\beta\lambda'} \tag{35}$$

and the viscous flow is now Non-Newtonian. According to HIRSCHFELDER et al. (1954, 624, 661-667), who regard EYRING's theory as only moderately successful in explaining liquid structure, claim that it is the only theory to give a simple relationship between Newtonian and Non-Newtonian flow.

Due to the small values for the frequency term v_m compared to $^{KT}/_h$ the relationship between the apparent (geomorphic) viscosity and the true (rheologic) viscosity as measured in soil mechanics laboratories,

$$\eta \;=\; f\, \frac{h}{KT}\; e^{\frac{E_0}{KT}}\, e^{-\frac{\frac{1}{2} f\lambda}{KT}} \tag{36}$$

is of a high order of magnitude putting the values for the apparent (geomorphic) viscosity in the same class as those for glasses.

The flow rate of glasses is so slow that viscosities cannot be measured at room temperature. The process is speeded up by fusing the glass and then extrapolating for the lower temperatures. Geomorphic soil creep is likewise of too slow a rate to measure the most interesting parameters and so recourse must be had to speed-up models but first there must be some form of theoretical justification.

diffusion – The diffusion coefficient is given by

$$D \;=\; \frac{\bar{r}^2}{\tau_0} \tag{37}$$

where $\bar{r}$ is the mean translational distance and τ_0 the mean residence time. There is also a numerical factor that depends upon the precise circumstances and on convention. The mean residence time is the reciprocal of the rate contant so,

$$D = \lambda'^2 S v_m e^{-\beta E_0} \tag{38}$$

Concentration dependence of diffusion in soils is not due to mutual interference as in sedimentation but is a structural effect following upon variation in the free volume.

The rate process theories of viscosity and diffusion regard the liquid state as a disordered solid, still maintaining fairly strong local order but with sufficient free volume to ensure fluidity. This is akin to the state of affairs in our blurred crystal model of soil structure. Application of the more modern and inclusive integral equation theories of the liquid state e.g. the BBGKY, Percus-Yevick, Rice-Alnatt etc. (BARKER & HENDERSON 1976), which approach from the gaseous direction is a much more advanced problem and will have to be left for the present.

It will also be apparent that there is considerable overlap between hole-and-lattice theories (FRENKEL 1926, 1946) and EYRING's theory and that within the area of overlap they have complementary emphasis; the one is a structure theory and dwells on constraints while the other is a theory about activity. In including a structure term in the basic equation (28) of geomorphic soil creep we veer just that much nearer to FRENKEL.

pressure – The effect of (geostatic) pressure is to increase the normal stress at the contacts so increasing the number of bonds by fostering their renewal and hindering their rupture. Conversely, negative pressure due to pore water (or entrapped air) will decrease the normal stress and have an opposite effect upon bonding.

Very high pressures increase the viscosity of liquids in an exponential manner. Explanation from the rate process point of view (EWELL & EYRING 1937) is that the activation energy is raised by an amount related to the increase in volume held to accompany viscous flow

$$E_{act} = E_{vis} + p \Delta v \tag{39}$$

where E is the activation energy under the assumption that no work is required in the formation of the holes needed for flow. This latter is identified with the energy of evaporation E, required to sever the bonds between a surface molecule and its neighbours. In the soil there is an analogous energy required to separate a particle from its immediate neighbours and also in some cases to create or enlarge the space into which it moves; somewhat akin to FRENKEL's concept of internal evaporation (FRENKEL 1946, 6). There is also an effect upon the structure term due to a change in the free volume. Thus

$$\eta_a = \frac{1}{\lambda' v_m \beta S(1 - p\theta)} e^{\beta(E_0 + p\varphi)} \tag{40}$$

where θ and φ are empirical parameters.

More interesting is the case of negative pressure. Increasing pore water pressure induces a force between the particles tending to separate them and opposed to any normal stress across the contacts. It therefore has the effect of lowering the activation energy

$$E_{act} = E_0 - \tfrac{1}{2} p \tag{41}$$

i.e. the opposite of (25).

Firstly, it will tend to reduce the inter-particle friction and so ease the mechanical translation of particles. Secondly, it will affect the chemical bonding. The normal geostatic stress over individual contacts will vary from the mean value with orientation. As pore water pressure is increased, the effect of the normal stress upon the activation energy will, at first be reduced and then, commencing at the weaker sites, be reversed, thus greatly increasing the rate of bond rupture and once broken the bonds will not be replaced. Continued increase of pore water pressure will extend the reversal throughout all contacts with the eventual stripping of all chemical bonding between particles. The activation energy will fall to the very low values of (2-5 Kcal/mole; 8.4-21 KJ/mole), those of hydrogen or of physical bonding and the soil will become a paste or slurry and act like a viscous liquid.

failure – Failure takes place when the internal resistance can no longer maintain structure against external stress. Analogus to (26) and giving the rate of change in the number of soundly bonded particles, we have

$$- \frac{dP}{dt} = Sv_m e^{-\beta E_0} \left\{ P e^{\frac{f_n \lambda' \beta}{2P_0}} e^{\frac{f_s \lambda' \beta}{2P}} - (P_0 - P) e^{-\beta \varepsilon_0} e^{\frac{f_n \lambda' \beta}{2P_0}} \right\} \qquad (42)$$

where P is the number of bonded contacts per unit volume and P_0 the initial number

While the normal stress is dominant, only sporadic failure of individual contacts will take place, the number of sound contacts remains statistically steady at a level that ensures a stable soil and the slow flow of geomorphic soil creep. Where this is not the case, the multiplier effect of the concentration of any directed external stress upon fewer and fewer contacts comes into play and failure takes place when the number of bonded particles reaches low values. As at the molecular level, the effect may require a long time to take off; scores of years of imperceptible motion terminated by an exponential catastrophe.

The qualifications made with regard to equation (26) need to be repeated here. One consequence of the complex cycle of operations that takes place between the time at which a particle leaves one equilibrium cell to the time at which it leaves the next is that the base number of particle contacts, Po, is not a constant. There may even be interruptions to the cycle during which a particle may be in limbo, subject to no significant stresses and merely idling within the soil structure. Such possibilities make the transformation from individual particle escape to wholesale mass movement and failure a much more complicated process than the straightforward application of (42) would imply. A start on the investigation of the cycle of operations has been made by PUSCH & FELTHAM (1980) but with respect to an analytical treatment the conclusion as to its present tractability given in the section on the failure of individual contacts is equally applicable here.

Wholesale failure of particle contacts and consequent accelerated flow will follow upon a sufficient change in the controlling parameters; a lowering of the effective activation energy, a large increase in the frequency term or by a large input of kinetic energy into the system.

In a typical geomorphic setting the normal stress is relatively strong and failure is of isolated particle contacts; independent, intermittent and geomorphologically activated. Accelerated flow, in which the slow diffusive behaviour of the soil mass quickens to a stick-slip variety and eventually, if conditions allow, to continuous fluid flow, can arise from the imposition of large loads so increasing the external force. Increased pore water pressure reduces the effective activation energy and tends to promote particle failure. At high values this may reduce the activation energy to below the level at which the downslope component of gravity becomes a relatively strong external force, flow ceases to depend upon geomorphic activation and the soil begins to move 'under its own weight'. At very high values the activation energy is so reduced that the soil acts as a slurry. Increase in the frequency of particle oscillation accompanied by a large input of kinetic energy can occur during earthquakes or artifically by vibration. As well as the large increase in v_m , the increase in kinetic energy is such that $\beta \rightarrow 0$ and $e^{-\beta E}o \rightarrow 1$, no matter what the activation energy may be; while sufficient energy is adducted to maintain the free volume above the critical void ratio to ensure liquefaction (WINTERKORN 1971).

fluidization – The fluid phase may be supplied by air, naturally as in debris flows or artificially in fluidization. Chemical bonding is lost and the energy imparted is greatly increased in both frequency and value. Free volume is increased and constraint on particle activity falls to gaseous levels.

The simplified version of (29) appropriate to fluidised media is

$$\bar{v} = 2\lambda'' v_m e^{-\beta E_0} \sinh \tfrac{1}{2} f \beta \lambda'' \tag{43}$$

where β is the reciprocal of the kinetic energy, E_0 the activation energy, v_m the frequency. now measured in times per second rather than in hours or days, λ'' is the mean particle translation, now more like a mean free path so that the structure term degenerates to unity. The external force is the only factor relatively unchanged from the geomorphic case, being the downslope component of gravity on a sloping fluidised bed.

This rate process model derived as an extreme case is virtually identical with that proposed by SCHÜGERL (1961, 1971), designed to interpret experimental results on the viscosity of fluidised beds. The mean displcement of a particle is given as

$$\bar{v}_p = a_p v \tag{44}$$

where a_p is the distance between adjacent holes and v is the rate constant

$$v = \frac{1}{t_0} e^{-\beta W^+} \sinh \left(\tfrac{1}{2} \beta \frac{a_p}{n_p \delta_p} F_p \right) \tag{45}$$

where t_0^{-1} is the frequency of particle oscillation, β^{-1} the mean kinetic energy, W^+ is the activation energy, F_p the external force, n_p is the number of particles per unit volume and δ_p is the distance between the centres of two adjacent particles. Thus the effective external force at particle level is derived by dividing the total applied force by the number of particles per unit volume as we have done before, only this time, due to the greater free volume, the distance between particles has to be taken into account. In fact in the original presentation δ_p appears as a qualification of v_p (SCHÜGERL 1971, eq. 6.21 p. 278), thus

$$\frac{\bar{v}}{\delta_p} = 2 \frac{a_p}{\delta_p} K_{0'} \sinh (F_p \xi \beta) \, (\text{sec}^{-1}) \tag{46}$$

where

$$K_{0'} = \frac{1}{2t_0} \, e^{-\beta W^*} \quad (\text{sec}^{-1}) \tag{47}$$

and
$$\zeta = \frac{a_p}{2n_p \delta_p} \quad (\text{cm}^3) \tag{48}$$

In many respects fluidization bears a closer parallel to geomorphic creep than does the creep behaviour studied by soil engineers.

If this is the case, then the magnitude of the activation energy for geomorphic creep needs considerable revision. Despite the cogency of the serial argument, the activation energies for thermally activated and geomorphologically activated creep are not the same. SCHÜGERL (1971, 280) quotes a value of 3×10^{-3} erg/particle (3×10^{-10} J) for smooth glass beads of 250 μm diameter (fine soft sand) in a fluidised bed. This is many orders of magnitude greater than the values found by soil engineers. The absence of chemical bonds and a reliance on electrostatic – VAN DER WAALs forces would tend to lower the activation energy but as well as static inter-particle forces, SCHÜGERL also mentions dynamic forces and the friction between adjacent particles moving with differing velocities. This frictional resistance provides the slowest link in the chain of action and governs the rate of the process.

On this interpretation, the activation energy cannot be due solely to the severance of chemical bonds as particles slide past one another, as assumed previously, but to the particle having to forge a passage between neighbouring particles and in some cases to create its own cell space. The rupture of chemical bonds, although taking place, does not constitute the slowest component. Inter-particle clearance times are several orders of magnitude faster than the frequency of particle displacement by geomorphic agents. It is only when flow becomes continuous that the rate of bond rupture and the associated activation energy governs the rate of soil deformation.

We return to equation (28)

$$v = v_m S e^{-\beta E_0} \, e^{\frac{1}{2} f \beta \lambda'} \tag{49}$$

and attempt a rough order of magnitude calculation of the activation energy for geomorphic creep. In order to do so we make the following assumptions.

i)   The mean rate of creep is taken as 1-2 mm per year (YOUNG 1972, 56). For a random walk, the relationship between the distance between the origin and the position after n steps, R_n, and the mean translation distance, r, is

$$\overline{R}_n^2 = n\overline{r}^2 \tag{50}$$

If we take the mean translation distance as ~ 0.1 mm, then at a frequency of one translation a day, after a year,

$$R_n = 1.9 \, \text{mm} \tag{51}$$

This, however, is for diffusive movements; drift velocities will be greater and so we take the rate of particle displacement a magnitude lower at once every ten days,

$$v = 1.16 \times 10^{-6} \text{sec}^{-1} \tag{52}$$

ii)   For a loose sandy soil, the void ratio is approximately 0.75, so, $V_0/V \sim 0.4$. The other component of the structure term S, is the probability of a particle being able to enter or to create an adjacent void and is concerned purely with the configuration permitting this and not the energy required to do so, which upon the present interpretation is part of the activation energy. Its value can only be vaguely assessed and for convenience we take it as 0.25, to give

$$S \simeq 0.1 \tag{53}$$

iii)   The frequency v_m refers to the oscillatory behaviour of the particle. The difficulty here is that the agencies tending to displace a particle normally act over an interval. If we assume that a particle is subject to some form of geomorphic stress for 10% of the time then

$$v_m = 1 \times 10^{-1} \sec^{-1} \tag{54}$$

Substituting

$$1.16 \times 10^{-6} = (1 \times 10^{-1})\, e^{-\beta(E_0 - \frac{1}{2}f\lambda)}$$

$$\ln(1.16 \times 10^{-5}) = -\beta(E_0 - \tfrac{1}{2}f\lambda')$$

$$11.36\frac{1}{\beta} = E_0 - \tfrac{1}{2}f\lambda' \tag{55}$$

iv) β^{-1} is a measure of the kinetic energy possessed by the particles and is most difficult to estimate. The mean mass of the particles is taken as $\sim 1.4 \times 10^{-3}$ gms. The velocities attained during displacement are small, possibly 1 mm/sec. However, the particles are not free. If we assume that the input of energy is such that if free the particles would attain velocities of ~ 1 cm/sec., then a straightforward calculation gives

$$\frac{1}{\beta} \simeq 7 \times 10^{-4} \text{ erg/particle } (7 \times 10^{-11} J) \tag{56}$$

v)   If the external force, f, is due to gravity then a straightforward calculation for a mass of 1.4×10^{-3} gms gives

$$f \simeq 1.37 \text{ dyne/particle } (1.37 \times 10^{-7} J) \tag{57}$$

Bearing in mind that it is the downslope component that is providing the directed external force we take

$$f \simeq 1.37 \times 10^{-1} \text{ dyne/particle} \tag{58}$$

We have already estimated λ' as 0.01 cm and so substituting in (55) we get

$$(11.36)(7 \times 10^{-4}) = E_0 - (6.85 \times 10^{-4}) \tag{59}$$

giving finally

$$E_0 \simeq 8.6 \times 10^{-3} \text{ ergs/particle } (7 \times 10^{-10} J) \qquad (60)$$

This 'Drake equation' exercise can give only a very rough estimate and every one of the component estimates can be seriously questioned. The outcome could be in error by several orders of magnitude but it appears to support the view that the value of the activation energy for geomorphic soil creep is nearer to the value found for fluidized flow than to the experimental activation energies found by soil engineers for rheologic soil deformation. This suggests that although under certain conditions soils behave plastically and the strain rate is governed by the strength of chemical bonding; in a geomorphic setting they can behave more like a fluidised medium in which the rate constant is dependent on the mechanical friction. The importance of the friction term brings us back full circle to Brownian motion theory and the Langevin equation (LANGEVIN 1908), for the free particle

$$\frac{du}{dt} = -\beta u + A(t) \qquad (61)$$

as the appropriate expression for particulate flow.

Apart from a numerical factor the diffusion coefficient comprises a scaling term (square of the mean translation distance) and the ratio between a frequency term and a friction term. In the classical formulation the latter is given as (CHANDRASEKHAR 1943, 25)

$$\frac{KT}{m\beta} \qquad (62)$$

where m is the mass of the particle and β the friction term, which we now replace by the symbol f to avoid confusion with the symbol for kinetic energy. Thus, in unit terms

$$D = \frac{KT}{f} \qquad (63)$$

In rate process theory the diffusion coefficient is given by (37) and τ_0 mean residence time is the reciprocal of the rate constant so,

$$D = \frac{\bar{r}^2}{\tau_0} = \lambda^2 \frac{KT}{h} e^{-\frac{E_0}{KT}} \qquad (64)$$

and for geomorphic soil creep

$$D = \lambda'^2 S v_m e^{-\beta E_0} \qquad (65)$$

The counterpart to the friction is given by the exponential term

$$f = e^{\beta E_0} \qquad (66)$$

and we arrive at an explicit expression for the friction coefficient in the Langevin equation (61).

In particulate flow, whether we deal with solids, liquids or gases, or whether we are concerned with geomorphic soil creep or fluidization, the elementary interaction comprises three components,

i)   the initial impetus to the given particle
ii) the environmental (friction) reaction
iii) the terminal hard-core reaction.

In the application of rate process theory to transport phenomen, the first is taken care of by the frequency term and the distribution of kinetic energy. The second is idealised as the activation energy, while the third is taken for granted in that a particle translation extends for just one inter-equilibrium distance. In KIRKWOOD's approach, the second component is treated with more respect and the friction term plays a central role in the development. His theory of irreversible transport processes (KIRKWOOD 1946, 1967, 1968) forms the natural starting off point for the next level of investigation.

In the meantime, the rate process approach must be put to the test. Although we possess in principle a quantifiable relationship between geomorphic creep and fluidised media before we can presume to use the results of fluidization experiments to investigate soil creep in the field and the laboratory, means must be devised to measure the parameters in (28). Of particular interest and importance would be a knowledge of the mean (and the distribution) of the kinetic energy of particles during geomorphic processes and a direct evaluation of the activation energy.

ACKNOWLEDGEMENTS

This work has been supported by a N.E.R.C. Research Grant which is gratefully acknowledged. Helpful discussion and encouragement have been received from Professor J.B. Thornes and Dr. N.J. Cox. The diagram was drawn by Mrs. Jane Pugh.

REFERENCES

ALDER, B.J. & WAINWRIGHT, T.E. (1959): Studies in molecular dynamics. I. General method. J. Chem. Phys. **31**, 459-466.
ARRHENIUS, S. (1889): Über die Reaktionsgeschwindigkeit bei der Inversion von Rohrzucker durch Säuren. Z. Phys. Chem. **4**, 226-248.
BARKER, J.A. & HENDERSON, D. (1976): What is liquid? Understanding the states of matter. Rev. Mod. Phys. **48**, 587-671.
BERNAL, J.D. & FOWLER, R.H. (1933): A theory of water and ionic solution with particular reference to hydrogen and hydroxyl ions. J. Chem. Phys. **1**, 515-548.
BOWDEN, F.P. & TABOR, D. (1950): The friction and lubrication of solids. Oxford Univ. Press. London.
CARSON, M.A. & KIRKBY, M.J. (1972): Hillslope form and process. Cambridge Univ. Press. London.
CHANDRASEKHAR, S. (1943): Stochastic problems in physics and astronomy. Rev. Mod. Phys. **15**, 1-98.
CHOWDHURY, R.N. (1978): Slope analysis. Elsevier. Amsterdam.
CHRISTENSEN, R.W. & WU, T.H. (1964): Analysis of clay deformation as rate process. J. Soil Mech. & Foundation Div. A.S.C.E. **90**, SM6, 125-157.
CULLING, W.E.H. (1963): Soil creep and the development of hillside slopes. J. Geol. **71**, 127-161.
CULLING, W.E.H. (1963): Theory of erosion on soil covered slopes. J. Geol. **73**, 230-254.
CULLING, W.E.H. (1981): New methods of measurement of slow particulate transport processes on hillside slopes. Erosion and sediment transport measurement. Proc. Florence Symp. IAHS Publ. **133**, 267-274.
CULLING, W.E.H. (1982): Stochastic processes. In: Quantitative Geography. 202-211. Ed. WRIGLEY, N. & BENNET, R.J., Routledge & Kegan Paul. London.
CULLING, W.E.H. (1983): Slow particulate flow in condensed media as an escape mechanism: I. Mean translation distance. CATENA (this volume).
EWELL, R.H. & EYRING, H. (1937): theory of viscosity of liquids as a function of temperature and pressure. J. Chem. Phys. **5**, 726-736.

EYRING, H. (1935a): The activated complex in chemical reactions. J. Chem. Phys. **3**, 107-115.
EYRING, H. (1935b): The activated complex and the absolute rate of chemical reactions. Chem. Rev. **17**, 65-77.
EYRING, H. (1936): Viscosity, plasticity and diffusion as examples of absolute reaction rates. J. Chem. Phys. **4**, 283-291.
FRENKEL, J. (1926): Über die Wärmebewegung in festen und flüssigen Körpern. Z. Phys. **35**, 652-669.
FRENKEL, J. (1935): The liquid state and the theory of fusion. Acta Physico chimica. **3**, 633-648, 913-938.
FRENKEL, J. (1946): Kinetic theory of liquids. Oxford Univ. Press. London.
GLASSTONE, S. (1946): Textbook of physical chemistry. 2nd edition. Van Nostrand. New Yori.
GLASSTONE, S., LAIDLER, K. & EYRING, H. (1941): The theory of rate processes. McGraw-Hill. New York.
HIRANO, M. (1975): Simulation of developmental process of interfluvial slopes with reference to graded form. Journ. Geol. **83**, 113-123.
HIRSCHFELDER, J.O. (1971): A forecast for physical chemistry. In: HIRSCHFELDER & HENDERSON (1971), 73-89.
HIRSCHFELDER, J.O., CURTIS, C.F. & BIRD, R.B. (1954): Molecular theory of gases and liquids. Wiley. New York.
HIRSCHFELDER, J.O. & HENDERSON, D. (1971): Chemical dynamics: papers in honour of Henry Eyring. Adv. Chem. Phys. **21**.
KIRKBY, M.J. (1967): Measurement and the theory of soil creep. Journ. Geol. **75**, 359-378.
KIRKBY, M.J. (1971): Hillslope process response models based on the continuity equation. Slopes: form and process. Ed. BRUNSDEN, D. Inst. Brit. Geog. Spec. Publ. **3**.
KIRKWOOD, J.G. (1946): The statistical mechanical theory of transport processes. I. General theory. J. Chem. Phys. **14**, 180-201 (included in KIRKWOOD, J.G. 1967).
KIRKWOOD, J.G. (1967): Selected topics in statistical mechanics. Ed. ZWANZIG, R.W. Gordon & Breach. New York.
KIRKWOOD, J.G. (1968): Theory of liquids. Ed. ALDER, B.J. Gordon & Breach. New York.
LAIDLER, K.J. (1969): Theories of chemical reaction rates. McGraw-Hill. New York.
LAIDLER, K.J. (1972): Unconventional applications of Arrhenius' law. J. Chem. Educ, **49**, 343-344.
LANGEVIN, P. (1908): Sur la théorie du mouvement Brownien. Comptes. Rendues **146**, 530-539.
LASAGA, A.C. (1981): transition state theory. Kinetics of geochemical theory. 135-169. Rev. Mineralogy v.**8**. Ed. LASAGA, A.C. & KIRKPATRICK, R.J.
MANDLEBROT, B.B. (1977): Fractals: form, chance and dimension. Freeman. San Francisco.
MITCHELL, J.K. (1964): Shearing resistance of soils as a rate process. J. Soil Mech. & Foundations Div. A.S.C.E. **90**, SM1, 29-61.
MITCHELL, J.K., CAMPANELLA, R.G. & SINGH, A. (1968): Soil creep as a rate process. J. Soil Mech. & Founations Div. A.S.C.E. **94**, SM1, 231-253.
MITCHELL, J.K., SINGH, A. & CAMPANELLA, R.G. (1969): Bonding, effective stress and strength of soils. J. Soil Mech. & Founations Div. A.S.C.E. **95**, SM4, 1219-1246.
MURAYAMA, S. & SHIBATA, T. (1961): Rheologic properties of clays. Proc. 5th Int. Conf. Soil Mechanics & Foundation engineering, 269-273.
PAULING, L. (1960): The nature of the chemical bond. 3rd edition. Oxford Univ. Press. London.
PUSCH, R. & FELTHAM, P. (1980): A stochastic model of the creep of soils. Geotech. **30**, 497-506.
RICE, S.O. (1944): Mathematical analysis of random noise. Bell System Tech. Jour. **23**, 282-332.
SCHÜGERL, K. (1971): Rheological behaviour of fluidised system. In: Fluidization. Eds. DAVIDSON, J.H. & HARRISON, D. 261-292.
SCHÜGERL, K., MERZ, M. & PELTING, F. (1961): Rheologische Eigenschaften von gasdurchstromten Fließbett-Systemen. Chem. Eng. Sci. **15**, 1-38.
STATHAM, A. (1981): Slope processes. Geomorphological techniques. Ed. GOUDIE, A. Allen & Unwin. London.
TABOR, D. (1979): Gases, liquids and solids. 2nd edition. Cambridge Univ. Press. London.
WINTERKORN, H.F. (1971): Analogies between macromeritic and molecular systems and the mechanical properties of sand and gravel. 751-765. In: HIRSCHFELDER & HENDERSON (1971).
YOUNG, A. (1960): Soil movement by denudational processes on slopes. Nature **188**, 120-122.
YOUNG, A. (1972): Slopes. Oliver & Boyd. Edinburgh.
YOUNG, A. (1974): Rate of slope retreat. Inst. Brit. Geog. Spec. Publ. **7**, 65-78.
ZIMAN, J.M. (1972): Principles of the theory of solids. Cambridge Univ. Press. London.

Address of author:
W.E.H. Culling, Bedford College, Regent's Park
London NW1 4NS, Great Britain

7 8 0 9